CW01081348

DEVELOPMENT OF POWER IN THE
TEXTILE INDUSTRY

FROM 1700–1930

Rev. Dr Richard L. Hills

DEVELOPMENT OF POWER IN THE
TEXTILE INDUSTRY

FROM 1700–1930

Rev. Dr Richard L. Hills

Landmark Publishing

Published by

Ashbourne Hall, Cokayne Ave
Ashbourne, Derbyshire, DE6 1EJ England
Tel: (01335) 347349 Fax: (01335) 347303
e-mail: landmark@clara.net

1st Edition

ISBN: 978-1-84306-350-6

© Rev. Dr Richard L. Hills 2008

The right of Rev. Dr Richard L. Hills as author of this work has been asserted by him in accordance with the Copyright, Design and Patents Act, 1993.

All rights reserved. No part of this publication may be reproduced, stored in a retrieval system or transmitted in any form or by any means, electronic, mechanical, photocopying, recording or otherwise without the prior permission of Landmark Publishing Ltd.

British Library Cataloguing in Publication Data: a catalogue record for this book is available from the British Library.

Print: Cromwell Press Ltd

Design by: Mark Titterton

Edited by: Ian Howe

Front Cover: Left high-pressure side of Brooklands Mill engine.

Back Cover: The high-pressure trunk guide of Leigh Spinners Number 2 engine with governor and flywheel in the background.

Title page: The rope drive at Mons Mill, Todmorden. The drum is formed from three pulleys side by side.

CONTENTS

INTRODUCTION

This book has its origins in the experience gained through setting up the Manchester Museum of Science and Technology during the later 1960s and transferring the exhibits to Liverpool Road Station nearly twenty years later. The purpose of the Museum was to display scientific discoveries and technological inventions that had made the North-West and Manchester the centre of the Industrial Revolution. The purpose was also to display the exhibits in such a way that they would rouse young people to take an interest in science and technology, the foundations of our present industrial age. To achieve this second purpose, we realised that our exhibits should be demonstrated as far as possible in ways similar to those in which they had been used in industry. This meant that we had to learn the skills how to operate them.

The Industrial Revolution was epitomised by the change from the handcrafts of spinning and weaving to power-driven machines. Although natural sources of power such as animals and water were used at first, it was the development of the rotative steam engine that enabled the textile industry to expand so dramatically. Therefore the textile mill engine, characteristic of the steam engine applied to other industries, had to feature prominently in any Manchester science museum.

The primary objective of this book is to outline the development of textile machinery from early times down to 1930 together with linked inventions in wool, silk, flax and cotton. However, cotton predominates because it was the spinning inventions of James Hargreaves, Richard Arkwright and Samuel Crompton that really changed the cotton industry from its domestic origins into one concentrated in mills. The second objective is to outline the increasing demand for power to drive the newly invented machinery. We shall see how the steam engine evolved from a device solely used to pump up water into a highly sophisticated machine based on scientific principles, capable of delivering over 2,000 h.p. The third objective is to explain how these machines worked through experience gained installing and demonstrating them at the Museum. Working them helped us to understand better the conditions under which people in the mill operated the textile machines – noise, dust or unhealthy cramped physical conditions. In contrast, the engines were kept generally in tip-top condition, sparklingly clean, as befitted the power source on which the whole of the mill depended.

I owe a great debt for the help received from so many people which has provided the background. Mill owners, their overlookers and engine tenters allowed me freely into their mills especially to photograph their engines. The photographs are nearly all mine. Staff in the Mechanical Engineering and Textile Technology Departments of the University of Manchester Institute of Science and Technology (UMIST) gave advice and help setting the machines to work again. Platts of Oldham helped with the removal and re-erection of the spinning mule from Elk Mill, generously donated by Shiloh spinners. Then Fred Hilditch set his mule to work again, teaching us to the best of his ability. The mill engines were donated by the National Coal Board, Courtaulds Ltd and Brain Melland, but they would have remained in situ had it not been for the labours of my museum technicians such as Frank Wightman, Harry Appleby, Sid Barnes, Joe Taylor and many others. They also kept the engines and textile machines running. To all these and to so many others I owe my great thanks. They gave the visiting public over twenty years of enjoyment seeing these machines run again. My thanks are also due to those who have helped with the preparation of this book including David Brearley, John Glithero, Robert Steeds, Tony Woolrich and of course Lindsey Porter and the staff at Landmark Publishing who prepared the book for its launch.

Richard L. Hills
March 2007

CHAPTER 1

THE FIRST TEXTILE MACHINES AND STEAM ENGINES UP TO 1785

Introduction

The Cotton Manufacture of England presents a spectacle unparalleled in the annals of industry, whether we regard the suddenness of its growth, the magnitude it has attained, or the wonderful inventions to which its progress is to be ascribed. Within the memory of many now living, those machines have been brought into use, which have made as great a revolution in manufactures as the art of printing effected in literature. Within the same period, the Cotton Manufacture of this country has sprung up from insignificance, and has attained a greater extent than the manufactures of wool and linen combined, though these have existed for centuries.[1]

So wrote Edward Baines in 1835. During the previous sixty years, the production of cotton textiles in Britain had been transformed from a domestic craft to one where spinning and weaving were carried out in large mills powered principally by steam engines. The reduction in price of cotton fabric brought about through mechanisation enabled Lancashire products to capture world markets so that this industry expanded way beyond what would have been needed to meet demand from Britain only. The newly invented machines which had made this possible were adapted to process other fibres such as wool and flax. The pace of change was dramatic; indeed, as Baines pointed out, 'a spectacle unparalleled in the annals of industry'. It could not have been achieved without other inventions in sources of power, particularly the steam engine, so that the developments in textile machines will be linked with developments of that prime mover. The descriptions of both textile machines and steam engines will be based on experience gained at the North Western Museum of Science and Industry in Manchester through collecting representative examples and setting them to work again for demonstrations.

Early Wool Textiles

First the earlier methods of textile production will be examined to see how, for thousands of years, there were few improvements and little mechanisation before this sudden extraordinary blossoming in the latter part of the eighteenth century. Archaeological excavations of Neanderthal sites dating from around 20,000 BC in the Dordogne region of southern France have not revealed any equipment for producing fabricated textiles so these people must have clothed themselves with skins. The earliest evidence of spinning and weaving comes from the Neolithic or New Stone Age cultures of the Mediterranean region around 5000 BC. These crafts must have developed over many hundreds of years but certainly by the time of the Neolithic cultures of Crete and pre-dynastic Egypt, spinning and weaving were well established. The Neolithic peoples, who arrived on the south-western coasts of Britain around 2500 BC, brought the crafts of spinning and weaving wool with them. They settled on the chalk country and are sometimes known by the name of their most famous encampment, Windmill Hill in Wiltshire.[2]

The production of cloth requires a series of quite complex operations. The fibres to form the yarns must be cleaned from dirt, or in the cases of flax and cotton from parts of their plants, to prepare them for spinning. The fibres need separating from each other so the right number to form the required thickness of yarn can be drawn out and laid parallel. Spinning involves twisting the fibres so they are bound together which gives strength to the yarn. Woven cloth contains two sets of threads. Warp is the first, consisting of parallel threads that are entered into the loom which may be either vertical or horizontal. The weaver then inserts the weft from side to side. Warp and weft may be different textures or colours to give the required character to the cloth. Finishing processes may involve bleaching and dyeing as well as cleaning and treating the cloth to give the final surface appearance. Such treatment may be almost as extensive as spinning and weaving.

Evidence for spinning at these early Neolithic sites has been found in the form of small circular stones or lumps of clay with a hole through them forming 'whorls'. The invention of the spindle and whorl was a great advance in civilisation. The method may have evolved in two stages. First, yarn spun by hand was wound around a stick to store it. Then a weight, the whorl, was added to the stick or spindle to act as a flywheel. A wooden hand-held spindle and whorl dated to around 1900 BC has been found in Egypt for spinning flax into linen. The principles for spinning on the spindle and whorl are the same as those for later machines. If the fibres are held in the same line as the spindle is pointing or at a slight angle and the spindle rotated, the fibres will be twisted together to form the yarn. If the yarn is held at right angles to the spindle and the spindle rotated again, the yarn will be wound on.

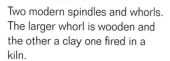

Two modern spindles and whorls. The larger whorl is wooden and the other a clay one fired in a kiln.

To spin with the hand spindle and whorl, first a short length of yarn must be wound onto the spindle and hooked round the tip, leaving a length free which can be joined onto the fibres ready to be spun. The spindle is suspended by the yarn and set rotating. Fingers of both hands pull fibres out of the mass already prepared, wrapped around a distaff, and allow them to be twisted together onto the end of the piece of yarn. In this way, drawing out or 'drafting' the fibres can be separated from the twisting. It is possible to spin a length of about three feet before the spindle touches the ground. This new length must be wound on. The yarn is unhooked from the spindle tip, wound onto the spindle and hooked up again to enable spinning to recommence. The spindle and whorl are light enough to carry anywhere and women worked with them even while walking. On a visit to Scotland in 1786, Alexandre de Rochefoucauld noted that, 'When passing through villages, I have seen spinning by spindle, but seldom and by old women, earning at most 4 pence a day'.[3] Spindles and whorls were still being used in that country as late as 1817[4] and in parts of Peru and the Andes even more recently. At the Museum we demonstrated this method to show that it is a desperately slow method of spinning.

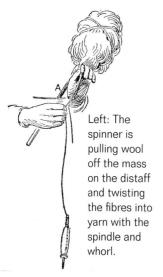

Left: The spinner is pulling wool off the mass on the distaff and twisting the fibres into yarn with the spindle and whorl.

Evidence of weaving on early British archaeological sites may be found in the weights for tensioning the warp of vertical looms. One end of the warp would be secured to a round beam at the top of the loom on which the finished cloth would be wound. This beam was supported at either end of a frame leaning against the side of the house so the loom occupied little space. The warp hung down and was kept tensioned through being tied in groups to the weights, which were often made of clay or stones. To weave plain cloth, every other warp thread was passed through loops tied round a heddle bar that was pulled forwards. The yarn for the weft was wound round the end of a long stick and passed through the shed created between the two sets of warp threads. The weft was beaten upwards to the rest of the woven

Vertical loom pictured on a Greek vase circa 560 BC.

cloth either with a short comb or a flat sword stick. The position of the warp threads was reversed by letting the heddle rod move back and another shoot of weft passed across in the other direction. Fragments of cloth found in excavations and modern reconstructions of vertical looms with multiple heddle bars show that quite complex patterns can be woven. Loom weights occur in excavations at Winchester, Rochester and Oxford dating to the twelfth century, but are rare by that time, showing that the vertical loom was being superseded by the horizontal type. In Winchester in the thirteenth century there were two weaving guilds, one for vertical looms and one for horizontal. Vertical looms survived in Lapland until the middle of the twentieth century.

Developments in Wool Preparation and Spinning

In ancient times, wool, a protein fibre, was plucked off sheep and probably teased out with the fingers ready for spinning. The Romans introduced iron shears to cut the wool off the sheep. Quality of wool varies according to the breed as well as the part of the animal so the fleece has to be sorted. A fleece sheared off a better-bred sheep today can be separated lock by lock and teased out with the fingers, leaving the fibres parallel for drawing out in the spinning, but this is slow and rough on the fingers. Another early method was to use a comb to smooth out the fibres. The first known references to combing date from 1500 BC in the Sumerian civilisation. By the twelfth century AD, this had developed into a pair of hand combs with their long, vicious iron spikes. Wool combing for worsted yarns became the preserve of men because of the weight of the combs. The process removed the short fibres (the noils) and left the long ones (the tops) parallel. Wool combing was not finally fully mechanised until the 1850s.

Modern hand shears similar to those used in ancient times.

For softer woollen yarns which used shorter fibres, the seed heads of the teasel plant, in Latin carduus, were mounted on a pair of handles and the wool teased out or carded by hand between the hooks on the teasels. This could not have been very effective because of the cylindrical shape of the teasel, although teasels were used to raise the nap on woollen cloth. Teasels were replaced by small wire hooks. Wire-drawing was introduced to Europe during the twelfth century. By the thir-

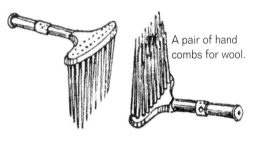

A pair of hand combs for wool.

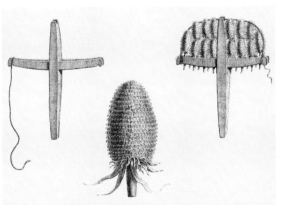

A teasel which would be mounted on the wooden cross for raising the knap on cloth.

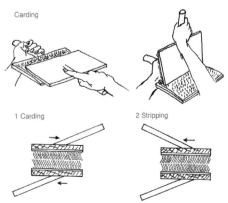

Carding

1 Carding   2 Stripping

Carding with a pair of hand cards.

teenth, the French had developed a pair of hand-held boards covered with bent wire hooks or points mounted in leather backing. Carding with hand cards tended to break the fibres as they were pulled apart. After working the fibres between the cards to open out the wool, the fibres were pulled off and rolled into a rollag for spinning. Since the fibres did not lie in the direction ready for spinning, sometimes they would be drawn out into a sliver or roving on one spinning wheel before being finally spun in a second similar operation.

Spinner seated at her Great Wheel

It is extraordinary to realise that in Western Europe the simple spindle and whorl remained the only method of spinning wool, flax and cotton until probably the middle of the thirteenth century or even later, when the first spinning wheels were introduced. The Luttrell Psalter, dated to around AD 1338, has a picture of the type that became known as the Great Wheel. The spindle was placed horizontally and ended in a point, on which the Sleeping Beauty could have pricked her finger. The whorl became a pulley driven by a band from a much larger wheel. The spinner used the right hand to turn the large wheel so that the spindle rotated with considerable velocity. The left hand held the mass of prepared fibres and drew them out away from the spindle at an angle. The yarn flicked over the end of the spindle as the twist was inserted. The problem was how to draw out the fibres without putting in too much twist to prevent further drafting while at the same time not putting in enough twist so the yarn fell apart. When the left hand had been drawn away from the spindle as far as was convenient, more twist could be inserted. Then the right hand reversed the wheel to unwind the few coils of yarn from the tip of the spindle back to where the yarn spun earlier had been wound on into a cop. With the right hand turning the wheel in the spinning direction again, the left hand brought the yarn to a right angle with the spindle and guided it onto the cop in order to wind on that length. When this length had been wound on, spinning could commence again. Spinning like this is much easier and faster than with the spindle and whorl.

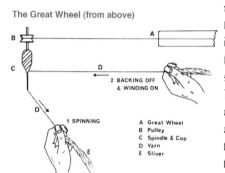

The Great Wheel (from above)

2 BACKING OFF & WINDING ON

1 SPINNING

A Great Wheel
B Pulley
C Spindle & Cop
D Yarn
E Sliver

Method of spinning on the Great Wheel.

There were at least two sizes of these wheels. The spinner sat at the smaller but stood at the larger, which was about five feet high. Standing gave a longer length of yarn spun each draw, but it was more difficult to control the winding on. Adam Smith reckoned that the Great Wheel more than doubled a spinner's production compared with a spindle and whorl. However, careful carding was essential if the spinner were to produce an even yarn while winding on also demanded skill to prevent snarls forming. As well as being used for spinning wool, the Great Wheel became associated with the early Lancashire cotton industry because on it could be spun a softly twisted yarn suitable for the weft in the fustian cloth woven in the area. It thus became the basis for the crucial inventions of James Hargreaves's spinning jenny and Samuel Crompton's mule which were to mechanise the textile industry at the end of the eighteenth century so dramatically.

Sometime, perhaps as early as AD 1400, a second type of spinning wheel appeared. No one knows its origins. It may have been invented in England and has been called variously the flyer or flax wheel because it was more suitable for spinning the linen warp threads for fustians which needed to be stronger and harder twisted. It was also suitable for the long fibres of worsted yarns. The horizontal spindle had a removable pulley wheel fitted at one end. The other end was broader, with a hole through which the yarn passed. This end was fitted with a horseshoe-shaped flyer which guided the yarn from the hole round to the side of a bobbin placed on the

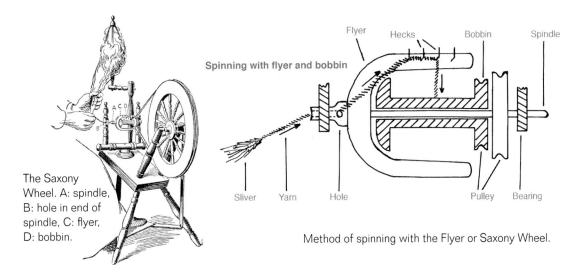

Spinning with flyer and bobbin

The Saxony Wheel. A: spindle, B: hole in end of spindle, C: flyer, D: bobbin.

Method of spinning with the Flyer or Saxony Wheel.

spindle shaft. The bobbin had a different-sized pulley from that on the spindle so that it rotated at a different speed. Both bobbin and spindle were driven from a much larger wheel.

The left hand paid out the fibres, which were twisted through the rotation of the spindle and wound onto the bobbin continuously through the difference in relative speeds. Leonardo da Vinci made detailed drawings of flyers in about 1490, but these may have been for twisting silk threads. It could have been Johann Jurgen who, around 1530, fitted the driving wheel with a crank operated by a foot pedal on what became called the Saxony wheel. Not only could the spinner turn the wheel faster, but this also left both hands free to control the drafting and pay out the fibres, again separating drafting and twisting. Even so it is difficult to achieve a yarn with even thickness and twist. But spinning is much quicker on this wheel than with the plain spindle type. It can take a good two or three hours to fill a bobbin holding two ounces (56g). Another advantage was that the full bobbin could be mounted directly onto a frame or creel for preparing a warp. The flyer wheel, with its continuous action, must have seemed more suitable for mechanisation than the Great Wheel. Indeed this was the type developed so successfully by another of the great spinning machine inventors, Richard Arkwright.

Drawing by hand

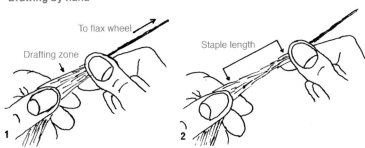

Method of using two hands in drafting or drawing.

The Horizontal Loom

The basic concept of the horizontal loom is very ancient, appearing in pre-dynastic Egypt around 3000 BC. Four corner posts would be stuck in the ground to support a beam with the warp wound round it on one pair with the cloth beam on the front pair. A sword stick could be passed through the warp threads to lift up the appropriate ones as well as beating up the weft. This method of warp selection for complex patterns could be seen being demonstrated in AD 2000 at the Ballenberg Open Air Museum in Switzerland. On ancient looms,

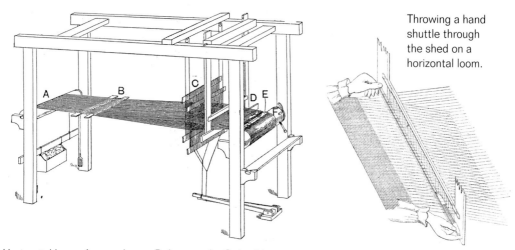

Throwing a hand shuttle through the shed on a horizontal loom.

Horizontal loom. A: warp beam, B: lease rods, C: healds or heddles, D: slay and reed, E: temple, F: cloth beam.

the weft might be passed across either in a ball or on the end of a stick. The horizontal loom appears in the West with a framing above the warp. The corner posts of the frame supported the warp and cloth beams. It allowed the weaver to work more conveniently and also permitted the introduction of shedding mechanisms to select warp threads. From the framing could be suspended heddle or heald frames to form a harness operated by foot treadles. A piece of cloth from York dated to the ninth or tenth centuries has a pattern which could only have been woven by a harness with six heddles on a horizontal loom.

Another important advance was the addition of the slay hanging from the framing in front of the healds. On this could be fitted the reed which consisted of a long comb, the teeth of which passed between the warp threads and beat up the weft more quickly and evenly than previous methods. The reed also kept the warp threads at their correct spacing across the width of the loom. The shuttle, with its pointed ends and with the weft wound onto a pirn or quill placed inside, increased the speed of weaving considerably. One limitation was the width of the cloth because the weaver had to be able to pass the shuttle through the shed in the warp with one hand and catch it with the other. Broader cloth still needed two weavers, one at each side. The horizontal loom was well established in England by the thirteenth century.

The beginning of mechanisation for selecting complex patterns and repeating them may have had its origins in the Middle East. Evidence from textiles shows that some form of figure harness was being used in Roman Egypt and Syria by the third century AD. Draw loom weaving was established at Constantinople by the tenth century and was being practised in Italy by the fourteenth. The pattern was tied into the harness before weaving started so repeats were possible. A draw boy lifted up appropriate warp threads which passed through eyes suspended in vertical lingoes or leashes. The pattern could be repeated across the loom by a number of lingoes being tied to the same cord in the top of the loom. The draw boy selected the right set of cords by separating a loop of string which was loosely passed around them. When the

The boy at the side selects the pattern on this draw loom. The weaver used an ordinary hand shuttle.

shed had been lifted open by the draw boy, the weaver threw the shuttle in the usual way and beat up the weft with the reed. Selecting the next part of the pattern in this way took such a long time that it was not worthwhile adding to draw looms Kay's flying shuttle after its invention. It was not until 1801 that the Frenchman Joseph Marie Jacquard patented his machine in which the patterns are recorded on punched cards. Although this could be operated faster by only the weaver, it could not match the exquisite detail of some of the larger draw loom patterns until bigger machines were developed during the nineteenth century.

The Jacquard apparatus is placed at the top of the loom and worked with a foot-pedal by the weaver himself.

The Fulling Mill

Right up to 1760, the wool textile industry remained based on domestic crafts, with one exception. Woollen cloth, such as the famous English broadcloth, had to be fulled to clean and compact it, then raised and sheared to give it a smooth finish. This led to the first textile machines to be driven by power. Trampling on the cloth by human feet in a trough of stale urine or fuller's earth was replaced by pummelling with a pair of stepped hammer-heads mounted at the ends of pivoted horizontal shafts which were lifted by cams on the axle of a waterwheel. No longer can the thumping of the stocks and the splashing of the waterwheel be heard in the countryside, for the mystique of fulling has long disappeared. There could be two types of fulling stocks. In one, the heads fell in a slanting direction which performed a scouring and cleaning process by throwing the cloth up and swirling it round in the trough. In the other type, for fulling or milling, the heads descended vertically to pound and shrink the cloth. Fulling stocks existed on the Continent at least by the eleventh century. In Britain, the earliest known were recorded in 1185 on lands belonging to the Knights of the Temple in Yorkshire and the Cotswolds. A charter granted to the Abbot of Stanley in Wiltshire in 1189 mentions a fulling mill, which suggests that they may have been fairly widespread by that time. Over one hundred and twenty are known in England before 1327. The fulling mill became an essential part of a manorial estate where there were suitable streams, so that the woollen industry migrated from towns to more rural regions where names such as Waulk or Pandy still survive, indicating sites of mills. By the middle decades of the eighteenth century, there were over one hundred

Italian fulling stocks depicted in V. Zonca, Novo Teatro di Machine et Edificii, 1607.

The fulling stocks at Jones Woollen Mill, Tan-y-grisiau, Blaenau Ffestiniog, North Wales.

in operation in the West Riding of Yorkshire, all probably water-powered. During the last quarter of that century, they were often adapted to become some of the earliest textile mills with the addition of carding machines. In the Netherlands, there were a few wind-powered fulling mills with vertical hammers.

The Importance of the English Wool Industry

For many centuries, Englishmen cherished the conviction that English wool was the best in the world. The tradition went back to early times, since wool produced in England enjoyed immense repute. Even in the tenth century, wool was raised for sale abroad. It was our chief raw material, the indispensable basis of our greatest industry and the most highly prized of our products in other countries. Wool entered into diplomacy; wool was a leading source of revenue; wool exported brought foreign exchange or the right to receive money abroad that could be spent on a campaign or royal meeting. The Cistercians, who were pre-eminent among the pioneers of wool-growing, at the time of the captivity of Richard I devoted a year's wool revenue towards his ransom. It was not only the cities of Bruges, Ypres and Ghent in Flanders which relied on English wool from which to make their finest cloth but also the merchants of Florence and other Italian cities who came to England in pursuit of wool.

At first it was the wool itself that was exported, but the taxes on it imposed around 1350 by Edward III to pay for his wars began to stimulate the production of cloth and helped to launch the famous English broadcloth which became so important in our export trade. The expansion of sheep-farming in England was continuous from the late fifteenth to the late eighteenth centuries. Even in 1757, Malachy Postlethwayte could write:

> The woollen manufacture being the great staple of England, it will remain her everlasting interest to support this branch as much as possible against all competitors as well as any such attempts to injure it either in Ireland or Scotland, and the British plantations, as well as the efforts of France or any other foreign rival to ruin it; for the loss of this capital branch will first ruin a great part of the landed interest, and banish our woollen manufacturers out of the kingdom, after that the rest of our other artists may soon go a wool-gathering too, according to our English proverb; for our woollen fabrics have provided a great support of most of our other, by promoting their sale in conjunction at the same time.[5]

The Linen Industry

The linen industry, although very ancient in England, has been overshadowed first by the wool and later by the cotton industries. The long, smooth, straight cellulose fibres created cloth with a very different feel to wool. A lengthy process was necessary to obtain the fibres, which put flax at a disadvantage compared with cotton, but the linen industry proved to be the basis out of which the cotton industry was to flourish. By the opening years of the eighteenth century, the annual crop of flax was prepared for spinning with a series of hand-operated devices. After flowering, the plant, about two feet high, was pulled up, dried in bundles and 'rippled', or pulled by hand through vertical iron spikes mounted on a board to remove the seed heads. The seeds were crushed to obtain linseed oil. Then the bundles were 'retted' or soaked in water for weeks to soften the woody material of the stalk surrounding the fibres. After drying again, the stalks were 'broken' through beating the bundle with a ribbed mallet or some similar tool before being 'scutched', in which a wooden blade was used to knock out the remaining pith and begin to separate the fibres; a dusty task.

In the eighteenth century, breaking and scutching might be performed by power-driven machines. The retted bundles might be passed between small-diameter water-powered rollers

Flax plants as pulled up and dried.

Hand-operated rollers for breaking up the pith in the stalks of retted flax at the Kortrijk windmill, Belgium.

The wheels with wooden blades used to scutch flax at the Kortrijk windmill. The stand on the right was foot-operated.

to break up the pith. In England, Abraham Hill patented a mechanical method for scutching in 1644, but it is not until 1717 that we find the first reference to a 'flax mill' in Northern Ireland and in 1726 to a 'lint mill' at Paisley in Scotland. These would have been water-powered while a little wind-powered flax scutching mill survives at Kortrijk in Belgium. Final separation of the fibres was achieved through 'hackling', in which the bundle was pulled by hand through finer and finer sets of iron spikes or combs, taking out short fibres and leaving the long ones lying nicely side by side. Bundles would be gathered together into a 'strick' ready for spinning on the Saxony wheel in the same way as for wool.

There was some mechanisation in the processes after weaving linen. During bleaching, the linen would have needed washing, which was done in revolving washtubs well before 1750. There were also crank-operated rubbing mills being installed in Scotland around the same time. When bleached, the linen cloth might be given a smooth surface either by the Dutch method of passing it between heavy rollers called 'callenders' or by the Irish method of beating or 'beetling' it with a row of small vertical hammers or stampers raised by cams as the cloth passed over a stout wooden roller. Through the great amount of effort required, beetling mills were usually water-powered. These machines were introduced to Ireland between 1725 and 1745 and into Scotland in the 1750s.[6]

The Silk Industry

It was the silk industry which, before the Industrial Revolution, had the most impressive machines for preparing threads for weaving. Silk, a protein fibre, originated in China, which has seen around five thousand years of sericulture. A cocoon of the silk moth looks such an unlikely source for a textile fibre since it appears solid and the filament, when released, is much too fine to use on its own. So to produce pure silk, the chrysalis inside the cocoon is killed by heating it; otherwise it will spoil the silk as it emerges to become a moth. Then the cocoon is placed in hot water to soften the gum which holds the cocoon together. The filaments from eight or so cocoons are reeled off together. Each cocoon would yield about 500 yards of a continuous filament suitable for pure silk fabrics. Even these eight filaments would still be too fine for practical use, so more strands would have to be twisted or 'thrown' together to build up the right thickness for weaving. At first the Chinese used the spindle and whorl, but these die out in archaeological excavations around 400 BC because they were replaced by a form of spinning wheel with the plain spindle.

Traditionally, sericulture was brought to the West by a couple of Nestorian monks who hid some silkworm eggs in their staffs to smuggle them out of China. This was in the reign of the Emperor Justinian who, in AD 530, took the silk culture of Corinth under his patronage and claimed the produce. Chinese methods of reeling and throwing must have been imported also, which may have been the source for the Great Wheel for spinning wool. By the thirteenth century, the Chinese had treadle-operated machines for reeling the silk off the cocoons as well as multi-spindle hand-turned machines for throwing.

Treadle-operated silk reeling machine ascribed to the early thirteenth century. The cocoons float in the basin in front of the operative on the right. The silk is wound onto the reel at the back.

A new type of 'throwing' frame appeared in Italy, possibly in Bologna in about 1272. Strict secrecy surrounded this invention, so nothing is known about its early history, but the frames were probably similar to a silk-throwing frame in a Luccan document of the fourteenth century which is basically the same as later ones. The Luccans had introduced these frames to Florence and Venice where they were driven by undershot waterwheels. The frames were circular with a drive shaft running vertically through the middle. On this was fixed a large upper wheel with cams which rotated horizontal reels. Below the reels were vertical spindles with flyers on which were placed bobbins filled with the silk. The spindles and flyers were rotated by a second large wheel on the vertical shaft so they gave the twist as the silk was drawn upwards off the bobbins onto the reels. These operated in the reverse way to the

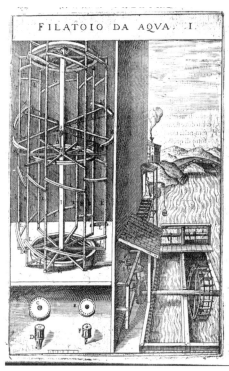

The Italian water-powered silk-throwing frame depicted by Zonca in 1607 showing the drive from the waterwheel.

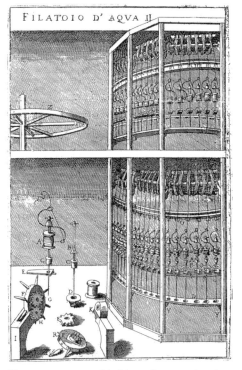

The arrangement of bobbins, flyers and reels on Zonca's silk-throwing frame.

later flyer spinning wheels. The Luccan document indicates that their frames had two rows of twelve reels with ten spindles to each reel. In 1385, a frame is described as having four rows of sixteen reels and six spindles per reel, giving a total of 480 sets of spindles. These frames were remarkable feats of mechanisation. They required only two or three operatives to join the threads, replace the empty bobbins and clear the full reels; thus they were able to perform the work done previously by several hundred hand-throwers.

James I encouraged the development of a silk industry in England but apparently planted the wrong type of mulberry tree to feed the silk worms. However, the industry expanded during the seventeenth century through refugees from religious wars on the Continent seeking safety in England and bringing their skills with them. In 1702, Thomas Cotchett set up a mill for 'throwing' silk by water power at the northern end of an island in the River Derwent at Derby. The mill contained Dutch silk-throwing machinery and was driven by a 13½ft (4m) diameter waterwheel built by George Sorocold. The enterprise quickly failed, perhaps through the type of machinery, but it was soon revived and extended by Thomas and John Lombe. Thomas was a silk merchant in London. His half-brother John went to Italy in disguise to see how the silk-throwing machinery worked there. On John's successful return to England in about 1717, Thomas patented the Italian types of machines[7] and began to build a larger mill beside Cotchett's, once again employing Sorocold as engineer. The mill was visited a little later by Daniel Defoe, who was suitably impressed:

> Here is a Curiosity of a very extraordinary Nature, and the only one of the kind in England: I mean those Mills on the Derwent, which work three capital Italian Engines for making Organzine or Thrown Silk, which, before these Mills were erected, was purchased by the English Merchants with ready Money in Italy; by which Invention one Hand will twist as much Silk, as before could have been done by Fifty, and that in a truer and better Manner. This Engine contains 26,586 Wheels, and 96,746 Movements, which work 73,726 yards of Silk-thread, every time the Water-wheel goes round, which is three times in one Minute, and 318,504,960 Yards in one Day and Night. One Water-wheel gives Motion to all the rest of the Wheels and Movements, of which any one may be stopt separately.[8]

The mill was still working in 1836 with its machinery virtually unchanged. A model is exhibited at Macclesfield Silk Museum. By the 1760s, these silk mills had spread to Congleton, Macclesfield, Stockport, Sheffield and Watford. They were the models on which later mills for spinning cotton, wool and flax were based. Also the fact that one type of fibre could be successfully processed on machines may have stimulated inventors to attempt to do the same with others. In the third edition of his book on Mechanics published in 1773,[9] William Emerson included a picture of a circular machine for twisting worsted and earlier another circular machine, this time for spinning cotton, was developed by Lewis Paul and John Wyatt. (See p21)

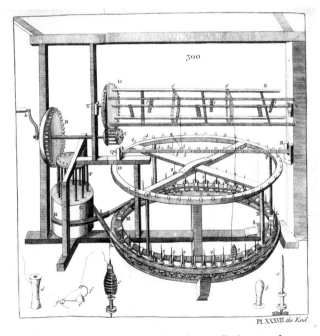

Machine for twisting worsted similar to silk-throwing frames.

John Kay's Flying Shuttle

Another machine which showed potential for being driven by power was the Dutch ribbon loom. One may have been made in Dantzig by Anton Moller in 1586 but there was great opposition to it there and also in Holland where it appeared later. These machines were being used in London by 1616 and in Lancashire by 1680 at the latest. They were gradually improved from weaving four to six ribbons originally to twenty-one by 1621 and eventually to as many as fifty. The shuttle for each ribbon, which was longer than the width of the ribbon, was knocked through the warp by vertical pegs mounted on a horizontal bar. An attempt to establish a water-powered factory in Manchester by Mr Gartside in 1765 failed because one person was still needed to tend each machine, to stop it should a warp thread break as well as changing the pirn in the shuttle when the weft ran out.

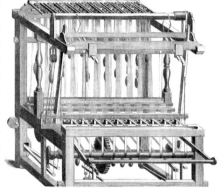

A hand-operated small-wares loom for weaving ten ribbons.

Yet the ribbon loom may have been important in the mechanisation of the textile industry if it was already known to John Kay when he patented his flying shuttle in 1733.[10] He certainly was acquainted with it when he patented improvements on it in 1745.[11] On the early horizontal loom, the weaver used one hand to pass the shuttle through the warp, catch it with the other and then beat up the weft with the first hand, changing hands continually. With the flying shuttle, the right hand held a picking stick or peg with cords attached to pickers sliding in shuttle boxes at either end of the slay holding the reed. A jerk of the picking stick moved the picker so that the shuttle was sent out of the box, across to the other side, while the other hand held the centre of the slay and beat up the weft with the reed. The weaver no longer had to swap the position of his hands each time. It was estimated that he could double his production even on narrow fabrics. On the broad loom, it enabled one man to do the work of two with a greater output. While this may be an overestimate, having seen a skilled weaver in China working an ordinary loom very quickly, the great advantage of the flying shuttle was that it enabled one person to weave cloth wider than he could reach with the stretch of his arms. The flying shuttle certainly made weaving much easier and faster. It was a very important addition.

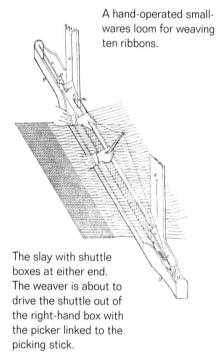

The slay with shuttle boxes at either end. The weaver is about to drive the shuttle out of the right-hand box with the picker linked to the picking stick.

It must have taken Kay a while to perfect his flying shuttle. He would have found that, when the shuttle was stopped in the shuttle box, a loose pirn with the weft wound round it might continue to rotate, forming a snarl. So the weft had to be drawn

A modern flying shuttle showing the wheels.

off from the end of a fixed cop skewered onto a spike in the shuttle. Kay took the cop formed on the Great Wheel. This feature continued with cops from Hargreaves's spinning jenny and Crompton's mule, a practice continuing right up to the 1970s. The race on which the shuttle ran across the loom had to be horizontal when the slay was pushed back. Therefore the race had to be at an acute angle to the reed, and the shuttle shaped likewise to fit. Kay mounted his shuttle on wheels so it moved easily. The wheels were set to send the shuttle in a slight curve so that it always remained pushing against the reed and did not fly out. The rod on which the picker was mounted in the shuttle box was also at a slight angle so that the rear end of the shuttle was lifted a little as it was driven out, again to stop it flying out. This type of shuttle would be incorporated into the power loom later. Kay came from the Lancashire area and by 1780 the flying shuttle had come into general use in the cotton industry as well as the Leeds woollen industry.

The Cotton Industry

The cotton industry probably displaced the woollen in the poor agricultural areas of the Pennines to the north and east of Manchester. It is not known how, when or why this industry started here. In about 1538, when John Leyland journeyed through Lancashire, he found the manufacture of cotton cloth already well established. He wrote, 'Bolton on the Moor has a market whose main commodities are cotton and course [sic] yarn. Several villages on the moors around Bolton manufacture cotton'.[12] In 1601, the name of George Arnould, fustian weaver of Bolton, appears in the records of the quarter sessions and more references to this type of employment appear in wills and other records in following years. Although the raw cotton, a cellulose fibre from the seed head or boll of the cotton plant, was imported from Turkey and areas round Syria, the industry expanded quickly in the Lancashire region for in 1621 a petition to Parliament stated that 'There is at least 40 thousand peeces [made yearly] and thousande of poore people set on working of these Fustians'.[13]

The flying shuttle certainly increased production and put pressure on hand spinners to produce more yarn. By the 1760s, lack of yarn caused a severe bottleneck to the expansion of the cotton textile industry because eight or more spinners were needed to keep one weaver supplied with cotton weft. More were needed to spin the linen warp for fustians which had cotton weft. Although women and children were employed throughout the length and breadth of the country, supply of yarn was always difficult and uncertain. Their equipment was hand cards for preparing the cotton and the Great Wheel for spinning the weft, a slow, intermittent process.

The Demand for Cotton Goods

During the second half of the seventeenth century, the East India Company organised a profitable trade, bringing back colourful calico and fine muslin cloth from India which became a popular form of dress. These increasing imports began to threaten the long-established wool trade, so much so that, in the years around the end of the seventeenth century, the wool interests began to take action. Shortly before 1700, petitions were presented to Parliament seeking prevention of imported silks and Indian painted and printed calicoes. This agitation culminated in the Act of 1700 when heavy duties were imposed on calico material, effectively pricing it out of the market. But this did not help the woollen industry because the small English calico-printing industry rapidly expanded and met the demand for cotton goods by printing imported white cloth. This naturally aroused the anger of the wool interests again and a further round of petitions to Parliament commenced in 1719 to try and extinguish the cotton trade in Great Britain. Those wearing calico were subjected to insults and violence from weavers of wool.

A further Act was passed in 1721 which prohibited any printed stuff made of cotton or mixed therewith. However muslins, neck cloths and fustians were specifically excluded from its scope. Therefore the mainstay of the Manchester trade, fustians which used linen warp and cotton weft, was not affected by the Act. The term fustian covered a wide range of goods, including herringbones, pillows for pockets and outside wear, strong cotton ribs and baragons, broad-raced linen, thicksets and tufts with striped dimities and lining jeans. Such a trade could not long remain outside the envy of the wool interests and this opposition came to a head in 1735. The wool supporters claimed that this trade ought to be included in the prohibition of 1721, especially as many Indian 'calicoes' were being imported as fustians. In return, the fustian manufacturers countered that this industry was beneficial because the cotton was imported from British plantations and the linen was the product of Ireland or mainland Britain itself which fitted in nicely with current economic theories. The Manchester Act of 1736 clarified the position and allowed Manchester and the surrounding area to continue with their manufacture of fustians by permitting the use of printed fustians made of linen and cotton, provided the warp was entirely linen. Those who wore pure cottons still might be fined £5, while those who sold them could be fined £20.

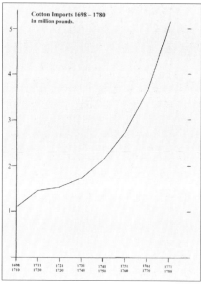

Cotton imports 1698–1780.

As the century progressed, a considerable demand arose for fustians and cotton cloth from overseas, particularly to supply the African trade. After 1750, the English cotton industry began to expand very considerably. People were beginning to realise that this industry would not necessarily prejudice the welfare of the wool industry. The value to the whole country of the cotton part of the export trade was recognised. In 1756, cotton velvets were first woven in England and the early 1760s saw renewed attempts at making all-cotton calico and the finer muslin. In 1766, the value of cotton goods made in England was £600,000. Import of cotton wool rose steadily to meet demand. But imports of cotton yarn show that, while these fell up to about 1750, they rose afterwards, indicating that the domestic hand spinners could not meet the total demand. Between 1698 and 1710, an average of 95,291lb of cotton yarn was imported. This dropped to an average of 46,316lb between 1741 and 1750 but rose to an average of 76,849lb between 1771 and 1780. The average import of cotton wool in those years was 1,095,084lb between 1698 and 1710, 2,137,294lb between 1741 and 1750 and 5,127,689lb between 1771 and 1780.[14] The increasing consumption after the 1760s was met by the invention of better spinning machines so that the import of cotton yarn fell rapidly in the following years. The article on 'Cotton' in Rees's *Cyclopaedia* written around 1808 summed up the quality of hand cotton spinning, probably spun on the Great Wheel:

> … [The spinning wheel] on which one person could with difficulty produce a pound of thread, by close and diligent application, the whole day. The goods then manufactured were strong and coarse, compared with those of the present day, and little or no thread finer than from 16 to 20 hanks in the pound, each hank measuring 840 yards, was then spun. It was subject, as may be readily conceived, to great inequalities, its evenness depending greatly on the delicacy of touch, which the spinner by long habit had acquired, and varied with every little difference in the extension of the thread during twisting, and revolutions of the spindle in portions of the same length.[15]

The count system determined the fineness of the yarn through the weight of so many hanks of 840 yards each: No. 1 count was the coarsest with 840 yards weighing one pound; 20 hanks, termed 20s counts, were coarse and 30s to 60s medium; 80s was beginning to be quite fine. New inventions, mostly based on existing principles, not only increased production but also improved quality and reduced price so that the cotton textile industry boomed in the last quarter of the eighteenth century.

The First Spinning Machines

The Spinning Machine of Paul and Wyatt

Of the many early inventors who tried to develop spinning machines, those who came nearest to success were Lewis Paul and John Wyatt. It has been claimed that Wyatt conceived a machine as early as 1730. He and Paul were probably corresponding about it in 1735. Paul took out two patents for machines to spin wool or cotton in 1738 and 1758.[16] In 1748, two methods of carding were patented.[17] The drawings in the 1758 patent show the spindles and flyers driven by a large horizontal wheel in a circular frame somewhat similar to silk-throwing machines. Placed above the spindles were the cotton rovings, wound on bobbins which rested on paying-out rollers. The fibres were twisted by the flyer method and the resulting yarn wound onto a bobbin.

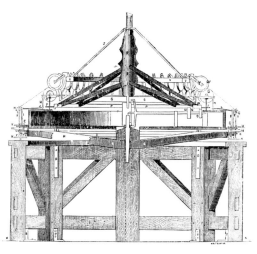

1758 patent drawing of Paul's spinning machine.

Their first mill with these machines was set up during the summer of 1741 in a warehouse in the Upper Priory, Birmingham. It was driven by two asses but was derelict within two years. After experimenting with a hand-powered mill at Holborn, London, Edward Cave found a suitable watermill at Northampton in 1742 which may have continued until 1755. Another mill was established by Daniel Bourn at Leominster, possibly in 1744. It was destroyed by fire in 1754 and not rebuilt although both Bourn and his partners had considerable hopes of it. These machines were complex and difficult to maintain in proper working order. But the main reason for Paul and Wyatt's lack of success was that their machine was based on an unsound principle for spinning cotton. They had failed to separate the drawing or drafting stage to thin down the sliver or roving from the twisting or spinning stage which was essential with the flyer method. They came very near to success.

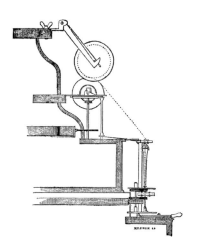

Detail of bobbin, roller, spindle and flyer from Paul's 1758 patent.

James Hargreaves's Spinning Jenny

During the 1760s, cotton became the 'lead' industry for textile inventions. It was James Hargreaves of Oswaldtwistle near Blackburn who began to alleviate the shortage of yarn with his spinning jenny, the first machine which successfully spun a number of cotton yarns at once. The story recounted in Rees's *Cyclopaedia* has a ring of truth about it. One day in 1764, an ordinary Great Wheel on which somebody was spinning was knocked over accidentally at his home. It remained rotating and gave Hargreaves his inspiration. His first machine with eight spindles differed little from the one described in the patent which he took out in 1770.[18] This had sixteen spindles placed at the back of a frame in an almost vertical position inclined slightly towards the spinner. They were turned by bands from a horizontal wheel on the right-hand side. Bobbins with rovings

Replica Spinning Jenny made for the Museum from
Hargreaves's 1770 patent.

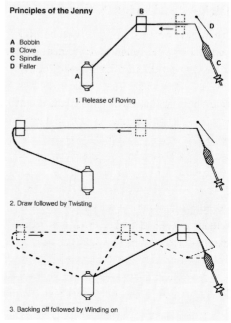

Principles of the Jenny

A Bobbin
B Clove
C Spindle
D Faller

1. Release of Roving

2. Draw followed by Twisting

Principles of the Jenny.   3. Backing off followed by Winding on

were mounted in a creel below the horizontal framing. The method of operation was similar to the intermittent action of the Great Wheel but, instead of the left hand controlling a single roving, it gripped a 'clove' made from two parallel pieces of wood to clasp the rovings. Lengths of roving were drawn through the clove. The clove could slide along the top of the framing to imitate the action of the spinner's left hand, drawing out the fibres as it was moved away from the spindles a distance of about 30in (750mm), while the right hand turned the horizontal wheel to put in twist. After backing-off, a foot pedal operated a faller wire to guide the spun yarn onto the spindles in the form of a cop while the clove was pushed back towards the spindles ready for the next draw.

Hargreaves was certainly no mechanical genius. A replica in the Museum based on the 1770 patent is a difficult, backbreaking machine to operate, partly through its low height. The drafting of the fibres is not separated from twisting so it is difficult to balance the right amount of thinning the sliver or roving and the right amount of twist. The yarns are constantly breaking and, even with rovings prepared on modern machinery, the finished yarns are uneven. It is not easy to wind on the yarn in a good cop. Only a lightly twisted yarn could be spun because a short length of spun yarn stretched between the tip of the spindle and the clove. Twist from this ran into the next length of roving drawn through the clove and too much twist could prevent the fibres from being drafted. But the finished yarn was suitable for the weft in fustians so that soon improved jennies of 80 spindles became quite common and later there were some of 130 spindles. By 1788, there were said to be some 20,070 jennies in use in the English and Scottish cotton industries. Even in 1811, Crompton found a total of 155,880 jenny-spindles at work. It was estimated that these larger jennies could supply sufficient weft for two looms. By 1776, the jenny had spread into the woollen districts, eastwards to Holmfirth in Yorkshire and southwards to Shepton Mallet in Somerset. It was important in the early stages of growth in the textile industry during the Industrial Revolution. Yet, through its intermittent action of first spinning and then winding on, the jenny was always operated manually and never by power although some were grouped into merchants' houses or mills. Because it soon outstripped production of hand-carded sliver and rovings, water-powered carding mills based on Arkwright's invention were built across the country after 1775 to supply it, but how many is not known.

Richard Arkwright's Waterframe

It may have been the gossip in Richard Arkwright's barber's shop in Bolton which turned his thoughts to inventing a cotton spinning machine since Bolton had long been a seat of the fustian industry. But Arkwright has never been credited with much mechanical aptitude and certainly did not have the tools necessary for constructing the gearwheels which would regulate the speed of his rollers for drawing out the cotton rovings. He turned to the flyer and bobbin system for twisting and winding on his yarn which, as we have seen, was a continuous operation. So far, there was nothing new, except that he placed four spindles with flyers and bobbins vertically near the bottom of his machine and drove them from a horizontal wheel in a similar way to Hargreaves. The size of his bobbin was 2in (50mm) between the flanges and the same diameter so frequent changes were necessary. At the top of his machine, he replaced human fingers with his crucial drawing rollers which have barely changed up to the recent invention of open end spinning. There were four sets, each consisting of a pair. The top roller of each pair was covered with leather and was kept firmly in contact with the bottom one by a weight. The bottom rollers were made from metal and wood with flutes cut along them. These lower rollers were connected together by gearing so that one shaft could turn them all. The pairs of rollers did not all turn at the same speed, for the back pair, where the thick cotton roving entered, rotated slowest and each succeeding pair turned faster. In this way, the roving was drawn out until the correct number of fibres was passed out between the nip of the front rollers where the twist from the flyer and spindle locked them firmly together and made the finished yarn.

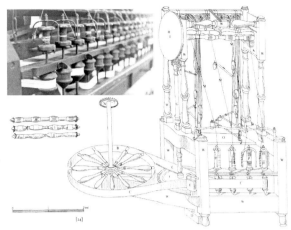

Arkwright's drawing of his spinning machine in his 1769 patent. Inset: Bobbins and flyers on a later waterframe.

Cotton Drawing Rollers

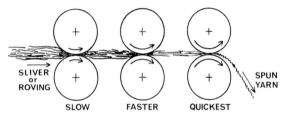

Patented by Arkwright in 1769.
Principle of drawing rollers.

Rollers and weights on a later waterframe.

The drafting of the fibres by rollers was separated from the twisting, making spinning much easier so that the skill was removed and Arkwright's machines could be minded by children.

Arkwright looked for someone to make his machine. His wife, Margaret Biggins, who came from Leigh, Lancashire, may have introduced him to another John Kay, a clockmaker from the same town. Earlier, Kay had helped Thomas Highs to build a spinning machine and one story says that Kay showed High's machine to Arkwright, who copied it and took all the credit. However, Arkwright added two crucial contributions. First, he realised that the different pairs of rollers must be set the correct distance apart to correspond with the staple length of the fibres being spun. Too close together and two pairs of rollers would grip the same fibre so it could not be drawn out but would break. Too far apart and the fibres would float in the gap and the drawing would be uneven, resulting in lumpy and broken yarns. In order to hold the fibres tightly in the nip of the rollers, Arkwright made his second contribution. He hung weights on the top rollers so they were pressed firmly against their lower counterparts. Neither Paul and Wyatt nor Highs weighted their rollers and neither did any of them realise the crucial importance of the staple length. Without sufficient weight, the twist will run through the nip and lock the fibres together in the drafting zone between the sets of rollers and prevent further drafting taking place. At the Museum, we found this happened when demonstrating an early original Arkwright spinning machine of about 1770 and had to increase the weights on the front rollers to make it work properly. Rees's *Cyclopaedia* gives weights on the Arkwright type of machines at Belper Mill, Derbyshire, as 2lb on the back pair, a few ounces on the middle but 20lb for the front.[19] No spinning machine with roller drafting will work without the correct spacing and weighting of the pairs of rollers. This is easier to achieve with cotton through its shorter staple length compared to wool or flax. But, because the drafting of the fibres depends on the proportional increase in speed between the pairs of rollers, if the rovings being fed in are lumpy and uneven, these characteristics will appear in the spun yarn. So high-quality rovings are essential.

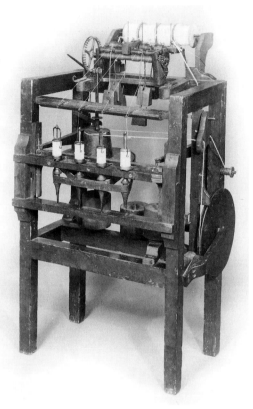

Early waterframe used at Cromford in about 1771.

In January 1768, Arkwright returned to his native town of Preston. A spinning machine was built in the old Grammar School, probably financed by John Smalley and David Thornley. The three agreed to form a partnership in May to take out their historic patent for the invention in the name of Arkwright, which was granted fourteen months later in 1769.[20] Thornley died a couple of years later. Arkwright's first machine with four spindles will fit comfortably on a table-top and can be turned by hand. The partners could have continued to make such small machines worked by hand for use in cottages, where they could have been readily copied, but Arkwright's business acumen told him that it would be easier to control licences of his patent if the machines were set up in mills and driven by power. Because of riots in Lancashire in which some of Hargreaves's jennies were destroyed, Arkwright and his partners moved to Nottingham where they established a mill powered by horses. From such a modest beginning, Arkwright would build up a large empire.

However, before this could happen, Arkwright had to solve the problem of supplying his spinning machine with rovings. This needed further investment so the partnership was expanded in January 1770 to include Samuel Need, a Nottingham banker, and Jedediah Strutt. In 1759, Strutt had laid the basis of his fortune when he obtained a patent for his Derby rib mechanism, a highly ingenious device added to William Lee's knitting machine of 1589.[21] It enabled the fashionable and more comfortable ribbed stockings to be knitted by machine instead of by hand. His invention was followed by a succession of others which enabled the framework knitter to produce almost every kind of mesh by mechanical means. In 1764, the knitting machine was adapted to make eyelet holes, the first step towards the manufacture of machine-made lace. While so far all these inventions remained hand-operated, they increased the demand for yarn so that Nottingham and its area offered many advantages to the prospective machine spinner.

Preparatory Machines

In 1771, the partners took the momentous decision to build a mill to be powered by water at Cromford near Matlock, even though their machinery was far from perfect. From this move, Arkwright's spinning machine became called the 'waterframe'. Groups of four spindles were driven by brass gearwheels. There were six groups in a line on each side of the framing. It was here also that development continued on more machines to prepare rovings for the waterframe, resulting in Arkwright's 1775 patent.[22] For the waterframe to be able to spin a continuous yarn, each spindle had to be supplied with a continuous length of roving which in turn had to be made from a continuous length of carded sliver. In other words, having mechanised one part of the spinning sequence, it was necessary to mechanise all the others to restore the balance. One invention stimulated another in quick succession until the whole character of textile production was changed completely from a domestic to a factory industry.

Descriptions and pictures of ten different machines for preparing cotton in particular were given in the 1775 patent. Some were of little significance, other than showing that Arkwright was trying to mechanise all the preparatory processes. For example, his opening and cleaning machines were never employed since at Cromford women continued to beat the cotton with sticks to open it and then pick out the dirt by hand. After this, the cotton had to be fed into the carding engine which Arkwright did by laying a length of cloth on a table and spreading cotton wool evenly on top. The weight and thickness of cotton per unit length here gave the quality control for the remainder of the spinning processes. The cloth with the cotton was rolled up on a lap machine and put at the back of the carding engine. The fibres were fed in as the cloth unrolled and fell to the floor. Later the cloth was found to be unnecessary.

In 1748, Bourn patented a carding machine[23] in which the cotton was carded by four consecutive cylinders the same size but he failed to find a way to remove the cotton from the last one. To give a continuous sliver from the carding engine, the whole of the surfaces of the cylinders had to be covered with wire hooks or points. Arkwright prepared a long narrow strip of card fillet which he wound in a spiral around the cylinders so there were virtually no gaps between the points. The cotton was

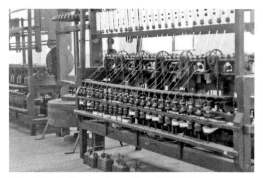
Pair of waterframes from Cromford Mill.

The machine for preparing the laps which were wound round the small roller.

CARDING ENGINE with FLATS

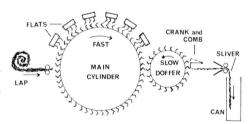
Principle of Arkwright's carding engine.

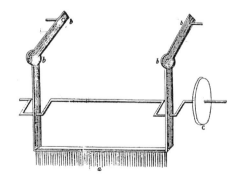
The crank and comb from Arkwright's 1769 patent.

Carding engine from Cromford Mill.

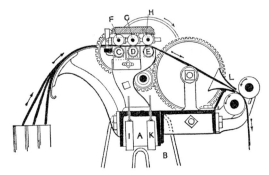

Principal working parts of Arkwright's drawing frame; CDE: fluted rollers, FGH: upper rollers, L: funnel to compact sliver.

teased out between the points on the main cylinder as it revolved and others on smaller diameter cylinders or flat cards around the upper circumference. A second doffer cylinder, smaller than the main one, rotated at a different speed to remove the cotton off the main one. This left the problem of how to take the cotton off this last cylinder. Where others had failed, Arkwright found the solution with his 'crank and comb'. Across the front of the doffer was mounted a strip of thin metal, the comb, so named because the bottom edge was cut into fine teeth. It was connected to a crank which raised and lowered it so that the teeth pushed the cotton off the wire points of the doffer cylinder. The cotton came off in a broad gossamer web. This was collected into a funnel and passed through a pair of rollers from where it dropped into a can placed in front.

Arkwright had found a way of preparing a continuous sliver but it still had many irregularities and was too thick to be fed into his waterframes. So he used more of his crucial rollers on a drawing frame. He passed, say, six slivers together through three pairs of rollers, each pair rotating more quickly to draw them out in the same ratio as the number of slivers fed in. The result was a sliver six times as long but more equal and smoother. This sliver still had to be reduced for spinning and some twist imparted. Arkwright's preferred solution was to pass the sliver through a further set of drawing rollers and allow it to fall into another can which was rotating so imparting twist to form rovings. Children wound these rovings onto bobbins ready for the waterframes. All these machines from the lap machine and carding engines through to the winding frames were driven by the waterwheel at the Cromford mill. Arkwright had mechanised cotton spinning, a far cry from the carding brushes and spindle and whorl. The speed of development of this complex machinery was extraordinary.

Revolving can frame from Cromford Mill.

The Cotton Industry Expands

While the machine was taking over from the handcraft, the yarn had to be sold. Cotton spun on a waterframe produced a hard twisted yarn more suited for warp than weft. But the various Parliamentary acts forbade the use of cotton warp. In 1773, Strutt erected a new mill at Derby specifically for the calico business but this new venture ran into difficulties with the Excise men who charged the highest rate of duty on the cloth since it was made entirely from cotton. Arkwright petitioned Parliament that calicoes made with his yarn, which was now called twist, should be charged at a lower rate since they were produced entirely in the Kingdom of Great Britain. In 1774, Strutt claimed that they had already expended over £13,000 and employed upwards of 600 people of all ages in spinning. The plea was allowed and their calicoes were able to compete on equal terms with fustians and linen cloth. At last Arkwright was able to overcome the hindrances preventing the development of his patent and start the enormous expansion of the cotton industry in the following decades. This was based largely on exports. Cotton manufactures rose from the sixth most valuable export in 1761 to the second in 1783. They surpassed in value silks in 1767 and linens in 1781. It was not until 1803 that exports of cotton manufactures surpassed the value of wool cloth exports, so displacing that industry from its historic primacy in the foreign trade of the realm.

The front of Samuel Greg's mill at Quarry Bank, Styal.

Soon both Arkwright and Strutt were building more spinning mills. In 1775, Strutt started mills at Milford and Belper. In 1776, a second mill was added at Cromford. Arkwright had interests in mills at Birkacre near Chorley, Lancashire, and at Bakewell, Derbyshire, begun in 1777. Then in 1780 Arkwright started mills at Masson near Matlock, Haarlem at Wirksworth, Derbyshire, and Shudehill in Manchester. He moved into Scotland at New Lanark in 1784. Smalley began his first mill at Holywell, Flint, in 1777. Through the spread of his empire, Arkwright's waterframe and carding machine became known throughout the land and capitalists flocked to buy them or for permission to use them. For example in 1775, Gardom and Pares paid £2,000 for an initial premium for the 1769 patent and £5,000 for the 1775 patent plus an annual tribute of £1,000 on their mill at Calver, Derbyshire. The licences seem to have been based on units of 1,000 spindles which would have needed 10 h.p. to drive them and their associated preparatory machinery. Arkwright himself said that by 1782 he had sold his machines to adventurers in eight counties who had invested over £60,000 in mills and equipment.

But other people copied his machines without permission so that Arkwright began prosecutions. While his patent of 1769 would expire in 1783, that for 1775 including the carding engine was valid until 1789. Accordingly Arkwright brought Charles Lewis Mordaunt to trial before the Court of King's Bench in July 1781. Mordaunt did not deny that he had infringed Arkwright's 1775 patent but pleaded that the specification was void because it was obscure and incomplete. This is certainly true if the drawings in the 1775 patent are compared with the one in 1769. After a six-hour hearing, the jury found the patent had no validity. Arkwright did not proceed with the other cases after this surprising verdict. The trade was thrown open so that many people started to build mills. Arkwright drew up his 'case' for extending his spinning patent to 1789 as well as confirming his 1775 patent and presented it to Parliament in February 1782. This failed, as did a second attempt a year later.

In the meantime, Arkwright decided to prosecute those spinners who, he alleged, had infringed the waterframe patent. The case against Peter Nightingale ended in Arkwright's favour in February 1785. This caused consternation in the textile industry because it reversed the judgement for Mordaunt and thereby Arkwright might be able to reclaim his carding patent and charge whatever price he chose. Since 1781, an estimated £300,000 had been invested in buildings and Arkwright machines, creating an industry which provided employment for some 30,000 men, women and children. The Manchester spinners were determined to attack the patent on all possible grounds and successfully applied for a writ of *scire facias* to have the verdict annulled. The case was heard in the Court of King's Bench on 25 June 1785 and went against Arkwright, turning on the lack of a sufficiently described patent. There was great celebration among the cotton spinners so that mill building continued apace.

A hasty survey was carried out by Patrick Colquhoun in 1788 which listed nineteen water-powered cotton mills in Scotland and 124 in England of which two-thirds had been erected in the past five years. These figures for England include two in Wales and one on the Isle of Man. His figures are almost identical to those recorded by Edward Baines in his History of the Cotton Industry from an unidentified pamphlet printed in 1787. Both agree that the greatest number occurred in Lancashire with 41, followed by Derbyshire with 22, Nottinghamshire 17 and Yorkshire 11. Mills were scattered in a further ten English counties as far south as Surrey. The Welsh ones were in Pembrokeshire and Flintshire. More mills were to be found in ten Scottish counties from Galloway to Aberdeenshire with the greatest concentration around Glasgow. Baines thought that this total of 143 mills 'would approach to correctness'.[24] The eager entrepreneurs, in their search for sites where they could find streams or rivers to power their mills, had had to cover nearly the length and breadth of Britain. The need for water power eclipsed the high transport costs of the raw cotton and spun yarn in the days before adequate canal, road and rail communications.

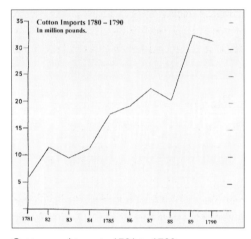

Cotton wool imports 1781 to 1790.

Cotton is an annual crop, imported at that time from the Mediterranean and the West Indies. Provided land could be found on which it could be grown and labourers (slaves) found to harvest it, production could be increased quickly to match consumption. It had the advantage that the cellulose fibres in the cotton boll needed little preparation to prepare them for spinning. The following figures for cotton imported from 1781 to 1789 show the initial impact on demand principally from the jenny and the water-frame. In 1781, only 5,101,920lb were imported, rising to 11,306,800lb in the following year. After a fall in imports, the figures reached 17,992,888lb in 1785 and 22,600,000lb in 1787, only to be eclipsed in 1789 with 32,576,023lb.[25] This shows a truly remarkable increase in consumption without a corresponding rise in prices.

The Impact of the Spinning Inventions

One visitor to Cromford in 1785 observed, 'I can only say the whole process of cleaning, carding, combing, twisting and compleating the yarn for the loom seems to be done almost without human aid.' Arkwright had invented 'a stupendous piece of mechanism, the first view of which irresistibly impresses the mind with the idea of magick'.[26] He had invented even more than this because, as Baines pointed out, 'When this series of machines was made known, and by their means yarns were produced far superior in quality to any before spun in England, as well as lower in price, a mighty impulse was communicated to the cotton manufacture'.[27]

The effects of this improvement were felt in the rest of the cotton industry. In his patent application of 1738, Paul had pointed out the great drawbacks of the domestic system:

> Whenever a clothier has occasion for a parcel of yarn to be spun to any particular degree of size or twist, he is obliged to have a much greater quantity spun than he often wants of that particular size or twist in order that among the whole he may pick out so many [threads] as will answer the present occasion; whereby the remainder often becomes a dead stock upon his hand for a considerable time.[28]

It is a great credit to Arkwright that he developed a system which spun a yarn 'many times stronger and leveller' than that from the spinning wheel. Mordaunt adopted the Arkwright system because, as he told Arthur Young in 1788, 'A total revolution in spinning has happened in these parts. Water engines make such fine level threads [that] spinning by hand engines is entirely abolished.'[29] Baines pointed out that, with Arkwright's yarn,

Weavers could now obtain an unlimited quantity of yarn, at a reasonable price; manufacturers could use warps of cotton which were much cheaper than the linen warps formerly used. Cotton fabrics could be sold lower than had ever before been known. The demand for them consequently increased. The shuttle flew with fresh energy, and the weavers earned immoderately high wages. Spinning mills were erected to supply the requisite quantity of yarn. The fame of Arkwright resounded through the land.[30]

People were also impressed with the size of the new mills. The original 1784 mill at New Lanark burnt down on 9 October 1788. It was replaced by one of five storeys, attic and basement 154ft (47m) long, 27ft (8m) wide and 60ft (18m) high. This was a typical size.[31] John Byng visited Cromford in 1790 and noted, 'These cotton mills, seven stories high, and fill'd with inhabitants, remind me of a first rate man of war; and when they are lighted up, in a dark night, look most luminously beautiful.'[32] The famous artist, Joseph Wright of Derby, was also fascinated by the Cromford mills illuminated at night and painted them several times with the windows ablaze and the moon shining overhead.

Early Sources of Power

The spinning inventions firmly established Lancashire and Yorkshire as the major textile producing centres of England. This was partly through their natural advantages with the streams running off the Pennines providing water for processing and power. These rivers also formed the means for transporting raw materials and finished goods along the Mersey and Irwell and the Aire and Calder navigations to and from ports. Later canals such as the Bridgewater and the Rochdale provided internal links. As the industries expanded and new water-power sites became scarce, the answer lay close at hand through the underlying coal measures which could be exploited to provide fuel for steam engines. Steam engines were being improved at the same time.

Horsepower

The small scale of early spinning mills made them well suited to be driven by animal power. Paul and Wyatt drove their first production machine at Birmingham with two asses. When Arkwright moved to Nottingham in 1768, he chose horses for his mill there as he envisaged in his patent. After Hargreaves had also moved there, he and his partner Thomas James had horses turning their carding machinery in 1777. The great advantage of animal power was its ready availability. No dams, leats or sluices were necessary as with water power and a horse-wheel was certainly less costly than a Boulton and Watt steam engine. The number of horses could be easily varied from one to ten or twelve to suit the amount of machinery being employed. The greatest disadvantage was that horses tired quickly, necessitating a number being kept to enable shift working, causing greater expense. In 1790, Arkwright decided to replace the horse-wheel in his second Nottingham mill with a steam engine. The wheel was 27ft (8m) diameter, 9ft (3m) high to the overhead gearing, situated in a room 11ft (3.5m) high. The drawing has a note on it: '6 strong horses at a time, Mr Arkwright said 9 horses'.[33]

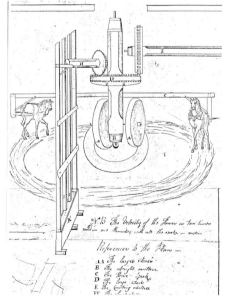

Two horses driving edge runners and stampers for an oil mill. (By permission of Birmingham Central Library, Boulton and Watt Collection)

Probably most horse-mills drove carding machinery for jennies and hand mules. A family of spinners may well have had a horse-wheel already installed in their barn for working agricultural equipment. It could have been quickly linked to carding engines which would have prepared either cotton or sheep's wool for their spinning machines. In the cellar of their Yellow factory in 1791, Horrocks Miller & Co. had a horse located 'which performed its dull round from day to day, turning the carding-engines in the room above'.[34] Here the cotton spinning was done on hand machines. At Lilley's Mill, Stalybridge, the horse-wheel which turned machinery for scribbling and carding engines for wool was replaced in 1802 by a steam engine, a very early example of steam power for the woollen industry in that area.

The importance of horsepower in the early days of mechanisation has been seriously underestimated. A number of mills built in Macclesfield and Congleton in the late eighteenth and early nineteenth centuries were situated away from known water sources and have no recorded primary power system. Between 1785 and 1826, only six sites out of sixty-eight mills erected in Macclesfield are known to have made use of water power, but many of the later ones would have had steam engines. Oldham, on the top of its hill, was poorly sited for water power. Between 1776 and 1778, six small cotton mills were erected there, three worked by water and three by horses. By 1791, there were eighteen and, because most of the best water sites had been taken, most of these later mills were driven by horses. In 1795, Royton had 'five mills moved by water, four horse mills for carding cotton, one fulling mill for the Rochdale baizes manufactured in the neighbourhood'.[35] Horsepower survived for a long time. In Oldham, Glodwick cotton mill was built in 1800 by Benjamin Clegg and was only converted to steam in 1815. A Congleton silk mill still had its stable and horse-wheel with cast iron gearing in 1812 while in Lower Hillgate, Stockport, there was a combination of a horsewalk working in conjunction with a 20ft-diameter waterwheel in 1821. Of the Yorkshire firms making returns to the 1834 inquiry into child employment, there was still one using animal power. Thomas Taylor of Barnsley had 'one horse . . . employed for winding yarn upon bobbins from the hanks, in a large chamber over the warehouse'.[36]

Water Power

However, most of those people equipping cotton mills adopted water power. It is thought that over half the mills in Colquhoun's list were on greenfield sites; the rest were either converted or new buildings at existing watermills. The greenfield sites were mostly higher up the valleys so had poorer water resources. Smalley selected a favourable site at Holywell because Saint Winefride's well provided a constant flow with little change in volume that rarely flooded or froze. Others were not so fortunate and the disadvantages of water power quickly became apparent. In spring and at other times, sites might be flooded, while in summer the water might run low or freeze in winter. The catchment area was limited, preventing the possibility of expansion. Mills had to be built where there was a suitable fall because streams could not be moved to them. Considerable capital might have to be invested in dams, reservoirs, sluice gear and channels to take the water to the mill wheel. But, once the high first costs had been met, running costs were low compared with other energy sources.

Marginal improvements might be added. For example, some sites might be developed with better storage reservoirs or improved outlets such as tunnels to take the water away from the mills. Then the arrangements for the wheels themselves might be improved along the principles laid down by John Smeaton who had found by his experiments with models in 1752 and 1753 that overshot or breastshot wheels working through the weight of water by gravity were more efficient than undershot wheels working by impulse where the water struck the blades.

Some mill owners were not so fortunate and could not augment or improve their water supply. In 1786, John Metcalfe of Carleton built a mill on the banks of a small stream that ran through his estate at Brough in Westmorland. He planned to have 2,000 spindles but found he could drive only 504; 'the water not answering my expectation'.[37] The mill was frequently stopped or only working half-time. Even Samuel Greg at Quarry Bank Mill, Styal, found the River Bollin failed to supply enough water in spite of extensive dams and storage ponds. In 1818, there is a note in the Greg papers that ten days' lost time would have to be made up in the following winter. The two water-wheels and the steam engine were unable to provide enough power since there were '256 spindles or Two drums upon an average standing for want of water'.[38]

One answer to shortage of water was to install an auxiliary steam engine. Watson and Son were obliged to do this at their Bromsgrove mill sometime before 1786 as they explained when opposing the Worcester Canal bill:

Wooden clasp-arm waterwheel for a fulling mill at the Skansen Open Air Museum, Sweden.

> The Summer Supply is not, upon Average, equal to Two Thirds of the Business. In the last summer it was barely equal to One Third, on which Account Messrs Watson were obliged to work at a Loss of, for many Weeks, from £10 to £15 a Week. A Fire Engine, erected at a very considerable Expence, was kept in constant Work from June to November, for the Purpose of enabling the Manufactory to be carried on.[39]

The fire engine at Watson's mill would have raised water from the lower to the upper millpond where it descended again around the waterwheel, thus helping to drive the mill. In 1792, Messrs Lawrence & Yates of Manchester had built a large cotton mill with 2,500 spindles near Manchester and, while they had plenty of water to drive them in wet weather, '… in very dry weather they have not water enough to turn 4 or 5 hundred – They have already an Engine upon the Saverian plan which they say raises water enough to turn 900 spindles and preparations and only burns 1 cwt of Coals pr hour'.[40] They were asking Boulton and Watt to provide them with another steam engine.

The Savery Engine

There were three types of steam engine on the market around 1780 for pumping water: the Savery engine, the Newcomen engine and the Watt engine. The earliest and simplest was patented by Thomas Savery in 1698, which he called 'The Miners' Friend' because he intended that it should be placed down a mineshaft to drain a mine. Steam from a boiler filled an enclosed receiver. Cold water was poured over the outside of the receiver to condense the steam inside and create a vacuum. Atmospheric pressure forced water from the bottom of the mine up a pipe into the receiver through a non-return clack valve. When the receiver was full, steam was re-admitted to force the water through another clack valve and up another pipe to the surface. The engine was controlled manually. Savery impressed members of the Royal Society with a demonstration model. Certainly models built for the Museum performed very convincingly. Yet, even though he was in contact with members of this august body and so had access to the latest scientific theories, Savery never mentioned in his book the necessity of regularly purging the receiver of air. It is doubtful if any engine were installed in a mine by Savery because the joints of the

J.T. Desagulier's experimental Savery engine which proved to be as economical as his equivalent Newcomen engine.

boiler and pipes could not be made strong enough to withstand the heat and steam pressure needed in mines with a high lift. A few were installed in and around London to supply houses with water.

Some textile mills turned to a modified type of Savery engine to recirculate water over their waterwheels. Only the vacuum phase was retained because that was sufficient to raise the water for a sixteen- or twenty-foot-diameter waterwheel. The water, once raised into the receiver, ran out directly over the top of an overshot wheel. Castings, which needed no costly boring or machining, were used for the pipes and receiver. Only the valves necessitated some fitting. For a mill which required an engine to supplement the water supply occasionally, this type of Savery engine seemed to be a cheap proposition. We do not know how many were installed in Manchester and in other parts of Lancashire by Joshua Wrigley. James Watt junior commented in March 1791 that Wrigley was erecting thirteen of his steam engines for driving cotton machinery through a waterwheel.[41] In 1795, John Aikin was impressed with these engines because they lessened the need for horses and their power could be increased simply by enlarging the receiver. He also praised Wrigley, 'who never applied for a patent, but imparted freely what he invented to those thought proper to employ him'.[42] John Farey, writing in 1827, said that:

> Mr Rigley contrived his engines to work without an attendant: the motion of the water-wheel being made to open and shut the regulator, and injection-cock, at the proper intervals. They continued in use for some years, but were at length given up in favour of better engines.[43]

James Watt was not impressed with these engines and told John Rennie in 1785, 'Joshua Wrigley is erecting a rotative Engine at Manchester, but if he does it no better than he does his cotton mills he will be beshet the re[ceive]r'.[44] A large one of 20 h.p. was erected by Messrs Salvin of Durham who found it fell 'short 1/2 of that power & to burn an immense quantity of coals; as will readily suppose'.[45] Two were erected by Wrigley in 1784 at Joseph Thackery's cotton mill at Garratt, on the River Medlock, then just on the southern edge of Manchester. Smeaton tested them and found that the smaller, with a receiver 16in diameter by 6ft long, had a duty of 5¼ million pounds weight of water raised to a height of 1ft by the consumption of a bushel of coals weighing 84 pounds. The larger had a 2ft-diameter receiver 7ft high and had a duty of 5½ million pounds. It burnt 32cwt of coals in 24 hours.

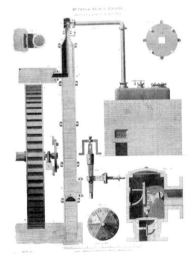

Peter Kier's modified Savery engine for working a waterwheel.

The only other figures we have for the performance of these Savery engines working waterwheels are for one erected by Wrigley to drive the workshop of Peter Kier in London. The water supply was controlled by a fly-ball governor. Kier claimed a duty for the engine alone of 17,325,000 pounds and when combined with the waterwheel, a duty of over 11,550,000 pounds.[46] These figures must be regarded with suspicion because usually there were complaints about the excessive coal consumption and this performance is better than the best known Newcomen engines. The drawback even of these later Savery engines working by suction only was that the receiver would be cooled to the temperature of the water being lifted, or much cooler than the cylinder of a Newcomen engine and cooler even than Watt's separate condenser. Then, to recreate the vacuum with the steam, the shell of the receiver would have to be heated again at least to the boiling point of water so there would have been considerable wasteful condensation of steam as it lost its heat to warm up the various parts. But this type of steam pump filled a small niche in the market. There were others besides Wrigley who built them and Wrigley himself continued to install them until shortly before 1800.

The Newcomen Engine

Like Savery, Thomas Newcomen had seen the need for a better machine to pump water out of mines. By 1712, he had developed a steam engine which he installed at a coal mine near Dudley Castle, then in Staffordshire. It is not known what scientific knowledge he had but his fire engine proved to be the first really dependable source of power in the history of civilisation when compared with wind and water. Its use spread rapidly across the country from the metalliferous mines in Cornwall to the coalmines of the Newcastle upon Tyne area. Although the date of 1760 is probably too early for the engine at Fairbottom Bobs between Oldham and Ashton-under-Lyne now preserved at Dearborn in the Henry Ford Museum, around that date such engines were draining collieries in the Manchester area. In March 1774, one with a cylinder diameter of 32 in was offered for sale at Bradford Colliery to the east of Manchester. So it was only to be expected that millowners would turn to these 'common' engines to act as returning engines to supplement the power of their waterwheels. Since no other example was likely to be forthcoming to display in the Manchester Museum of Science and Technology founded in 1969, the Mechanical Engineering Department of the then University of Manchester Institute of Science and Technology agreed to construct a one-third scale model of the engine at Dudley Castle. Our problems in operating it showed the difficulties which Newcomen had to overcome.

The Newcomen engine at Fairbottom Bobs between Oldham and Ashton-under-Lyne now at the Henry Ford Museum, Dearborn, USA.

One-third scale working model of the first successful steam engine which Thomas Newcomen built in 1712 to pump water from a colliery near Dudley Castle, Staffordshire.

Newcomen suspended the pump rods down the mine by chains from one end of a beam pivoted in the middle. The volume of water raised each stroke would remain the same, provided the length of the stroke did not alter. So a virtually constant power output was needed on the uplift of each stroke. It was the weight of the pump rods which returned the steam piston, hung by chains at the other end of the beam, to the top of the steam cylinder so no power was produced from steam in the second half of the cycle. To start the cycle, steam from a boiler underneath filled the cylinder with the piston at the top and drove out any air through a snifting valve. Although knowledge of the nature of the atmosphere and gases was rudimentary at that time, Newcomen recognised that he could not form a good vacuum when air was present instead of steam. So he sealed his piston with a layer of water, something we in the Museum found essential to prevent ingress of air past the piston, and he also fitted a snifting valve through which air could be blown out.

The crucial development probably occurred by accident. The engine will make a stroke if left to cool naturally, but this is very slow. Like Savery, Newcomen tried to cool his steam cylinder externally, in his case by placing it in a jacket of cold water. But the solder filling a flaw in the cylinder wall gave way. The result was spectacular. The piston on his model engine came down so rapidly into the vacuum thus formed that it smashed the bottom of the cylinder. Marten Triewald, one of Newcomen's assistants, commented:

> The hot water which flowed everywhere thus convinced even the very senses of the onlookers that they had discovered an incomparably powerful force which had hitherto been entirely unknown in nature – at least no-one had ever suspected that it could originate in this way.[47]

Newcomen had the genius to realise what had happened and quickly fitted another valve to admit a jet of cold water into the cylinder to condense the steam. At the Museum, we found that direct injection dramatically improved the operation of the engine so that it worked much more quickly and efficiently.

But then appropriate valve gear had to be added to control the engine because the length of the stroke is determined by the opening and closing of the valves which also give the whole timing of the engine through pegs on the plug tree suspended from the beam. This again shows Newcomen's genius. With the piston at the top of its stroke and with the cylinder full of steam, the steam valve is shut. The water injection valve opens quickly with a weighted lever called the 'F' lever from its shape. This admits the maximum jet of water to cool the cylinder and piston in order to create the necessary degree of vacuum for atmospheric pressure to force down the piston against the weight of the pump rods and water to be raised at the other end of the beam. But once everything is cold and as the piston descends, there is less need for cooling, so this valve is gradually closed by the 'F' lever. This gives the correct functioning of this valve. Thus on the down stroke, work is done by the action of atmospheric pressure on the moving piston.

To stop the descent of the piston, a lot of steam must be admitted quickly to raise the temperature, destroy the vacuum and drive out any air through the snifting valve. This also allows the condensate in the

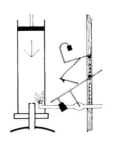

1) Piston at top of cylinder, catch is raised, letting 'F' lever fall and open valve.

2) As piston descends, peg on plug tree pushes down 'F' lever till the catch holds and shuts the valve.

Water injection valve on the model Newcomen engine.

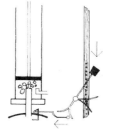
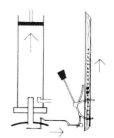

1) At bottom of stroke, peg on plug tree pushes 'Y' lever over until weight overbalances and opens steam valve.

2) At top of stroke, another peg pushes 'Y' lever up until it over-balances the other way and shuts steam valve.

Steam valve on the model Newcomen engine.

cylinder to drain away through a pipe. The steam inlet valve is operated by the 'Y' lever. On the long leg of the 'Y', which is upside down, is a weight which, as the lever pivots, suddenly overbalances and forces the steam valve open quickly, admitting the maximum amount of steam. The piston rises, exposing more of the cold walls of the cylinder so the supply of steam must be continued until the piston reaches the top. The 'Y' lever does not move until a peg on the plug tree hits a short arm of the 'Y', when the weight overbalances in the other direction and snaps the valve shut, stopping the piston rising. Again Newcomen had found a solution that best suited the operating conditions. While there was a complex set of levers, these valve gears worked so well that Smeaton copied them on the engines he built in the 1770s. It was difficult to control the Museum replica. The operating pegs had to be set correctly. Too much steam pressure made the piston rise too quickly so the chains by which it was suspended became slack and then might snatch. Not enough steam and the piston might not rise to the top of the cylinder to reset the valves. It took three months making small adjustments before the engine ran satisfactorily. The drawback of this type of engine lay in the alternate heating and cooling of the mass of the cylinder. Yet Newcomen was successful in creating an engine which formed the basis for further development over the next two hundred years. We found it to be a temperamental machine through its susceptibility to variations in boiler pressure and in the length of the stroke. It was this feature that most concerned engineers in the eighteenth century when they endeavoured to convert the single-acting Newcomen to drive a cotton mill directly.

Arkwright's Newcomen Engines

Having added a second mill at Cromford, Arkwright was in difficulties with the water supply and in November 1777 made enquiries with Boulton and Watt about a steam engine to raise water for his waterwheel. No order resulted. A further enquiry followed in 1780 when Watt wrote to Boulton:

> Mr. Arkwright of Cromford sent for me last night, he has built a mill and the miners have lett down his water so that it cannot move. He is much more modest than he was the last time . . . but as he does not pretend to improving the fire engine now I had little to say against him.[48]

While this may refer to the mills at Cromford which drew their water from a lead-mining sough, Arkwright could have been enquiring about an engine for the Haarlem Mill at Wirksworth which was apparently completed and perhaps working by June 1780 when a young man was killed while attempting to climb on its waterwheel. A steam engine with a 30in cylinder and 5ft stroke was installed here which is most likely to have been the first in any textile mill. It operated two pumps, twenty-four hours a day, and burnt 70cwt of coal per twenty-four hours. It was seen in 1782 by John Southern, the manager of Boulton and Watt's engine operations at Birmingham, who reported to Boulton that Arkwright had been deterred from ordering a Boulton and Watt engine by Francis Thompson who had said such engines were subject to disorder and were too complex. From this, it has been inferred that the Haarlem engine was built by Thompson who installed others in lead mines in that district. Hence it has been assumed that the Haarlem engine was a Newcomen-type atmospheric engine pumping water over a waterwheel. Arkwright also showed Southern a model engine which he described as 'farr execaded Mr. Boulton or Pickards or any other'.[49] This could have been a model of a rotative engine supplied by Thomas Hunt.

Following the destruction of his Birkacre Mill by rioters in 1780, Arkwright leased land in Manchester at Shudehill where he built a mill 171ft long, 30ft wide and five storeys high. This was the first large spinning mill in Manchester and Arkwright may have built it to impress the powerful Manchester merchants. There was only a small stream, quite inadequate to power the mill. It appears Arkwright intended his mill should be driven by rotative steam engines. In 1783, Hunt advertised a steam engine of his own design, 'Whereby MILLS, for any purpose whatever, can be set to work, in any place or situation, without having recourse either to Men, Horses, Wind, or even a Stream of Water'.[50] He provided an illustration of a pioneering design for a rotative Newcomen atmospheric engine on which the pump rod was converted into a connecting rod and turned a flywheel by a 'wrought Iron-Crank'. The flywheel had gear teeth around its periphery for driving the mill shafting. He also offered a model of his engine at the price of two guineas. Perhaps one was sold to Arkwright and was seen by Southern, raising the possibility of Hunt's involvement at Haarlem.

In 1785, Hunt was listed in Browne's Bristol Directory as 'Pump maker, machine Engine maker'. Earlier, Hunt had installed pumping equipment in Cornish mines as well as some form of rack and chain pump operated by horses at the Penrhyn Du Mine on the Lleyn Peninsula in North Wales.[51] In his advertise-

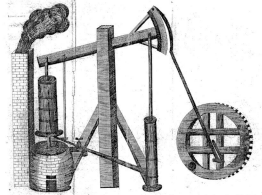

A View of a Machine upon an intire new Construction whereby Mills of every kind and for any purpose whatever can be set to work in any place or Situation without having recourse either to Men, Horses, Wind, or even a Stream of water Invented by Thos. Hunt of London.

Hunt's drawing of his rotative Newcomen engine. As drawn, the connecting rod is too long and the crank in the wrong position. (By permission of Birmingham Central Library, Boulton and Watt Collection)

ment, he pointed out the he had erected over twenty of his rotative steam engines in places such as London, Southampton, Bristol and Liverpool for driving a wide variety of mills, so he had wide engineering experience. He also listed 'two at Manchester, belonging to Mr. Arkwright, employed in his cotton manufactory'.[52] These last engines had probably been installed by the middle of 1781 when Boulton wrote to Watt, 'I have heard of no Engine improvements at Manchester except what Arkwright has pretended to . . . The Manchester folks will now erect Cotton Mills enough but want engines to work them.'[53] Hunt's basic design later became a popular type in many textile mills whose owners wished to avoid infringing Watt's patent. While the two at Arkwright's Shudehill Mill could have driven separate parts of the mill, they might have been connected, one either side of the flywheel, as was frequently the case after 1830. If the cranks were set at 180°, the power output ought to have been reasonably smooth as one single-acting cylinder would have had its power stroke after the other. But for reasons unknown, these engines were failures.

Watt was not impressed and in October 1783 wrote to Joseph Wilkes, a cotton spinner of Measham, 'We told Mr. Arkwright that the machine which he proposed to erect at Manchester could not answer; but he was obstinate & the event verified our prediction'.[54] James Bateman, who established an iron foundry in Manchester in 1782 and would become a serious rival to Boulton and Watt, noted in July 1783, 'Mr. Arkwright's works to go by fire engine are all to pieces'.[55] From this comment, it is unlikely that Bateman installed the Newcomen type of atmospheric steam engine with a cylinder 64in diameter by 7ft 6in stroke which was set to work at the Shudehill Mill that year to replace Hunt's engines. John Wilkinson was boring cylinders 63in diameter at Bersham for Boulton and Watt so might have made this one, or perhaps it came from Coalbrookdale. The engine supplied a waterwheel about 28ft diameter by 8ft wide through two pumps. When seen in 1790 by John Marshall, it was devouring a 'fantastic quantity of 5 tons of coal each working day of fifteen hours'.[56] In April 1792, Peter Ewart reported that 'the old engine is giving way every day'.[57] It was replaced by a 40 h.p. Boulton and Watt double-acting sun and planet rotative engine in 1793. It had worked for nine years and has been considered to be the first steam engine in a textile mill, but those by Hunt were earlier.

The Efficiency of Newcomen Engines

The power of a Newcomen engine is determined by the extent to which the cylinder is cooled. But, as the cylinder has to be reheated before the next stroke can commence, a considerable amount of steam is condensed wastefully. Smeaton found that the volume of steam needed for each stroke was 3.75 times one cylinder full. Watt arrived at an equivalent figure. When testing Newcomen engines in the Newcastle upon Tyne area in 1769, Smeaton found that the duty ranged from 3.22 million to 7.44 million pounds.[58] The Museum model engine with electric immersion heaters recorded 3.4 million. Watt settled on a figure of 7 million for a Newcomen engine when calculating premiums due on his patent engines. After conducting experiments and modifications on a small Newcomen engine at his home at Austhorpe near Leeds, Smeaton was able to raise the duty for a new pumping engine he built at Long Benton Colliery to 9.1 million. John Curr's pumping engine at Attercliffe Common Colliery, Sheffield, achieved 9.38 million in 1790. Watt and others had experienced great difficulty with badly bored cylinders but by the date of the Shudehill engine better ones were available through improvements to boring machines by Smeaton in 1770 and Wilkinson in 1775. This may have helped to raise the duty figures. At Shudehill, the bore of the water pumps was 31in diameter, the number of strokes 11 per minute and the length 7ft 6in, with coal consumption at 5 tons each day of 15 hours. These figures result in a duty of over 10 million which is the highest yet known for a common Newcomen engine. Perhaps the large size of the cylinder, in which the surface area of the walls was less in proportion to the volume, and the small height to which the water had to be raised compared with a mine may account for this record performance. But this was eclipsed by the much better duty reached in Watt's engines with the separate condenser which would soon be introduced into textile mills. Yet the Newcomen engine was a great pioneering achievement and was the basis for Watt's and later developments.

James Watt's Pumping Engine

The third type of engine available before 1780 was the pumping engine invented by Watt which was more economical than the others because he condensed the steam in a separate vessel from the working cylinder. During the winter of 1763 to 1764, he had been asked by the University of Glasgow to repair a model of a Newcomen engine. He was puzzled by its high consumption of steam and cooling water. He launched into a series of experiments in which he determined the volume of steam generated from a particular volume of water, the specific heats of some materials which showed him how much heat was needed to warm up the various parts, the latent heat of steam which showed him how much fuel was needed to generate steam from water as well as how much cold water was needed to cool and condense that steam. To make a more economical engine, he was faced with the dilemma that the cylinder of the Newcomen engine ought to be as hot as the steam that entered it to avoid wasteful condensation but, to create a good vacuum, it had to be cooled below 100°F (38°C). These conditions were mutually opposed to each other.

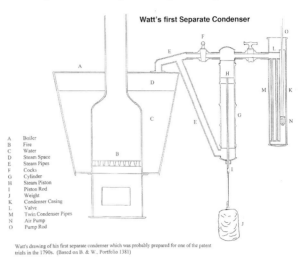

Watt's first Separate Condenser

A	Boiler
B	Fire
C	Water
D	Steam Space
E	Steam Pipes
F	Cocks
G	Cylinder
H	Steam Piston
I	Piston Rod
J	Weight
K	Condenser Casing
L	Valve
M	Twin Condenser Pipes
N	Air Pump
O	Pump Rod

Watt's drawing of his first separate condenser which was probably prepared for one of the patent trials in the 1790s. (Based on B. & W., Portfolio 1381)

Watt's first separate condenser. (By permission of Birmingham Central Library, redrawn from Boulton and Watt Collection)

While walking on the Green of Glasgow one Sunday afternoon in the spring of 1765, he had his flash of inspiration for his perfect steam engine. He could keep the cylinder hot all the time if the condensation were carried out somewhere else, in a separate cold vessel connected to the working cylinder by a valve. When this valve was opened, steam from the hot cylinder would rush into the vacuum and be condensed in what became called his separate condenser. He could maintain the heat of the steam firstly by enclosing the cylinder, by placing a cover on top with a gland through which the piston rod passed, and secondly by using steam to push down the piston instead of the cold atmosphere. In addition, if he surrounded the cylinder with a casing, steam could be admitted between that and the outside of the cylinder wall to keep it hot. The condensate and air which collected in his separate condenser were removed by an air pump worked off the beam. The condenser was placed in a tank of cold water. Watt claimed that, in the course of a few hours, he had thought out this scheme for his perfect engine which wasted no steam.

Although he had dramatically augmented contemporary knowledge of the properties of steam, we shall see that some of his concepts were flawed through lack of a true understanding of the laws of thermodynamics. He succeeded in implementing his theory of keeping the hot part of the engine separate from the cold but failed to understand the need for there to be a gradual fall in temperature between the two (see p.62). He built models of steam engines with separate condensers and air pumps to prove his theories and was delighted when these showed a great saving in fuel. These experiments were sufficiently convincing for him to form a partnership with Dr John Roebuck, who provided the finance for Watt's 1769 patent.[59] This coincided with the same year as Arkwright's first patent for his spinning machine. When Watt tried to build a larger engine at Roebuck's house at Kinneil in Scotland, he hit problems. This engine never performed to Watt's satisfaction. He had to leave it to earn his living as a civil engineer by surveying canals and then Roebuck himself became bankrupt. The engine languished until May 1773 when Watt and Roebuck settled their financial affairs and Watt received it as his due. He immediately dismantled it and despatched the parts to Birmingham. He followed a year later.

Trials in Birmingham convinced Matthew Boulton that it could become a practical working engine but he realised that the term of the patent would expire shortly. Therefore he urged Watt to apply to Parliament for an extension, which was granted in May 1775 for a further twenty-five years until the beginning of June 1800. The year 1775 of course coincided with Arkwright's patent for his preparatory machinery. While a better-bored cylinder supplied by Wilkinson improved the performance of Watt's engine, it was not until October 1775, when Watt changed from cooling his condenser solely by immersing it in cold water to direct injection like Newcomen, that he finally achieved a satisfactory, economical pumping engine. This was the engine which brought Watt and his new partner, Boulton, fame and eventually fortune through the firm of Boulton and Watt.

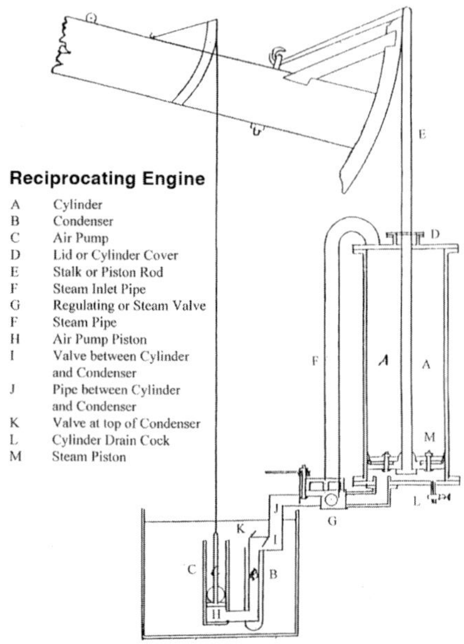
Reciprocating Engine
A Cylinder
B Condenser
C Air Pump
D Lid or Cylinder Cover
E Stalk or Piston Rod
F Steam Inlet Pipe
G Regulating or Steam Valve
F Steam Pipe
H Air Pump Piston
I Valve between Cylinder and Condenser
J Pipe between Cylinder and Condenser
K Valve at top of Condenser
L Cylinder Drain Cock
M Steam Piston

Watt's 1769 drawing of his engine with the separate condenser. This drawing was not included in his patent.

The first of Watt's new engines that was set to work for a commercial customer was at Bloomfield colliery near Birmingham with a 50in diameter cylinder. The inaugural ceremony was held in March 1776 when it was christened the 'Parliamentary Engine', after the Act extending Watt's patent. Two engines which were set to work during the summer of 1778 in Cornwall confirmed the superior efficiency of the Watt engine over the Newcomen. These were a new 52in cylinder engine for Ting Tang mine and a replacement for Smeaton's engine at Chacewater. Here not only was the Watt cylinder at 63in smaller but his engine proved capable of draining the mine where Smeaton's had failed. The performances of these engines convinced people that Watt's engine was better than either Savery's or Newcomen's. Performance figures of Watt's later engines showed even better figures. In 1778, Smeaton tested one at Spon Lane on the Birmingham Canal, when he recorded 18 millions. The 58in diameter engine at Hawksbury colliery, tested in 1779, also gave a result of a little below 19 millions. The later figure of 26.6 millions for some other engines seems to have been a little higher than the average for Watt engines in Cornwall. The double-acting engine at Wheal Maid returned 24,783,395lb in August, a saving of 70% compared with a common Newcomen engine. [60]

The only Watt pumping engine used to supplement the water for a waterwheel in a textile mill was ordered by Stockdale and Thackery in late 1785 for their cotton spinning mill at Cark on the southern edge of the Lake District. They had already installed a gin or wheel turned by six horses, but this and the waterwheel proved inadequate for driving the machinery in their five-storey mill during dry seasons. The Cark engine was a standard Boulton and Watt single-acting pumping engine with kingpost trussed beam and archheads.[61] The pistons were suspended by chains. Dimensions of the new steam engine cylinder and water pump were the same, 33in diameter by 8ft stroke, with the water being raised 20ft partly by suction. The special water pump was situated at a lower level to the engine. The boiler was a wagon type with rectangular flue running through the centre. Watt charged one third of the savings of fuel when compared with an equivalent Newcomen engine. Probably these premiums proved to be too high for other mill owners to copy this engine. The future lay with rotative engines driving the machinery directly.

Summary

The twenty years up to 1785 saw remarkable changes in the textile industry, especially in the cotton branch. Production was cheapened through the newly invented spinning machines so that demand for cotton goods rose enormously. The quality was improved and skill was transferred from hand crafts to machines. This demanded much increased sources of power both in scale in the actual mills as well as in aggregate. Horse and water power quickly proved inadequate to meet the demand so that mill owners had to turn more and more first to supplementary steam engines and then in the following years to steam engines that would provide direct rotary power.

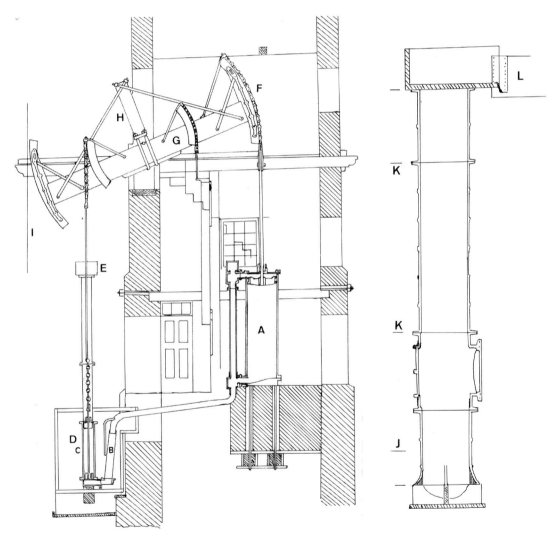

The Boulton and Watt single-acting engine for Cark Mill, 1785. **A** Cylinder; **B** Condenser; **C** Air Pump; **D** Condenser Tank; **E** Hot Water Supply for Boiler; **F** Archhead; **G** Beam; **H** King Post; **I** Pump Rod.
(By permission of Birmingham Central Library, redrawn from Boulton and Watt Collection)

The water pump for Cark Mill **J** Lower Surface of Tail Water; **K** – K Pump Barrel, 9ft 6in; **L** Launder to Waterwheel.
(By permission of Birmingham Central Library, redrawn from Boulton and Watt Collection)

NOTES: CHAPTER 1

1   Baines (1835), p. 6.

2   Ponting (1971), pp. 8 & 5.

3   Cooke (2003), p. 42.

4   Nasmith (1900), p. 9.

5   Postlethwayte (1757), p. 147.

6   Shaw (1984), p. 224.

7   Patent 422, 9 September 1718.

8   Cooper (1983), p. 37, quoted from Defoe, Daniel, *A Tour thro' the Whole Island of Great Britain*, 3rd edn, 1742.

9   Emerson (1773), p. 248.

10 Patent 542, 26 May 1733.

11 Patent 612, 18 April 1745.

12 Lawton (2004), Vol. 2, p. 1030.

13 Hills (1970), p. 6.

14 Wadsworth & Mann (1931, reprint 1965), p. 170.

Annual average consumption of cotton imported into Great Britain, 1698–1780, after deduction of exports.

Year	Cotton Wool (lb)	Cotton Yarn (lb)
1698–1710 (average of 12 years, 1705 missing)	1,095,084	95,291
1711–1720 (average of 9 years, 1712 missing)	1,476,107	77,538
1721–1730 (average of 9 years, 1727 missing)	1,505,273	88,181
1731–1740	1,717,787	97,807
1741–1750	2,137,294	46,316
1751–1760	2,759,916	64,139
1761–1770	3,681,904	75,887
1771–1780	5,127,689	76,849

15 Rees (1972), Vol. 2, p. 173, article 'Cotton'.

16 Patent 562, 20 July 1738 and Patent 724, 29 June 1758.

17 Patent 636, 16 December 1748.

18 Patent 962, 13 July 1770.

19 Rees, (1972), Vol. 3, p. 390, article 'Manufacture'.

20 Patent 931, 3 July 1769.

21 Patent 722, 19 April 1758 and Patent 734, 10 January 1759.

22 Patent 1,111, 16 December 1775.

23 Patent 628, 20 January 1748.

24 Baines (1835), p. 219. See also Aspin (2003), p. 469.

25 M'Connel (1905), p. 29 and Baines (1835), p. 347.

Cotton Imported

Year	The Cotton Wool applied to the manufacture was (lb)	When manufactured supposed to be worth (£)
1781	5,101,920	2,000,000
1782	11,306,800	3,900,000
1783	9,546,179	3,200,000
1784	11,280,238	3,950,000
1785	17,992,888	6,000,000
1786	19,151,867	6,500,000
1787	22,600,000	7,500,000
1788	20,467,436	N.A.
1789	32,576,023	N.A.
1790	31,447,605	N.A.

26 Aspin (2003), p. 13.

27 Baines (1835), p. 183.

28 Patent 562, 20 July 1738.

29 Aspin (2003), p. 17.

30 Baines (1835), p. 183.

31 Butt (1971), p. 220.

32 Cooper (1983), p. 287, quoted from Byng, John, *The Torrington Diaries*, 1790.

33 Birmingham Central Library, Boulton and Watt Collection, Portfolio 56.

34 Hogg (c.1913), p. 170.

35 Aikin (1795), p. 238.

36 Giles (1992), p. 124.

37 Aspin (2003), p. 42.

38 Hills (1970), p. 108.

39 Aspin (2003), p. 43.

40 B. & W. Col., from P. Ewart, 6 January 1792.

41 Ibid, J. Watt jun. to J. Watt, 13 March 1791.

42 Aikin (1795), pp. 174–5.

43 Farey (1827), Vol. 1, p. 122.

44 B. & W. Col., J. Watt to J. Rennie, 20 August 1785.

45 Ibid, from P. Ewart, 7 December 1791.

46 Hills, R.L., 'A Steam Chimera', *Transactions of the Newcomen Society*, Vol. 58, 1986–7, p. 37.

47 Triewald (1734), p. 3.

48 Fitton & Wadsworth (1958), p. 80, J. Watt to M. Boulton, 12 October 1780.

49 Fitton (1989), p. 57; B. & W. Mss, 'Minutes of Conversation & Notes with Mr. Arkwright's view upon the subject of employg B & W's Engines'.

50 B. & W. Col., J. Hunt's Drawing, Muirhead IV, Misc.

51 I wish to thank Dr J.P. Glithero for drawing my attention to Hunt's drawing and subsequently calculating the performance of his engine. For Hunt's work at the Penrhyn Du mine, see Hills, R.L. & Gwyn, D., 'Three Engines at Penrhyn Du, 1760–1780', *T.N.S.*, Vol. 75, No. 1, 2005.

52 B. & W. Col., J. Hunt's Drawing, Muirhead IV, Misc.

53 Ibid, M. Boulton to J. Watt, 7 August 1781.

54 Fitton (1989), p. 65; J. Watt to J. Wilkes, 20 October 1783.

55 Tann (1970), p. 75, from B. & W. Col., J. Bateman to J. Seale, 6 July 1783.

56 Aspin (2003), p. 73.

57 B. & W. Col., P. Ewart to J. Southern, 30 April 1792.

58 Farey (1827), Vol. 1, pp. 166–8 and 234.

59 Patent 913, 5 January 1769.

60 Hills (2005), p. 169.

61 B. & W. Col., Portfolio 560.

CHAPTER 2
STEAM COMES INTO ITS OWN, 1785–1830

The Expansion of the Cotton Industry

While the expansion of the cotton textile industry through the inventions of Kay, Hargreaves and Arkwright was seen to be dramatic enough to contemporaries, the pace quickened even more in the 1780s and 1790s with further mechanisation through developments of existing machines and invention of new ones. In fact so numerous were the improvements that:

> The man who one year laid out a considerable sum in the purchase of a jenny of the best and most approved make, found himself, in the course of the year following, so much behindhand, that with his utmost industry he could barely turn out a sufficient quantity of yarn to repay him for his present labour, in consequence of alterations which threw the productive power of his machine into the shade.[1]

A jenny with 30 spindles for spinning wool at Higher Mill, Helmshore.

The wear on the handles of the clove and crank for turning the main wheel shows how much this jenny has been used.

Industrialisation spread to the wool and linen sectors with further demands on sources of power.

Baines recorded the dramatic percentage increases in the import of cotton wool in the decades between 1741 and 1831:

Rate of Increase in the Import of Cotton-wool in the Periods of Ten Years from 1741 to 1831.

From	1741 to 1751	81 per cent
	1751 to 1761	21½ "
	1761 to 1771	25½ "
	1771 to 1781	75¾ "
	1781 to 1791	319½ "
	1791 to 1801	67½ "
	1801 to 1811	39½ "
	1811 to 1821	93 "
	1821 to 1831	85 "[2]

The effect of Arkwright's and Hargreaves's machines can be seen in the years between 1771 and 1781 but the really spectacular growth in the next decade was due to the introduction of Crompton's mule. The period between 1811 to 1821 reflected the boom after the Napoleonic Wars while the slower rise in the final decade resulted from a slump around 1825 although this period saw the introduction of Richard Roberts's power loom which helped to reduce the price of cotton cloth. The quantity of cotton wool imported and entered for consumption taken every five years shows the scale of these increases even though these figures do not reflect variations in intermediate years (see graph and note 3). In 1785, this was 17,992,888lb which, ten years later, was 25,207,603lb. It had reached 58, 878,163lb in 1800 and shot up to 123,791,826lb in 1810. After a decline at the end of the Napoleonic Wars, in 1820 the rise continued to 152,829,633lb in 1820 and 269,616,460lb in 1830.[3] Corresponding wool imports in 1800 were probably 8,609,000lb and in 1830 31,646,000lb.[4] Guesses of production of wool produced in the United Kingdom are 94,373,640lb in 1800 and 111,160,560lb in 1828. These figures show

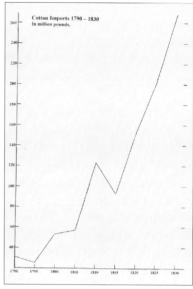

Cotton imports 1790 to 1830.

how the cotton industry outstripped the wool sometime after 1800. Soon after 1830, Baines wrote: 'The *spinning machinery* created the cotton manufacture. But this branch of industry has unquestionably been extended by means of the steam-engine far beyond the limit which it could otherwise have reached.'[5] It would be the combination of Crompton's spinning mule and Watt's rotative engine on which this later expansion would be based but it would take some years for both to achieve their positions of pre-eminence.

There were comparatively few cotton spinners before 1800 who possessed over 4,000 spindles. In 1803, New Eagley Mill near Bolton had 4,500 spindles. In the same year, 'Soot-Poke' Mill in Stalybridge had 4,200 spindles. The largest group of mills in that area at that time was at Rassbottom where the combined spindleage was 34,000. In 1811, Queen Street and Grosvenor Mills, both in Stalybridge, had 9,600 spindles each. At the same time in neighbouring Dukinfield, the Old Mill held 5,760 spindles and the New, the largest in the town, 12,480. Mill sizes would continue to increase in the years up to 1830 when the larger ones had around 20,000 spindles.

Samuel Crompton's Spinning Mule

While Arkwright's waterframe produced a hard spun warp and Hargreaves's jenny a softer spun weft suitable for fustians, neither machine could spin the finer counts necessary for muslins. The pull on the yarn from the bobbin on Arkwright's waterframe caused fine yarns to break while the drafting method on the jenny could not cope with higher counts. Samuel Crompton wove fine cloth in his home at Hall-i-th-Wood near Bolton. He became so exasperated with the defects of the jenny for spinning fine yarns that he set about improving it in 1772. He continued with experiments on his own machine until he perfected his 'spinning mule' in 1779. He built it all himself, mostly from wood with a few metal parts made at the local blacksmiths, and kept it carefully hidden in the attics.

He adopted the plain spindle method so spinning was intermittent. Whereas Hargreaves had his spindles stationary, Crompton mounted

Hall-i-th-Wood, near Bolton.

his on a wheeled carriage that moved away from the creel holding the rovings. The rovings were passed through pairs of drafting rollers similar to Arkwright's, although Crompton denied knowing about Arkwright's invention. In this way, Crompton separated the drafting and twisting. The gearing for the rollers was engaged so that they drew and paid out the fibres as the spinner turned a wheel which also rotated the spindles to insert some twist to the yarn. He pulled the carriage with the spindles away from the rollers until it reached its fullest extent. He then disengaged the rollers but could continue to rotate the spindles until the yarn had received sufficient twist. This slightly stretched the yarn, making it more even; an important feature in mule spinning. He reversed the spindles a few turns to unwind the coils of yarn from their tips to the end of the cop. While turning the wheel in the spinning direction again and pushing the carriage back in, he wound on the spun yarn to form the cops on the spindles.

We created a demonstration hand mule from parts of a twentieth-century one for the North Western Museum of Science and Industry in Manchester. The spinning sequence was made much easier than with the jenny and the carriage almost moved itself out but skill was still needed to wind on a good cop. While it was easier to control the faller wire for winding on with the hand rather than the foot, with only a single faller wire it was difficult to guide the yarn into well-shaped cops. Winding on too quickly broke the yarns while too slowly might form snarls. The mule handles the cotton fibres more gently than the waterframe and it is more flexible than the jenny so that hard or soft spun yarns can be produced on it as well as much finer ones.

Crompton's first mule had forty-eight spindles. To begin with, he used it only to supply his own loom with warp and weft. But as he was spinning finer counts than the waterframe, he realised he could sell them. Soon he was selling 80s counts which was thought to be impossible to produce. It was much finer than could be spun on the Great Wheel and was much sought after for muslins. In 1780, he left off weaving to concentrate on spinning. Such was the interest shown in his yarn that people began to invade Hall-i-th-Wood to try and find out how he was making it. He was driven to distraction by their curiosity and did not know what to do for he was unwilling to destroy his machine. Since he could not afford to take out a patent, eventually he agreed to accept the offer of a liberal public subscription if he would make his machine known. But once he had revealed his machine, many people failed to pay what they had promised. However, he did receive enough to make a new mule with fifty-two spindles. Up to 1783, Crompton's mule could have been held to have infringed Arkwright's 1769 patent, hence the importance to cotton spinners of seeing that that patent was not extended. In 1783, there were only a thousand mule spindles in existence. Improvements were added by others almost immediately after Crompton revealed his mule, such as better drafting rollers, an improved method of driving the spindles as well as a greater number of spindles. In 1787, it was estimated that there were 550 mules and 20,700 jennies which, together with waterframes, contained 1,951,000 spindles.

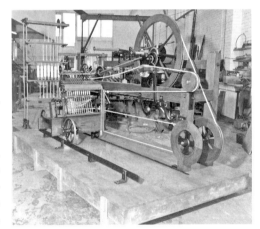

Replica of part of a mule owned by Samuel Crompton probably around 1810.

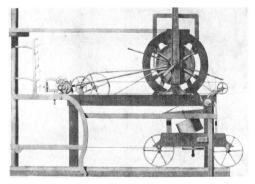

A drawing of the 1790s of one of M'Connel's mules.

In 1789, Peter Drinkwater began building a mill for fine spinning a little to the south of Piccadilly in Manchester and installed hand-operated mules of 144 spindles. The preparatory machinery, based on Arkwright's, was to be powered by a Boulton and Watt steam engine. This was a typical combination at this period. By February 1795, McConnel and Kennedy, fine spinners and machine builders of Ancoats, Manchester, wrote to a customer recommending even larger mules:

> In respect to what number of spindles may be most profitable is very difficult to fix, as what was thought best only 2 years ago is now thought too small. 216 [spindles] is now made to run as light as 144 used to then. We are making now from 180 to 288 spindles.[6]

They also pointed out in another letter, 'the gearing for water spinning would be charged according to the manner it was done'.[7] They were referring to driving mules partly by water power. Most effort was needed in the spinning phase when the rollers had to be turned, the spindles rotated and the carriage drawn out. At the end of the draw, twisting on the head took less and the short backing-off phase even less. However, winding on and pushing the carriage back in required an intermediate amount. Hence in mule spinning, the amount of power absorbed differed in each of the four phases. The first hand mules would have needed about one tenth of a horsepower, which can be achieved only by a very fit man.

In 1790, William Kelly tried to mechanise all these phases on his mules at New Lanark and drive them by water power. He patented his mechanisms in 1792, hoping to be able to spin with young people.[8] But the methods he tried for backing off and winding on were unsuccessful. However, the application of power to the spinning sequence became common in most mills. This enabled one spinner to manage a pair of mules placed opposite each other with the aid of a child piecer to join broken yarns. While one mule was spinning under power, the spinner was manually winding on on the other. Crompton had placed his driving wheel on the headstock at the right-hand end of his mule. Kelly made one mule right-handed and the other left so that the headstocks were opposite each other. No longer did the spinner have to walk from one end of one mule to the further end of the other, but he had to alternate from being right- to left-handed each time he changed mules.

This disadvantage was removed soon after 1792 when Wright, who had served his apprenticeship to Arkwright, conceived the idea of placing the spindles on a carriage that stretched either side of the headstock. He drove his experimental mules, which soon reached 400 spindles, with a horse gin. Gradu-

An early semi-powered mule in the Vienna Technical Museum.

Pair of semi-powered mules around 1830. The spinner is winding on on the left one.

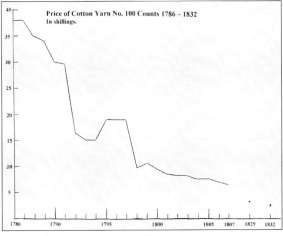

Price of Cotton Yarn No. 100 Counts.

ally these double semi-powered mules superseded the older single ones so that, by placing them in pairs, one spinner could manage four times the number of spindles compared with the former method. In addition, the carriages were lengthened even further so that in 1796 there were mules with 650 spindles, which was probably about the limit that a spinner could wind on or put up by hand. M'Connel estimated that one horsepower was sufficient to drive 350 semi-powered mule spindles, probably without preparation machinery. The mule proved to be a much more versatile and popular spinning machine than either the waterframe or jenny so that the price of fine yarn fell drastically. In 1786, the price of cotton yarn count number 100 was thirty-eight shillings. Ten years later this had fallen to nineteen shillings and then it was down to seven shillings and two pence in 1806. After many fluctuations, it was only two shillings and eleven pence in 1832 (see graph and note 9).

When Crompton was petitioning Parliament in 1812 to receive a grant of money in recognition of the value of his invention, he took to London samples of yarn spun on the mule. They ranged from count 1, very coarse, to count 310, incredibly fine, in fact as fine as any ever seen before. His survey of 1811 found that there were 4,209,570 mule spindles (including 22,600 billy or stretching spindles) compared with 310,516 waterframe and 155,880 jenny spindles. The number of waterframe spindles was an underestimate because he failed to include some of the mills in Derbyshire but this still indicates the dominance of the mule. A survey in 1797 for the Government carried out by insurance companies showed that the number of mills had increased to 900, valued at £2,500,000, most of which would have contained mules. They employed directly about 60,000 people. The comment was passed on this report:

> What has been at present surmised is almost past belief, That a Manufactory of so great magnitude could have been raised within 20 years and that from a raw material imported, more especially when we consider the immense capital which must be required to support it.[10]

Preparatory Machinery

Some of the immense capital had been invested in preparatory machinery. Having seen that it was possible to improve the spinning machines, people turned their attention to other parts of the textile processes. For example, the Revd Edmund Cartwright patented power looms in 1785 but failed to solve all the problems. The story of the power loom will be told later in Chapter 3. At the start of processing the cotton, Eli Whitney in America contributed his important invention of the saw gin in 1793. This removed the cotton fibres from the seeds in the boll more effectively than by hand and enabled a new range of American cottons to be grown and sold profitably. The cotton arrived in England much cleaner so that more discriminating selection and more uniform classification could take place.

New inventions in the opening and other processes preparatory to carding were not introduced extensively prior to 1800. A batting machine patented in 1801 with a series of rods to beat and open up the tufts of cotton did not find much favour except for fine cotton. For coarser cottons, two machines came into general use a little before the turn of the century. The devil or willow was a vicious machine, consisting of a drum with large spikes which revolved in a casing also set with spikes. Lumps of cotton from bales were carried round

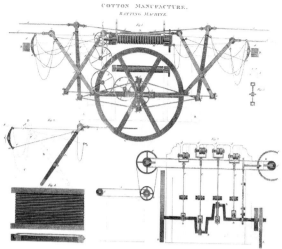

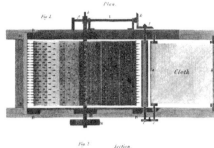

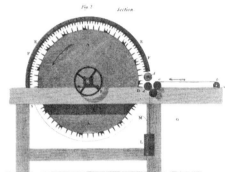

Batting machine c.1808.

The devil for opening lumps of cotton.

by the drum and torn apart between the spikes. Women might remove any dirty or discoloured and damaged cotton passing out of this machine but this job was mechanised by the scutching machine. Although it was invented in Scotland by Neil Snodgrass in 1797, it was not introduced into England until 1808. It was based on the principle of the threshing machine. Beaters working against a drum separated the cotton from the seeds and dirt. While the refuse fell out, the cotton was carried forward on a draught of air and rolled up into a lap which could be placed at the back of the carding engine. Scutchers reduced the labour needed for opening and cleaning the cotton to a twentieth of that used before. They filled the last gap in the complete mechanisation of cotton spinning so that by 1810 every process of converting a bale into finished yarn could be performed efficiently by machines.

The revolving can frame was replaced by one of either two machines. The earlier, called the stretching frame or slubbing billy, was introduced by 1795 and was an adaptation of the mule, working on the same basic principles but producing a cop of lightly twisted roving. In 1797, M'Connel and Kennedy recommended the following machinery for an Irish cotton mill:

A slubbing billy as used in the woollen industry.

	£. s. d.
12 Carding Engines with 18 in. Cards at £27	324. 0. 0
20 Heads Drawing Rovins [sic] @ 75/-	75. 0. 0
2 Stretching Frames 90 Spindles each @ £57	114. 0. 0
30 Mules 180 Spindles each to go by power @ £57	1,620. 0. 0
	£ 2,133. 0. 0[11]

A steam engine of 8 to 10 horsepower costing £800 would be required to drive this machinery, consuming about 14cwt of coals per day. Stretching frames or slubbing billies were soon phased out, possibly because winding on was a skilled operation and it was an intermittent process. They had been replaced mostly before 1836 by the bobbin fly frame with its continuous production.

Arkwright had tried to make rovings on a fly frame but had not succeeded. In many ways, it was a larger version of the waterframe with roller drafting to draw out the slivers into rovings. Light twist was inserted by rotation of flyers and the roving wound onto bobbins. But herein lay the difficulty because the thicker roving quickly increased the diameter of the bobbin. Yet the velocity of the circumference had to remain constant to prevent the roving being drawn out further. Therefore the bobbin speed had to diminish as it was filled. The bobbins had to be driven positively as well as the flyers so their respective speeds could be accurately controlled and some method of altering the speed had to be devised. A belt was moved slowly along a pair of opposed cones which gave a smooth and gradual way of varying the speed. Driving the flyers and bobbins at their respective speeds was solved by John Kennedy and Henry Houldsworth with a differential motion sometime before 1812. It was found that the roving was likely to jam against the bobbin flanges and break as it was being pulled off when placed in the spinning machine. Therefore around 1830, the flanges of the bobbin were removed to leave only a tube. The length of travel along the tube as the roving was being wound on was made progressively shorter each layer, forming a cone at each end. This form of package remained unaltered on roving and slubbing frames until the demise of cotton spinning in Britain around AD 2000.

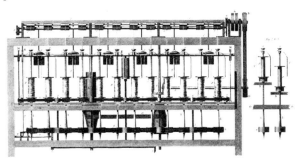

A roving or fly frame of 1808.

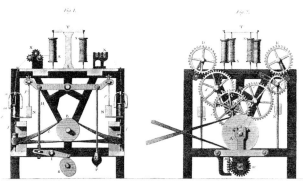

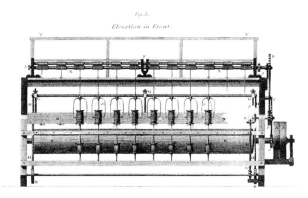

A throstle spinning frame of 1808.

Arkwright's waterframes consisted of groups of four spindles with their set of drafting rollers driven by gearwheels. Probably these brass wheels wore too quickly if they drove longer rollers. Early in the nineteenth century, stronger cast iron gearwheels replaced the brass ones. A single set of these placed at one end of the frame could drive a continuous length of rollers for all the spindles. This new type of spinning machine became known as the throstle, reputedly from its singing sound. Robert Owen was already using throstles at New Lanark when he visited Stanley Mill near Perth in December 1802. He recommended replacing some of their waterframes by throstles 'because you can put more spindles in the same space and they work with less power and cost less to make'.[12] In 1808, Rees's *Cyclopaedia* mentions one with 112 spindles,

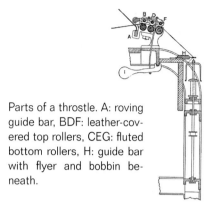

Parts of a throstle. A: roving guide bar, BDF: leather-covered top rollers, CEG: fluted bottom rollers, H: guide bar with flyer and bobbin beneath.

66 on each side. It was simpler, cheaper and needed less power than the equivalent waterframe but its disadvantage was that all the spindles had to be stopped when the bobbins needed changing, whereas on the waterframe this was necessary only for a group of four. Productivity was greater but it seems not to have found much favour until the later 1820s when a heavier, hard twisted yarn of superior strength was in demand for the warps of cloth woven on Roberts's newly introduced power looms. The throstle was later developed into the ring spinning frame.

In 1817, the following attempt was made to estimate the importance of the cotton spinning industry:

90,000,000   Pounds of Raw Cotton consumed annually in the United Kingdom.

8,437,500   Pounds loss in Spinning the above being 1½ ounce per pound.

81,562,500   Pounds of yarn spun in 1817.

40   Average No. of Hanks per pound

3,262,500,000   Hanks Spun in 1817,

3   ounces of coal required to produce the Power to Spin 1 Hank of No. 40

611,718,750   Pounds of Coal Consumed annually.

11,328   Horse Power required, supposing 180 lb. of Coal equal to the Power of one horse and 300 working days in a year.

5,437,500   will be about the total number of Spindles employed of every description supposing each spindle to turn off 2 Hanks per day on an average and 300 working days in a year.

The total number of persons employed in Spinning Cotton will be 90,625 Supposing each individual on an average to produce 120 Hanks per day of No. 40. 300 working days in the year. N.B. – 910 1/3 Tons of Coal consumed daily.[13]

Inventions in Other Textile Industries

Mechanisation based on experience gained with cotton soon spread to the other textile industries. In his 1769 patent, Arkwright claimed that he could spin wool, but it is unlikely that he made any serious attempts. The carding engine was adapted to process short staple wool with a series of small cylinders and clearers set around the main cylinder to tease out the fibres. The wool was removed from the doffer cylinder with Arkwright's crank and comb. Carded slivers were turned into slubbings on slubbing billies with a longer stretch than those in the cotton industry.

Carding engine for wool with small cylinders and clearers round the top of the main cylinder.

While the mule had driven the jenny out of the cotton industry very quickly, it took much longer for the jenny to disappear from the woollen industry. A list in 1815 of workpeople at Benjamin Gott's Bean Ing Mill in Leeds contained only two mule spinners. In 1830, this had increased to fifteen with still thirteen jenny spinners. It was only after the introduction of the self-acting mule in 1830 that the mule began to make any headway either in Yorkshire or the West of England. Throughout the early nineteenth century, the West Riding could show cotton mills spinning with the mule and worsted spinners using the waterframe or throstle, while the woollen industry retained the spinning jenny in both cottages and factories. The first ordinary mules were installed in the West of England industry around 1828 and, while the strike of 1829 hastened their introduction, they did not entirely oust the jenny for a long time with one surviving in a Trowbridge mill until 1925. One jenny was used in a mill at Dobcross in Yorkshire until 1916 and another on Anglesey until perhaps the start of the Second World War.

As early as 1781, three men worked secretly in Keighley to build a worsted spinning machine with roller drafting. The *Leeds Mercury* of 1 November 1785 carried an advertisement for a machine with twenty-four spindles which could make better worsted yarn and do as much as six people with common spinning wheels. On the other side of the Pennines, in 1784 a partnership of Robert Addison, John Satterthwaite and Thomas Edmondson started to replace an old corn mill at Dolphinholme on the Wyre with a four-storey mill 'for the purpose of spinning and manufacturing worsted'.[14] The mill, machinery and associated houses were insured for £2,300 in June 1786 so the factory was working by then. Arkwright's drafting rollers could be set far enough apart at about six inches to draft the longer combed wool fibres which were more equal in staple length since combing removed the short ones. In 1790, Edmund Cartwright patented a combing machine, but it was suitable only for coarse wool.

Flax fibres presented an even greater challenge through their longer length of often well over twelve inches, because they needed support in the drafting zone. In 1787, John Kendrew and Thomas Porter obtained a patent for two machines to spin flax, which is generally accepted as the first useful commercial system.[15] To insert the twist, they used flyers and bobbins. Their first machine prepared the flax by drawing it over a revolving cylinder covered with heckles but they had difficulty in removing the tow from the heckle spikes. On their second machine, the cylinder was covered with leather. Round part of the circumference of the cylinder were mounted weighted rollers so the flax was drawn out between the large cylinder and these rollers, before passing through a funnel to the final delivery rollers. They equipped a water-powered mill at Adel near Leeds. Then in January 1788 they licensed John Marshall to use their machines. With the help of the brilliant young engineer, Matthew Murray, Marshall began experiments in Scotland Mill. Murray replaced the cylinder and rollers with a pair of revolving sheets of leather or revolving sheets of carding material. The fibres were fed in and drawn out by pairs of rollers. He patented this in June 1790[16] but a similar idea had been patented by Cartwright five weeks earlier.[17] Marshall moved to Holbeck, closer to Leeds, where he installed Murray's machines in a mill that was ready for use in September 1791. On Wrigley's advice, it was at first driven by a Savery engine and waterwheel. Murray's machines were such a success that Marshall expanded his business, spending over £20,000 on mills and machines between 1794 and 1798. But the linen industry was never to regain the prominence it once had through being overshadowed by its ever-expanding rival, cotton.

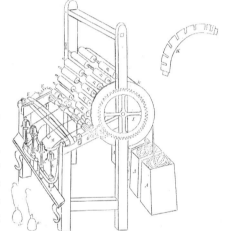

John Kendrew and Thomas Porter's patent in 1787 for flax spinning.

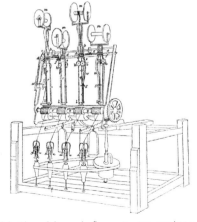

Matthew Murray's flax-spinning machine.

There were also developments in the finishing industries. Watt's second father-in-law, James McGrigor, owned a bleachworks near Glasgow. He had approached Watt about improving his water-wheels in 1781 and sought advice about drying the linen during the bleaching processes. Watt sent drawings of a machine with hollow copper drums or cylinders which could be heated by steam as the cloth was drawn over them. This drying machine was constructed by Watt's former apprentices. It must have been taken up elsewhere in Scotland because in 1814 Sir David Brewster asked Watt to describe it for the *Edinburgh Encyclopaedia*. Watt's drawing does not show how he proposed to drive his drying cylinders but they must have been connected to a waterwheel. The machine soon spread to the Lancashire bleachers. In 1820, when T.B. Crompton of Farnworth, Lancashire, was considering how he could dry long lengths of paper made on the papermaking machine, it is said that he took a roll of wet paper to a textile mill where he had it run over the drying cylinders.

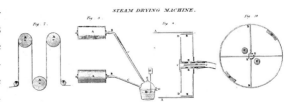
James Watt's steam-heated drying cylinders

These drying cylinders would have been very useful to Thomas Bell for his calico printing machine. Bell had the pattern engraved into copper cylinders but had problems removing excess colour before printing. He visited Watt in 1770, who suggested that Bell should try 'lantern horn or tortoise shell' for the doctor blades.[18] Watt commented, 'They keep their whole process secret' and we have no more information about Bell until he took out a patent in 1783 for a machine with six printing rollers and steel doctor blades.[19] A further patent was granted the following year.[20] His machines had to be driven by power, in early instances by a waterwheel. They were being used at Masney, near Preston, by Messrs Livesey, Hargreaves, Hall & Co. in 1786.

A twelve-colour printing machine of 1888 driven by a three-cylinder steam engine.

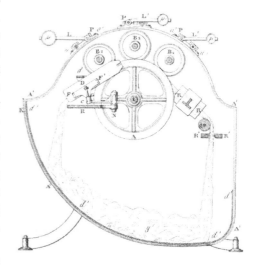
A milling machine for woollen cloth.

The time-honoured fulling stocks began to be replaced in 1816 when William Lewis of Brimscombe, Gloucestershire, patented a milling machine in which the cloth was squeezed as it passed through.[21] Then in 1833 John Dyer, a Trowbridge engineer, patented an improved version[22] in which the cloth was sewn up into a long continuous length. It was milled by rollers forcing it through a hole or spout from where it dropped down into the fulling liquid, where it soaked before being pulled out and pushed through the hole again. Dyer had three pairs of rollers, one pair set at right angles to the other. His machine was often used in conjunction with stocks. It does not seen to have come into general use until the 1850s.

After fulling, the nap or surface had to be raised with teasels mounted in handles, which remained a hand operation until the beginning of the sixteenth century. Then teasel heads were mounted round the periphery of

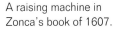

A raising machine in Zonca's book of 1607.

Teasel gig raising machine at Tan-y-grisiau Woollen Mill, Blaenau Ffestiniog.

Hand shearers at work c.1635.

a drum turned by a waterwheel. The cloth was moved over the drum. Since this machine might put people out of work, a law was passed against it in 1551–2, but by the early eighteenth century anyone who wanted one built it. There is some doubt whether this was the same type of machine which caused riots when it was introduced to the West Riding around 1816. Gott did not use it at his mill until after 1820.

By this time, the highly skilled task of shearing the nap on woollen cloth had also been mechanised. Hand shears were extremely large and heavy. Various attempts, such as that in 1784 by James Harmer, a clergyman of Sheffield, to place several pairs of shears in a frame and operate them by cranks, were unsuccessful. The first version of a rotary machine was made by an American, Samuel Griswold Dore (or Dorr). His first frame consisted of a wheel of twelve 'spring knives', fixed like spokes and set at an angle of about 45° to the horizontal. Under this wheel, and on the same axle, rode a second one carrying four 'tangent knives', which lay almost flat upon the cloth. As the two wheels rotated above the surface of the cloth, they acted in the 'manner of shears'. Dore came to England where he patented his invention in 1793.[23] Little more was heard of his machine in Britain, probably through his death in 1794, but his son and others patented several improvements. In a patent of 1815,[24] John Lewis of Brimscombe claimed that he

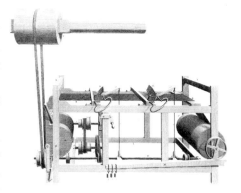

Attempt to mechanise hand shears c.1810.

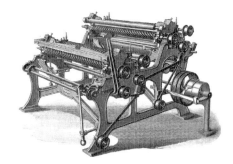

Quadruple cropping machine with the shearing knives around the cylinders.

had brought together a number of desirable features for shearing cloth in one machine. The local story current in the Stroudwater district is that Lewis obtained his idea from Budding, a lad who worked for him. Budding invented the lawnmower with the blades on a rotating barrel or cylinder which he patented in 1830. In the shearing machine, the cloth was moved under the rotating cylinder which could be the same width so only one operation was needed for each side. His machine spread quickly in the Gloucestershire woollen industry so that, by 1830, hand shearing was extinct there. With it, a comparatively untrained operator accomplished twenty times what had previously needed the skill of the handicraft shearmen.

Development of Mill Structures and Line Shafting

As the size and length of the spinning machines increased through improved construction, and better opening and carding machinery became available, larger buildings were required. Also, since the lubricating oil and cotton created a considerable fire risk, mill owners began to search for ways of erecting a fireproof building. One of the pioneers was William Strutt, son of Jedediah, who experimented in 1792 with a cotton mill at Derby and a warehouse at Milford. Iron columns supported the long wooden floor beams. The floors between the beams were built with brick arches and the exposed wood plastered. The floors on the arches were stone slabs. Then in 1796 to 1797, Charles Bage replaced the wooden beams with cast iron ones in his flax mill at Shrewsbury. Here even the roof trusses were iron castings so the whole mill was virtually incombustible. This first iron-framed building in the world still survives. So also does the iron-framed Belper North Mill built in 1804 to replace an earlier one with wooden floors which burnt down, confirming the advantages of iron construction.

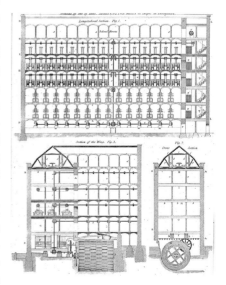

Belper North Mill, 1804, showing the iron-framed structure and drive from the waterwheel.

In the early silk mills, all the machinery from the waterwheel to the throwing frames was built of wood except for the bearings and a few other small parts. The wooden ladle boards of the waterwheel were fixed to wooden rims supported by wooden arms mortised into or clasped around the wooden axle shaft. This took the drive directly to a similarly constructed gearwheel driving more wooden gearing and shafting to reach the machines. In later mills, a heavy vertical shaft took the drive up the mill to the various floors. At each level, bevel gears linked the vertical shaft to horizontal ones running the length of the mill just below the ceilings. The shafting was thick with enormous couplings and large pulleys rotating at about 40 r.p.m. All this obscured the light and needed a great deal of maintenance and constant oiling. Should a spinner start a machine too quickly, there was a danger that teeth on the gearwheels might be stripped, causing stoppages for repair. There was loss of power through friction in gears and bearings. All this was improved when the cumbersome wooden gearing and shafting was replaced first by cast iron and then by wrought iron.

When Simon Goodrich visited Manchester in November 1799, he saw mills where the shafts and gears were cast iron, made as light as possible consistent with the necessary strength. The teeth of the gearwheels needed no trimming and he noted that they ran with very little noise, only a smooth humming. William Fairbairn arrived in Manchester around 1814 and worked for the millwright, Thomas C. Hewes, from whom he may have learnt about the principles of his suspension wheels and line shafting. In 1817, Fairbairn joined with James Lillie to set up as millwrights. They were asked by the mill owners A. & G. Murray to repair some line shafting. Fairbairn realised that a shaft turning at 80 r.p.m. will transmit

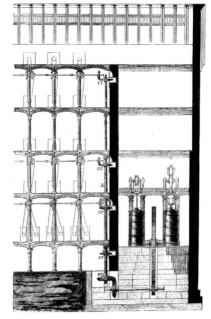

The method of taking the power from the steam engine through a vertical shaft and then along the different floors by horizontal shafts.

100 h.p. with no more stress than 50 h.p. at 40 r.p.m. He replaced the earlier shafting with slender rods of wrought iron suspended from light frames and with lighter, stronger pulleys. The speed was increased to as much as 300 r.p.m., thus transmitting more power. This allowed larger textile mills to be built in which the machinery could be driven more quickly. In turn, this meant that the machinery had to be built to more sophisticated designs with cast or wrought iron parts replacing earlier wood. It also meant that the mills demanded increased power from their waterwheels or steam engines.

The maze of shafting and belts needed to drive the power looms at Pennington Mill, Leigh.

Sources of Power

Wind Power

The ever-increasing range of powered textile machines, the ever-increasing range of textile industries in which machines were used and the ever-increasing demand particularly for cotton textiles led to increasing demands for power. Windmills were seldom used in textile mills in spite of improvements such as those made by Edmund Lee with his fantail to keep the sails facing into the wind and Andrew Meikle and William Cubitt to the sails with reefing shutters. Samuel Unwin built a spinning mill around 1770 at Sutton in Ashfield powered by horses and a waterwheel. To augment the water supply from the River Idle, he built a windmill on the roof of the mill to pump water back into the upper reservoir, not to drive the machinery. This proved inadequate, so by about 1790 a steam engine was added. In 1791, Peter Ewart visited a spinning mill at Stockport where the manager, when asked what they did if there was no wind, replied, 'We play us'.[25] In 1800, there was a windmill driving cotton machinery on Carrow Hill in Norwich, where winds would have been stronger, but even so wind was too unreliable a source of power for driving spinning machinery.

Water Power

Until well into the nineteenth century, water remained the preferred source of power so that more mills were erected on rivers and streams wherever possible. For example, on the edge of the Pennines where the River Etherow flows through the Longdendale valley, four mills were erected in the ten years from 1785 to 1795. The first textile mill in neighbouring Glossopdale was completed probably in 1784, and a further four mills were built there that year. In 1800, there were sixteen and by 1830 over thirty. None of these was mentioned in Colquhoun's list so would have been carding mills or later mule mills. Most probably relied entirely on water power. Boulton and Watt did not supply any steam engines here and the coal mined in the locality was of poor quality.

If these early mills needed only ten horsepower to drive their machinery with 1,000 spindles, then the rivers at many early sites had the potential to provide more than this. Greg's mill at Styal was built in 1784 and extended with a second waterwheel around 1800 by Ewart. Its capacity rose from 2,425 to 3,452 spindles by 1805. He enlarged the storage reservoir with the present fine stone arched dam in 1799. Then a further extension of the mill followed in 1820. The tailrace for this new wheel was diverted into a long tunnel to take the water further downstream to obtain a greater fall. From probably originally around ten horsepower, the power generated rose to around 100 h.p. This last wheel was constructed from iron, 32ft in diameter, 21ft wide and weighed between 36 and 43 tons. In March 1823, this wheel drove 9,600 spindles. At New Lanark, the Falls of Clyde provided plenty of water so that eventually four spinning mills were built on the site. In 1795, these mills contained 12,000 spindles and the power generated was about 300 h.p. The power that could be generated here when the river had an average flow was about 650 h.p. At other good water power sites such as Belper and Darley Abbey on the River Derwent, clusters of mills were also erected.

In the West Mill at Belper, completed in 1797, there were two enormous wooden wheels. The smaller, for use in times of flood, was 48ft long by 12ft diameter. The larger was 40ft long by 18ft diameter. The ladles were mounted in rings and staggered across the breadth so that the incoming water hit one section after the other in rapid succession to avoid giving a shock to the wheel which would have been the case had the water struck the whole forty-foot length at once. The wheels were made in the form of a cask or barrel but the ladles did not quite touch this central drum to allow the air to escape when the water poured in, the arrangement acting as a form of ventilated bucket.

Gradually iron replaced wood everywhere. Smeaton is credited with some of the earliest cast iron axles around 1770 but they did not prove entirely satisfactory. John Rennie used cast iron for gearing and other parts in 1784 at the Albion corn mills in London. Soon most parts of a waterwheel were made from cast iron. The main gearwheel ran in a pit alongside the waterwheel. The power was transmitted from the rim of the waterwheel, through the spokes, along the axle and then through the spokes of the gearwheel. This arrangement put great strain on the spokes, which had to be suitably strong and heavy. When cast iron segments were used to form the rim of the waterwheel, it was realised that the gearing could be incorporated into the casting and the mill shafting driven from a pinion engaging with it. In this way, the power was taken off from the point where it was being generated by the falling water. The spokes no longer transmitted power, so they became merely struts to hold the rim in place. Soon they were made from light wrought iron tension rods, similar to spokes in a bicycle wheel. The first of these suspension wheels may have originated at Gott's Armley Mill in Leeds around 1810. Ewart soon built one at Styal and the same principle was used there again for the 1820 wheel. Many more were installed by Hewes and Fairbairn. Between 1825 and 1827, Fairbairn built a massive pair of wheels, 50ft diameter by 10ft 6in wide, for the Catrine cotton mills in Ayrshire, which developed 240 h.p. Later, Fairbairn improved the design by re-introducing ventilated buckets, resulting in increased power with less waste of water. Through improvements such as these, water power was kept abreast of steam and at the best sites developed even more power than individual steam engines up to at least the 1830s.

Early suspension wheel showing the wrought iron radial tension rods.

The massive suspension wheel at Egerton Mill, near Bolton, 63ft in diameter, that developed 150 h.p.

The 1859 composite waterwheel with wooden spokes and wrought iron tie rods at Abercegir Woollen Mill, mid-Wales.

Steam Power

Using any steam engine to pump water over a waterwheel incurred double penalties. There was the inefficiency of the steam engine itself when converting the heat from the burning coal into a usable form of energy and then there was the inefficiency of the waterwheel. Smeaton showed that around one third of the theoretical power had to be deducted to allow for the losses within the waterwheel itself. Southern wrote to Peter Ainsworth of Bolton in 1790:

> They [Boulton and Watt] wish you to observe that a 10 horse engine applied to pumping water for waterwheels, will not produce the effect of 10 horses in the machinery; it may take a 16 or a 20 horse engine to do that according to the construction etc. of your waterwheels. It will be much your interest to erect an engine to turn the machinery directly . . . An engine to pump water comes more expensive, and does little more than half the effect when that is thrown on a wheel.[26]

Southern was, of course, referring to the more efficient Watt engine with its separate condenser. The expense would have been greater with the Newcomen engine. Yet in 1781, Smeaton preferred the waterwheel and steam engine system because it drove the machinery more smoothly and there would not be any sudden stoppage should the engine break down.

Early Attempts at Rotative Steam Engines

The first inventors like Hunt had no choice to obtain direct rotary drive but by adapting the Newcomen engine. Once the superiority of Watt's separate condenser became recognised, attempts were made to pirate it without permission. There were two problems in producing rotary motion from a Newcomen engine. First, the engine only produced power on the downward stroke and second, the stroke was irregular both in length and frequency. While the crank was well known for converting circular motion into linear, using it in reverse to create a rotary motion from a Newcomen engine was probably thought to be impossible owing to the variability of the stroke. Accordingly early attempts were focused on adaptations of racks driving pinions either with teeth round only a part of their circumference or ratchets. Such devices turned by waterwheels or men operating cranks were illustrated by Angostino Ramelli in 1588 being used to raise water with reciprocating pumps. When Triewald installed a Newcomen engine in 1725 to pump water out of the Dannemora copper mine in Sweden, he also erected a winch mechanism to wind ore out of the mine. Two racks, engaging with gearwheels on the winch barrel, were moved by rods linked to the reciprocating motion of the engine beam. Stone-filled chests acted as counterweights to return the racks during the upward dead stroke of the engine. Opposing ratchets were fitted in the gearwheels so that one rack turned the winch one way and the other in the reverse.[27] This was probably the first attempt to provide rotary motion directly from a steam engine but was unsuccessful.

One way of overcoming the dead stroke was to install a pair of single-acting atmospheric cylinders. This was proposed by a Dutchman, N.D. Falck, in his pamphlet of 1776. Instead of racks, he used chains around a ratchet wheel mounted on the main shaft of his engine. The cylinders worked alternately. Boulton was sceptical about Falck's claim that this engine would 'raise more than double the quantity of water that can be raised by any other common engine of the same dimensions, in an equal space of time, and with the same quantity of fuel'.[28] In 1791, Isaac Manwaring patented an engine with a similar layout of two atmospheric cylinders but racks engaging with a gearwheel replaced the chains.[29] The oscillating gearwheel was fitted with ratchets for rotary motion. His engine was improved by Bateman and Sherratt with a connecting rod to drive a crank. One was erected at Thackery's cotton mill at Garratt in Manchester in 1792. Manwaring condensed the steam in the cylinder but Bateman and Sherratt exhausted it into a separate condenser similar to Watt's, from where the

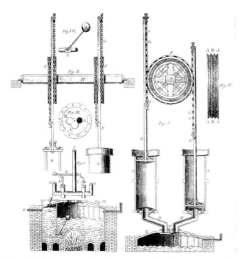

N.D. Falck's twin-cylinder atmospheric engine with chains and ratchet wheels.

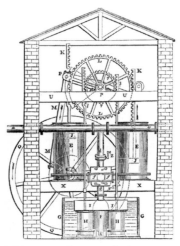

I. Manwaring's twin-cylinder atmospheric engine, with F: separate condenser, H: twin air pumps, driving a crank and flywheel.

condensate was removed by a pair of air pumps. Farey commented that these were 'better than the air-pump of Mr. Watt's double-engine, which is a single action, and exhausts only once each complete stroke'.[30] This engine was rated at 46.5 h.p. at 21.4 strokes per minute and was still in use in 1825. Isaac Perrins, one of Watt's engine erectors, bribed the engineman and was able to gain access to this mill where he saw the condensing apparatus which contravened Watt's 1769 patent. Investigations by James Watt junior and M.R. Boulton found that Bateman and Sherratt had installed another at Thackery's Cark Mill near Lancaster, with probably a further six elsewhere.

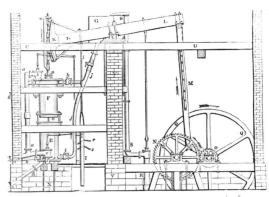

F. Thompson's twin-cylinder atmospheric engine with a top cylinder (F) inverted over the lower one (E).

Rack and ratchet or 'click' devices were tried by various engineers including Matthew Wasborough who took out a patent in 1779.[31] He added a flywheel for the first time on a steam engine, which proved to be a great advantage, helping to smooth out the running. He erected engines at Bristol and Southampton. James Pickard, who had one at Birmingham in 1780, found that the ratchet gear continually got out of order and so substituted a crank but retained the flywheel. The engine answered so much better than anything which had been tried before that the same principle was adopted by other engine builders. But the problem of the single-acting cylinder remained. Thompson patented a solution in 1792 by inverting a second atmospheric cylinder above the usual one on a beam engine with connecting rod, crank and flywheel replacing the pumps.[32] Both pistons were fixed to a common rod which passed through a stuffing gland in the top of the upper cylinder and was linked to the beam by double chains. On the down stroke, atmospheric pressure pushed down the lower piston in the usual way while the return was made by the air forcing the upper piston into the top cylinder. Thompson installed five engines in mills before his early death; two with 40in cylinders were at Arnold worsted mill, Nottingham, and Macclesfield cotton mill; two with 27in cylinders at Ancoats Lane and Levers Street cotton mills in Manchester and one with 22in cylinders at Sutton cotton mill near Mansfield. The fuel consumption was found to be considerable.

One reason for Marshall installing a Savery-type engine at his flax mill was that Wrigley also was in favour of the steam engine and waterwheel combination for its greater smoothness. Wrigley told Marshall that there was:

Nothing gained by a Crank instead of a Waterwheel because of the great weight they are obliged to use at the beam end. J[oshua] W[rigley] says the Boulton & Watt's Crank engines are the only ones that will produce a motion sufficiently regular for spinning.[33]

Wrigley was referring to the common rotative atmospheric engine with a single cylinder like Hunt's. Aikin noted in 1795 that most of the steam engines used in and around Manchester were made and fitted up by 'Mr. Sherrard . . . a very ingenious and able engineer', and that these were 'in general of a small size, very compact, stand in a small place, work smooth and easy, and are scarcely heard in the building where erected. They are now used in cotton mills and for every purpose of the water wheels where a stream is not to be got'.[34]

The layout of the ordinary Newcomen atmospheric engine was followed with a single-acting cylinder at one end of the beam. At the other, to return the piston to the top of the cylinder, either a heavy weight was fitted on the beam or the connecting rod to the crank was made extra heavy. Farey commented:

The common rotative atmospheric engine relied on the heavy weight of the connecting rod (M) to pull the piston to the top of the cylinder (E).

These atmospheric engines act very well if the work or resistance opposed to them is constantly the same so that the counterweight of the connecting rod may be properly adjusted to half the descending force of the piston, in order to make the pressure upon the crank-pin of equal force in ascending as in descending. But they are not so well adapted . . . where . . . the resistance must be perpetually changing.[35]

One which survived for many years at Crank Mill, Morley, was built by Lord Dartmouth in 1791 to power this woollen mill. The engine house contained only the cylinder and half the beam, leaving the rest of the beam, the crank and flywheel exposed at the end of the mill rather like a mine pumping engine. It was replaced only in the mid-nineteenth century.

The load in a textile mill would be changing constantly, with machines being stopped or started as well as the different power requirements in the cycle of spinning mules. But it would be very difficult to adjust the power generated in a single-acting Newcomen cylinder, so the engine would become unbalanced and might fail to get over dead-centre. It might

Half the beam, the heavy connecting rod, crank and flywheel of the atmospheric engine were in the open at the end of Crank Mill, Morley.

stop or worse still turn backwards. The mess of material in the textile machines is best left to the imagination. Bateman and Sherratt soon added separate condensers and air pumps similar to Watt's on these common engines as well as on Manwaring's type. Boulton and Watt obtained injunctions against Bateman and Sherratt in May 1796 so that Bateman and Sherratt agreed to pay the premiums for use of the separate condenser on their own engine and deposit a bond of £4,000 as security against further infringements. Bateman and Sherratt continued to build common atmospheric engines which they designed to be fitted with separate condensers once Watt's patent expired in 1800. When this happened, Bateman and Sherratt had great success with this line of business. A beam engine ascribed to them survives at the Etruscan Bone Mill, Etruria.

Boulton and Watt Rotative Engines

Aikin said that Boulton and Watt had 'far excelled all others in their improvement of the steam engine',[36] while Farey acknowledged that those 'who took care to study Mr. Watt's models very closely, succeeded so far as to establish themselves in the business'.[37] It had taken Watt many trials over many years to evolve a world-beating design that remained the most successful type of steam engine for textile mills until at least the 1850s. Before he reached this position, Watt had dreamed of a rotary engine for driving machinery directly without the intermediary of a waterwheel. In February 1766, he told Roebuck about a 'simpler circular steam-engine' he had been planning. This was his steam-wheel, rather like the wheel of a car in which steam could be admitted through three sets of valves consecutively into sections of the tyre. It pushed against a valve in one direction until it raised a liquid weight, usually mercury, to a sufficient height in the opposite direction to overcome the resistance and start the wheel turning. The mercury passed through the next valve and steam was admitted to the next section while in the first it was exhausted to the separate condenser. In 1770, Boulton agreed to conduct experiments on a steam-wheel at Birmingham because he foresaw a fortune in prospect if it could power post-chaises, canal boats and sugar mills as well as other machines. Although one was erected at Birmingham and trials carried out on it in early 1775, Smeaton was proved correct when he told Boulton that 'It would not do'.[38] People like Samuel Roe of Macclesfield, who enquired about one for driving his silk mill, were recommended to purchase a reciprocating pumping engine for a waterwheel.

It was not until 1779 that Boulton tried to rouse Watt's interest in rotary engines again but Watt complained that he was overwhelmed with erecting pumping engines in Cornish mines. Yet in December that year Watt had models made by Richard Cartwright of engines with cranks and weights to return the piston back to the top of the single-acting cylinder. Cartwright proudly boasted about these remarkable inventions in the Waggon and Horses, the local hostelry to the Soho Manufactory. Pickard soon learnt about Watt's ideas and quickly took out a patent in August 1780.[39] Watt was furious when he discovered how one of his schemes had been stolen from him.

In June 1781, Boulton pointed out how 'the people in London, Manchester, & Birmingham, are Steam Mill Mad', and that they should hurry and take advantage of the demand.[40] Watt needed little encouragement to plan alternatives to the crank. Although Watt thought that designing and constructing rotative engines would barely cover their costs, he drew up a lengthy patent during the latter part of the summer in 1781 for five different ways of creating rotary motion from reciprocating. Four of these included a weight to act during the return stroke. The fifth was the suggestion revived by William Murdock of the sun

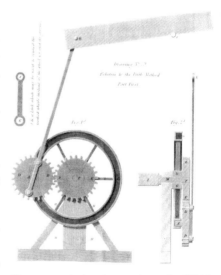

The sun and planet gear drawn for Watt's patent granted in February 1782.

and planet motion. This had a gearwheel fixed on the end of the connecting rod meshing with a second on the main drive shaft in a form of epicyclic gearing. Boulton played with a model one Sunday instead of going to church and solved the problem of retaining the gears in mesh with a simple link. The link appears in the drawings appended to the 1781 patent[41] almost as an afterthought. The layout had the advantage of increasing the speed of the flywheel. With the sun and planet motion, Watt avoided infringing Pickard's patent and Boulton and Watt continued to use it on some engines as late as 1802, by which time it had been generally replaced by the crank.

The next patent enrolled in 1782[42] covered the use of steam expansively and the double-acting engine. Watt had written to William Small in May 1768 about using steam expansively in his steam wheel. He repeated this in the 1782 patent because he found that if the steam inlet valve were closed for part of the duration of the stroke, the steam would continue to expand. He discovered that, if it closed or 'cut off' at one quarter of the stroke, 'the effect produced is equal to more than one-half of the effect which would have been produced by one whole cylinder full of steam'.[43] While the cylinder needed to be larger to obtain the same power, Watt had found a principle for a more economical engine but one that had variable power with more at the beginning of the stroke than the end. While Watt himself did not use the expansive principle much on his rotative engines through the low pressure of the steam, it became important later as pressures rose, but the dilemma remained: how to even out the variations in power. Up to 1778, there was no steam valve between the top of the cylinder and the boiler except for one to isolate the boiler in emergency. Therefore the full pressure of the steam acted on the piston throughout the stroke. Boulton and Watt found that this valve could become a throttle valve to vary the steam pressure acting on the piston. It became an important way of regulating the power developed but at the expense of wire-drawing, or lessening the pressure of steam before it reached the cylinder.

The 1782 patent also included the double-acting engine that Watt claimed he had proposed fourteen years earlier, which would place it in 1767. Here the steam not only pushed the piston down

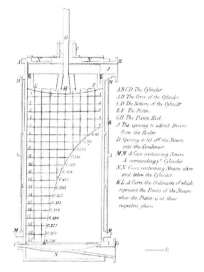

Watt's diagram showing pressure of steam expanding in a cylinder taken from his patent granted in July 1782.

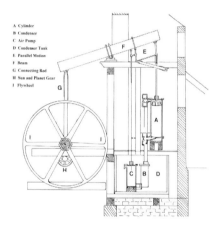

The double-acting Watt rotative engine with sun and planet gear supplied to the Robinsons for their Papplewick Mill near Nottingham. (By permission of Birmingham Central Library, redrawn from Boulton and Watt Collection)

but then more steam pushed it up again. Boulton wondered whether by 'that means [they could] turn a crank completely round the circle and then we are secure because a Com[n] engine can't be made to work up and down'.[44] One advantage was that double the power could be exerted in the same time, resulting in a smoother-running engine, but this came at the expense of more complex valve gear. Watt fitted these double-acting engines with four drop valves, two for the steam inlet and two for the exhaust. They were paired at either end of the cylinder, giving short steam passages, a potentially good arrangement thermodynamically, but Watt failed to operate the inlet valves separately from the exhaust so there was no variable cut-off. This meant that the cylinder would have remained at the same temperature as the incoming steam and so, when the steam

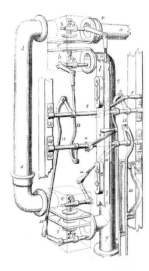
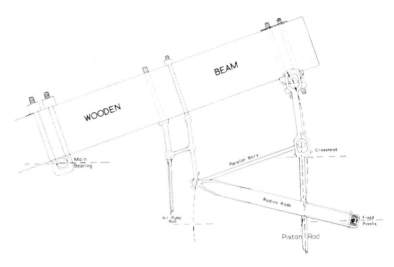

Watt's arrangement of four plug valves for his double-acting rotative engines.

Watt's parallel motion taken from one of the drawings for the Papplewick engine. (By permission of Birmingham Central Library, redrawn from Boulton and Watt Collection)

passed to the condenser, it also remained at a similar temperature, needed more cooling water to condense it. Weights hung on rods closed and by a tumbler system kept the valves shut. On the Watt engine preserved at Sydney, New South Wales, these weights are submerged in the water in the condenser tank and may have acted as dampers to prevent the valves hitting their seats too hard.

On the double-acting engine, the chain by which the piston was suspended from the beam had to be replaced with a positive linkage. Methods of achieving this formed a large part of a patent in 1784.[45] Some of Boulton and Watt's early rotative engines were fitted with a rack on the piston rod engaging with a sector on the end of the beam, but this could not be patented. Watt specified three other ways. One was to have a pair of fixed slide bars to guide the crosshead on the piston rod and link the crosshead to the beam with a connecting rod. Another was to have a pair of radius rods opposed to each other. Half the length of the main beam formed one of the rods. The centre of the vertical link joining their free ends moved in a straight line giving the three bar motion and this point was connected to the crosshead. But in this arrangement, the lower radius rod had to extend beyond the centre line of the cylinder as far as the cylinder was from the middle of the beam, which took up a lot of space.

Then Watt started 'a new hare' at the end of June 1784 when he realised he could make a more compact version by in effect shortening the top rod or beam to only half the length and joining the top of the rod for his air pump to the link on the three bar motion. The remaining part of half the beam formed an extended rod over the steam cylinder and a second link was suspended from it to the top of the piston rod crosshead. Another horizontal rod joined the lower ends of the vertical links to form a parallelogram. Watt had completed his parallel motion, which elegantly and simply provided the solution of joining the piston rod moving in a straight line to the end of the beam moving in an arc. It removed the need for counterweights and almost completed Watt's development of the rotative beam engine in a form which became the standard mill engine for at least another sixty years. No wonder Watt wrote in 1808, 'Though I am not over anxious after fame, yet I am more proud of the parallel motion than of any other mechanical invention I have ever made'.[46]

The First Boulton and Watt Rotative Engines for Textile Mills

The first rotative Boulton and Watt engine supplied to a textile mill was not a great success. The Robinsons at Papplewick, a little north of Nottingham, wanted a steam engine, fearing that the then Lord Byron in his estate of Newstead Priory on the headwaters of the River Leen might cut off their water supply. Boulton and Watt received an enquiry in June 1785. Rennie was sent to lay out the foundations, which were later found to be out of true so that the engine was misaligned. Castings from Bersham went astray and were located at Manchester only in December, with the result that the engine was not set to work until February 1786. Then the person trained to run the engine died. Perhaps it was lucky that the lawsuit against Lord Byron terminated in the Robinsons' favour, but that meant that the engine was not used much and so was not a good advertisement for Boulton and Watt.

Boulton and Watt fixed on a premium of £5 per horsepower per annum for their rotative engines outside London and £6 in the capital. This probably put off many enquirers, particularly those who wanted an engine only to supplement their water power in times of drought or flood. Yet more engines were ordered for cotton mills in the Nottingham area up to 1791 than any other. There were seven averaging 8 h.p. up to 1790. One of exceptional size at 30 h.p. went that May to Major John Cartwright, brother of Edmund, for his ambitious power loom weaving mill which failed. There were another six in 1790 and 1791, followed later with the replacement of Thompson's atmospheric cylinders for Davison and Hawksley's worsted mill at Arnold but then no more. Cotton spinning around Nottingham never developed to the same extent as in Lancashire.

It was not until April 1789 that an enquiry received from the Manchester area resulted in the supply of a successful engine. Drinkwater wrote a long letter about driving the preparatory machinery for his hand mules. He was worried because so many of the other engines then being erected in that town caused a public nuisance through smoke pollution. He said that 'the public yet are not all inclined to believe otherwise than that a Steam Engine of <u>any sort</u> must be highly offensive'.[47] In 1785, Watt had patented a smoke-consuming furnace for steam boilers which was unsuccessful.[48] After this, he developed a furnace with a sloping grate and special method of firing which was a great improvement. It was fitted to the boiler for Drinkwater's engine and helped convince Mancunians that steam engines need not be offensive.

Drinkwater also enquired about an invention which:

> I understand is of a Nature soly [*sic*] calculated to secure more effectually an equal motion under different degrees of heat from the fire – a Property so extremely essential in preparing cotton to work fine yarn – that I wou'd on no act. have you deny me the use of this instrument.[49]

He was referring to the centrifugal governor which Boulton had seen regulating the millstones at the Albion Mill. Rennie had probably added one through his millwrighting experience. Who adapted it to control the throttle valve on a steam engine remains unknown but it was quickly added by Boulton and Watt from their experience with their expansive engines. Watt claimed 'It will not permit 2 strokes per minute of increase in velocity though all the work were taken away at once'.[50] If the speed of the textile machines varied, the different parts would not run smoothly owing to backlash in the gearing, causing thicker or thinner places in the cotton slivers, rovings and through to the finished yarns. So governing the engine speed against variations in load became an essential and highly refined part of the equipment of any textile mill. Drinkwater decided to order an 8 h.p. engine.

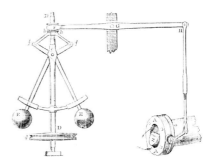

Watt's 'whirling regulator' or centrifugal governor adapted for steam engines.

Early Distribution and Power of Steam Engines

We have seen that Boulton and Watt by no means had the monopoly of supplying steam engines before 1800. References have been found to forty-six engines built by this time by Bateman and Sherratt, thirty-eight of them in Lancashire, mostly in the Manchester area. Since the firm's records have not survived, there is no way of knowing what percentage this forms of their total production. A list of all known engines in Lancashire and Cheshire other than Boulton and Watt's up to 1800 contains the names of seventy-four firms, but this is certainly an underestimate. It has also been estimated that in the Yorkshire wool industry before 1800, there were eighty-one engines in use, probably including six by Boulton and Watt.

The archives of Boulton and Watt are the most comprehensive of any steam engine building firm at this period. From them we can learn not only numbers produced, but type, increase in power and distribution. Between 1775 and 1800, out of a total of probably 596 engines, they supplied 308 rotative ones. Of these, 116 were for textile mills with the majority going to cotton mills. When questioned by Parliament in 1811 about Crompton's petition, Watt thought that about two-thirds of the engines they had erected were for Crompton's mules. Between 1785 to 1795, the firm supplied forty-seven engines to cotton spinning mills, totalling 736 h.p., averaging 15.6 h.p. Between 1795 to 1800, there were 35 engines, totalling 637 h.p., averaging 18.2 h.p. Farey claimed that there were probably 32 engines totalling 430 horsepower in Manchester before the expiry of Watt's patent in 1800. In fact, he was referring only to those supplied by Boulton and Watt, but even so he underestimated their numbers. Thirty-four have been traced with sun and planet gear and five with cranks totalling 612 h.p. and 127 h.p. respectively. Then from 1801 to the end of 1805, a further thirty-six engines were delivered to the Manchester area, most of them definitely for cotton spinning, with a total of 985 h.p., so averaging 27.4 h.p. Figures Baines received in 1832 for England and Wales show that the horsepower in 934 mills with steam engines averaged 28.39 h.p.

Of the earlier Boulton and Watt sun and planet engines, the largest was the 40 h.p. replacement in 1791 for the atmospheric engine at Shudehill. Their average size works out at 18 h.p. In 1800, orders were placed for a 45 h.p. crank engine for Mitchell Holt & Co. and a 40 h.p. one for A. & G. Murray. But they were eclipsed in 1801 by a 100 h.p. engine ordered by Phillips, Wood and Lee for the Salford Twist Mill. This was the largest engine for a textile mill found in the Boulton and Watt archives until well into the 1820s. In 1824, Boulton and Watt supplied an engine of 80 h.p. to the Oxford Road Twist Company in Manchester and another of the same size to the nearby Chorlton Mills of H.H. Birley. But most before 1830 were around 20 h.p., pointing to the small scale of many spinning operations.

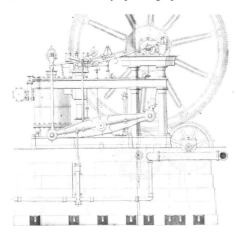

A side lever engine of around 1830 designed by Fairbairn for Bailey's Mill, Stalybridge.

In Yorkshire, Boulton and Watt supplied fourteen engines to textile mills starting in 1792. Six were for cotton spinning, five for wool, including the largest of 40 h.p. in 1792 for Wormauld, Fountain and Gott's Bean Ing Mill, one for worsted at Sheffield and two for flax, including a 28 h.p. replacement for the Savery engine at Marshall and Benyon's flax mill in Leeds. But from 1796, Boulton and Watt received few additional orders from the Yorkshire area. Henry Lodge at Halifax had one in 1801 and a second in 1802. The only other orders were two placed by Gott, the earlier in 1824 for an 80 h.p. conventional beam engine followed in 1829 for an 80 h.p. side lever type. That in 1824 was to drive gig machines for raising the nap on cloth and to relieve his old engine which was greatly overloaded. The side lever engine was based on the compact marine engine where a pair of beams were situated low down, one either side below the cylinder to give a self-contained unit. It possibly originated in a design by Murray in Leeds around 1805. Presumably Yorkshire mill owners supported local manufacturers such as Fenton and Murray of Leeds and so did not order more from Boulton and Watt.

It was only in 1798 that the first Boulton and Watt engine was ordered in Scotland. Seven were supplied to cotton mills and two to flax mills before 1800. More orders followed so that around thirty were supplied between 1800 and 1810. The spread of Boulton and Watt engines into the well-established traditional woollen manufacturing areas of the West of England did not occur until after 1800. An engine, not supplied by them, may have existed at Frome soon after this date. In spite of the proximity of the Somerset coalfield, transport difficulties probably delayed the introduction of steam to the Bradford on Avon and Trowbridge woollen mills until after the opening of the Somerset Coal Canal in 1805. Then J. Cooper & Co. of Trowbridge ordered a small 6 h.p. bell crank engine. This had a compact layout which also was sometimes supplied for early steam boats. Boulton and Watt received orders for fourteen engines up to 1820, with an average size of 14 h.p., the largest being one of 32 h.p. in 1816 for W.H. Jones in Bradford on Avon.

There was a similar picture in the Gloucestershire area where coal from the Forest of Dean could have been brought up the Stroudwater Navigation opened to Stroud in the summer of 1779. However, water power sufficed in the valleys there until 1802 when the first steam engine was installed at Bowbridge Mills to supplement the waterwheel, though its manufacturer and size are unknown. The first of Boulton and Watt's engines to arrive in a Gloucestershire mill was a 6 h.p. bell crank design purchased by H. & G. Austin in 1803. Between then and 1827, they supplied a further thirty engines, fifteen of them in the three years 1821 to 1823, averaging 17 h.p., with the more powerful ones being ordered in the latter part of the period. Only eight were the traditional beam engine built as part of the structure of the engine house. The most popular were twelve six-column beam engines where the beam and entablature were supported on six columns independently of the building. There were also six side lever engines.

While in the older wool industries water remained the predominant source of power for at least the first half of the nineteenth century, the cotton industry placed much greater reliance on the steam engine. While he was preparing his book in 1832, Baines received the results of surveys recently carried out in Great Britain on the cotton industry which showed the preponderance steam had achieved.

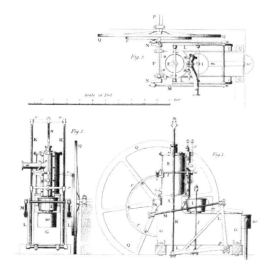

A bell crank engine.

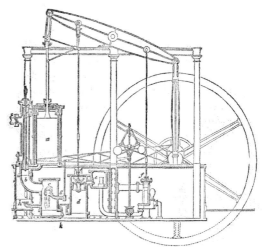

A beam engine with the entablature and upper framing supported on six columns, so independent of the engine house.

General Summary of Cotton Mills in the United Kingdom

Districts	Number of Mills	Horse Power Steam	Water	Number of Persons Employed
In England & Wales	1,000	27,049	7,343½	185,031
In Scotland	125	3,200	2,480	31,099
In Ireland	29	604	380	4,695
Total in the United Kingdom	1,154	30,853	10,203½	220,825[51]

Lancashire had not only the greatest number of cotton mills but also the greatest horsepower of steam engines. The only region where water power predominated was on the edges of the Pennines in Derbyshire, where there was an abundance of streams and rivers falling off the high hills.

Cotton Mills in England

Counties, etc.	Number of Mills	Horse Power Steam	Water	Total number of Persons Employed
Lancashire	657	21,387	2,831	137,352
Yorkshire	140	956	1,429½	9,453
Cheshire	71	3,210	847	20,736
Derbyshire (High Peak Hundred)	56	676	921	5,851
North of Staffordshire, Denbighshire and Flintshire	10	284	65	1,876
Total	934	26,513	6,093½	175,268[52]

Improvements to the Beam Engine

Around 1800, steam engines were transformed through the substitution of iron parts in place of wood for their supporting pillars, main beams and connecting rods. At this period, Boulton and Watt were lagging behind other engine builders, notably Fenton and Murray. After his success with flax-spinning machinery, Murray left Marshall and formed a partnership with James Fenton and David Wood, probably in 1797. They established their own workshops, a later one of which became known as the 'Round Foundry' from its circular shape. Murray concentrated on building steam engines. In 1799, Murdock was sent from Birmingham to Leeds to try and discover the secret of Murray's much better castings. M.R. Boulton wrote gleefully to James Watt junior that Murdock 'by plentiful doses of ale succeeded in extracting from him [one of Murray's foundry men] the arcane and mysteries of his superior performance'.[53] In desperation to try and improve the quality of their castings, Boulton and Watt even ordered a boat-load of moulding sand from the same source as Murray. Industrial espionage continued. Watt junior bought land adjacent to Murray's to prevent him expanding, but three years later had not succeeded in emulating him. One of the earliest engines built by Boulton and Watt entirely from cast iron was supplied to the Salford Twist Company in 1801. This mill was the first in Manchester to have a fireproof structure similar to that at Shrewsbury and later was one of the first to be lit by gas. Drawings for the main beam of this engine show that a sort of 'space-frame' was proposed. Another suggestion was for an elliptical shape but without the strengthening moulding round the edge which later became the normal type.

Around 1800, Boulton and Watt in Birmingham and Fenton and Murray in Leeds were looking for a simpler form of valve gear than Watt's plug type and an improved way of operating it. In 1799, Murdock had patented a sliding valve worked by an eccentric on the crankshaft.[54] Ports with flat faces were made at either end of the cylinder in order to keep the steam passages into and out of the cylinder short. Murdock connected the upper and lower valves by a hollow rod that served for an eduction pipe to the upper end of the cylinder. Two valves took the place of four in Watt's type. Later the valve was made as a single casting, stretching between the ports for the whole length of the cylinder. It was flat on the side next to the ports and semicircular on its back. The exhaust passage was cast into the whole length of the valve to carry the steam away to the condenser. This valve achieved short steam passages at the expense of a very heavy valve which was difficult to keep steam-tight with packing round the back. It soon became standard on all but the largest slow-speed rotative engines built by Boulton and Watt. This valve was developed into a pair of 'D' slide valves, one for each end of the cylinder, joined by a rod. These combined lightness with short steam passages but the inconvenient semicircular shape and packing were retained.

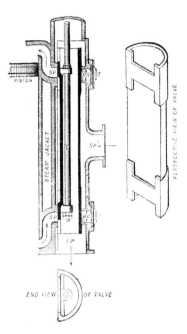

Murdock's long 'D' slide valve.

The essential differences in Murray's box type slide valve, patented in 1802,[55] were that it was kept against the port faces by the steam pressure and was quite short and light. This single valve replaced Watt's four. It had the disadvantage that it needed long steam passages to take the steam in and out of the cylinder. However, there was no trouble with packing and much less power was required to drive it than the Murdock type. It became the basis for most types developed later. To make his valve, Murray invented a planing machine which machined the valve faces to fit accurately. With any single slide valve, the relationship of the inlet opening to that of the exhaust will remain the same. Murray realised the advantages of valve 'lap' for expansive working. If the inlet side of the valve face were extended, that side of the valve would give a shorter opening of the port, allowing some expansive working.

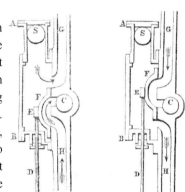

Murray's short box-type slide valve.

The Haydock Beam Engine

Increasingly, the cotton industry relied on the beam engine as demand outstripped natural sources of power that could be obtained from either horses or water. It was realised that the explanation of the development of the steam engine in any Museum of Science and Technology in Manchester would be incomplete without a beam engine. The only one which was offered was that at the Richard Evans & Sons colliery maintenance depot at Haydock. It had probably been moved to that situation around 1860. It has been suggested that it could have been one of the engines used to wind wagons up the railway inclines at Edge Hill in Liverpool but this seems unlikely for two reasons. First, the dimensions are wrong because the engines there had a 6ft stroke while that on the Haydock engine is only 5ft.[56] Then the engines at Liverpool were designed for a steam pressure of 35 p.s.i. whereas the slide valves on the Haydock engine are the low pressure type for perhaps 10 p.s.i.

Top of the cylinder of the Haydock engine before removal.

Wooden panelling covering the flywheel of the Haydock engine before dismantling.

The Haydock engine is a typical 'Watt' engine as used in textile mills and other applications around 1830 with cast iron parts except for rods and crankshaft. It is double-acting with Watt's separate condenser, his parallel motion to connect the piston rod to the beam and his centrifugal governor. However, the slide valves are separate 'D' valves at each end of the cylinder with packing around their backs. This was the type installed on the Butterley engine at Stretham near Ely dating to 1831. This type with short steam passages to the cylinder is good thermodynamically but the pressure from the packing round the backs of the valves had caused bad wear on the rubbing faces. The main beam had been plated at the cylinder end. As no fracture could be observed, this was assumed to have been added to balance the heavy cast iron connecting rod. In its house at Haydock, wooden panelling covered the flywheel which had gear teeth cast into the six segments of its rim. The rim could have been replaced when the engine was moved as it was a feature claimed to have been introduced by Fairbairn after 1832 and the crankshaft is long enough to have had a gearwheel fitted on its end.

When the engine was offered, it was accepted as a step of faith because the Museum was housed only in a temporary building with no prospect of any permanent home. Mr Reg Platt, an iron founder in Widnes, offered storage and help with its removal. The building which protected this engine from the weather also formed the supporting structure. Luckily the building was due for demolition so that we were able to free parts of the engine by knocking down the walls. However, it was recognised that such a 'house-built' engine might cause problems in re-erection later. The separate condenser, the crank bearing, the base of the vertical pillar and the cylinder are all secured on top of separate masonry blocks capped with stone slabs while the entablature and framing around the beam are supported by the walls. As all these are at different levels, there were problems of vertical as well as horizontal alignment to ensure that the centre lines of the cylinder, air pump, beam and crank pin would all be correct.

The crank pedestals, the pillar supporting the beam and the ends of the entablature under the beam were secured by long bolts passing right down the supporting masonry in holes. While this allowed a little sideways movement for accurate alignment,

The cylinder being lifted out of the partly demolished Haydock engine house.

on most bolts it was impossible to access the lower ends and hold them so that, once a nut had been loosened, the bolt dropped and turned freely so that the nut could not be unscrewed any more and had to be cut off. Reg Platt was able to borrow a mobile crane to lift out the freed parts. This certainly made their removal much easier than using block and tackle, especially as we had removed the roof beams which had been used as lifting points. The crane could only just reach the beam, which was the heaviest single part. With the beam away, the walls could be lowered and flooring removed to expose the cast iron framing around the beam and the entablature. The ends of all these parts were supported on more stone slabs built into the brickwork. These stones can sometimes still be identified in walls of old mill buildings where there have been beam engines. The tie rods for the main entablature cross beam ran a long way down through the walls and could not be removed, so the entablature had to be lifted off carefully. The flywheel spokes ended in a 'T' shape which meant that each rim section had to be taken to the top position and pulled out sideways before it could be lowered. This was a difficult balancing act, made more so when one spoke was discovered to be broken at its base. The cylinder and valve chests came out in one piece, to be followed by the condenser and air pump at the very bottom of the engine.

The cylinder being lowered onto Reg Platt's lorry with Frank Wightman in foreground.

The cylinder of the Haydock engine erected with parallel motion above at Liverpool Road Station.

The flywheel of the Haydock engine re-erected at Liverpool Road Station with the cylinder in the background.

The engine could not have been retained in situ so this was the only way of preserving this historic machine. Its removal and subsequent erection showed early engineering techniques, such as the method of aligning bearings by first positioning a sole plate and then mounting the pedestal more accurately on top with wedges. It also brought home the massive structure of the mainly cast iron parts for the comparatively little power produced, probably about 20 h.p. at about 20 r.p.m. When we had re-erected this engine and started to run it, we found one error in Watt's designs. He had immersed his separate condenser in a tank of cold water both to act as a surface condenser and also to prevent air entering the condensing chamber and destroying the vacuum. When he changed to jet condensing, he drew the cold water from this source, which we found became warm through the heat of the steam going into the condenser, thus reducing the efficiency of the jet. We also noted at the top of the governor stand an addition to his centrifugal governor in the form of a cast iron ball. This could have been added as a fail-safe feature to close the throttle valve in the event of the governor failing. Also it would work as a weight to prevent the governor balls rising and closing the throttle valve until a predetermined speed had been attained. If this were its reason, then it anticipated the American Charles Porter's weighted or 'loaded' governors by many years. This engine is certainly much easier to control than the Newcomen one and is a fitting tribute to the genius of Watt and the early pioneers.

The Grasshopper Engine

A compact form of beam engine called the 'grasshopper' can be traced back to 1805, when Oliver Evans installed one in a boat in America. It had a vertical cylinder. The piston rod was jointed to one end of a beam above the cylinder. Radius rods from brackets on top of the cylinder to the beam kept the piston rod moving vertically. The beam was only half the length of a normal one, terminating at the central pivot where it met a vertical support which could oscillate a little. The connecting rod was placed between cylinder and beam support. This type of engine became nicknamed 'grasshopper' from its action that mimicked the rear legs of the insect. It never achieved much popularity because it was unbalanced, with the weights of the piston, connecting rod and beam all being on the same side of the beam support. Reg Platt presented the example he saved from Widnes Technical College to the North Western Museum of Science and Industry in Manchester. We found that the top of the cylinder had a worn bell-mouth, due to the pivots for the radius rods being misaligned, probably from new. This was corrected and the engine ran well with its heavy flywheel.

Impressive Progress

Baines summed up the progress the industry had made by 1830 in a rather flowery passage showing his intense pride in the achievements and progress up to that date:

It will be perceived that the operations are numerous, and every one of them is performed by machinery, without the help of human hands, except merely in transferring the material from one machine to another. It is by iron fingers, teeth and wheels, moving with exhaustless energy and devouring speed, that the cotton is opened, cleaned, spread, carded, drawn, roved, spun, wound, warped, dressed, and woven. The various machines are proportioned to each other in regard to their capability of work, and they are so placed in the mill as to allow the material to be carried from stage to stage with the least possible loss of time. All are moving at once – the operations chasing each other; and all derive their motion from the mighty engine, which, firmly seated in the lower part of the building, and constantly fed with water and fuel, toils through the day with the strength of perhaps a hundred horses. Men, in the meanwhile, have merely to attend on this wonderful series of mechanism, to supply it with work, to oil its joints, and to check its slight and infrequent irregularities; – each workman performing, or rather superintending, as much work as could have been done by *two or three hundred men* sixty years ago. At the approach of darkness, the building is illuminated by jets of flame, whose brilliance mimics the light of day, – the produce of an invisible vapour, generated on the spot. When it is remembered that all these inventions have been made within the last seventy years, it must be acknowledged that the cotton mill presents the most striking example of the dominion obtained by human science over the powers of nature, of which modern times can boast. That this vast aggregate of important discoveries and inventions should, with scarcely an exception, have proceeded from English genius, must be a reflection highly satisfactory to every Englishman.[57]

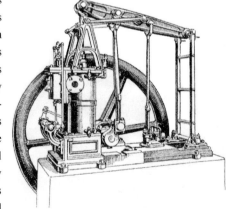

A grasshopper beam engine by Easton and Amos, 1862.

Baines had forgotten that the crucial invention enabling this industry to expand so dramatically was the steam engine developed by James Watt, the Scot.

NOTES: CHAPTER 2

1   Gaskell (1833), p. 43.

2   Baines (c.1835), p. 348.

3   Ibid, p. 347.

Cotton-wool Imported and Retained for Consumption 1785 to 1830, figures every fifth year.

Year	Consumed, lbs.
1785	17,992,888
1790	30,603,451
1795	25,207,603
1800	51,594,122
1805	58,878,163
1810	123,791,826
1815	92,525,951
1820	152,829,633
1825	202,546,869
1830	269,616,460

4   Baines (1875), p. 80.

5   Baines (c.1835), p. 227.

6   M'Connel (1905), p. 32, to Taylor & Heywood, 28 February 1795.

7   Ibid, to Taylor & Heywood, 11 February 1795.

8   Patent 1,879, 15 May 1792.

9   Baines (c.1835), p. 357.

Price of Cotton Yarn No. 100 from 1786 to 1832 in shillings and pennies. 1786, 38/0; 1787, 38/0; 1788, 35/0; 1789, 34/0; 1790, 30/0; 1791, 29/9; 1792, 16/1; 1793, 15/1; 1794, 15/1; 1795, 19/0 (spun from Bourbon cotton); 1796, 19/0 (spun from Bourbon cotton); 1797, 19/0; 1798, 9/10 (from Sea Island cotton); 1799, 10/11; 1800, 9/5; 1801, 8/9; 1802, 8/4; 1803, 8/4; 1804, 7/10; 1805, 7/10; 1806, 7/2; 1807, 6/9. After many fluctuations, in 1829, 3/2; 1832, 2/11.

10 Aspin (2003), p. 476.

11 Lee (1972), p. 21; M'Connel & Kennedy to G. Hannay, Bangor, Northern Ireland, (undated), 1797.

12 Cooke (2003), p. 79.

13 M'Connel (1905), p. 49.

14 Aspin (2003), p. 305.

15 Patent 1,613, 19 June 1787.

16 Patent 1,752, 1 June 1790.

17 Patent 1,747, 27 April 1790.

18 B. & W. Col., MI, 1/16, 'Journal', 7 November 1770.

19 Patent 1,378, 17 July 1783.

20 Patent 1,443, 9 July 1784.

21 Patent 4,013, 5 April 1816.

22 Patent 6,460, 13 August 1833.

23 Patent 1,945, 9 April 1793.

24 Patent 3,945, 27 July 1815.

25 Hills (1994), pp. 210–11.

26 B. & W. Col., J. Southern to P. Ainsworth, 28 June 1790.

27 Lindqvist (1984), p. 249.

28 Falck (1776), p. 1.

29 Patent 1,792, 10 February 1791.

30 Farey (1827), Vol. 1, pp. 663–4.

31 Patent 1,213, 10 March 1779.

32 Patent 1,884, 25 May 1792.

33 Musson & Robinson (1969), p. 399.

34 Aikin (1795), p. 177.

35 Farey (1827), Vol. 1, p. 422.

36 Aikin (1795), p. 177.

37 Farey (1827), Vol. 1, p. 677.

38 Muirhead (1854), Vol. 2, p. 64; Letter 131, W. Small to J. Watt, 23 February 1774, (Boulton 340.39)

39 Patent 1,263, 23 August 1780.

40 Tann (1981), pp. 54–5; M. Boulton to J. Watt, 21 June 1781.

41 Patent 1,306, 23 February 1782.

42 Patent 1,321, 4 July 1782.

43 Ibid.

44 Dickinson & Jenkins (1927), p. 140; M. Boulton to J. Watt, 20 April 1781 (B. & W. Col.).

45 Patent 1,432, 25 August 1784.

46 Dickinson (1936), p. 139.

47 B. & W. Col., from P. Drinkwater, 3 April 1789.

48 Patent 1,485, 9 July 1785.

49 B. & W. Col., from P. Drinkwater, 21 November 1789.

50 Ibid, to P. Drinkwater, 25 November 1789.

51 Baines (c.1835), p. 394.

52 Ibid, p. 389.

53 B. & W. Col., M.R. Boulton to J. Watt jun., 17 January 1799.

54 Patent 2,340, 29 August 1799.

55 Patent 2,632, 28 June 1802.

57 Bailey, M.R., 'Robert Stephenson & Co., 1823–1829', *T.N.S.*, Vol. 50, 1978–9, p. 127 (Wishaw (1842), pp. 196-7).

57 Baines (c.1835), p. 244.

CHAPTER 3
CONSOLIDATION, 1830–1860

Continued Expansion

The period 1830 to 1860 covers some important inventions which further increased the numbers and the sizes of spinning mills and weaving sheds. Among them were the self-acting mule, the condenser carding machine, the combing machine and the power loom. These almost wiped out hand production in all the textile industries but especially in combing and weaving. Imports of cotton continued to rise. In 1831, 266,360,000lb were retained for home consumption. In 1835, this was 339,379,683lb. The averages for the following years were:

1839–41	426,300,000lb
1844–46	523,300,000lb
1849–51	588,000,000lb
1857	764,007,000lb
1859–61	910,000,000lb[1]

Comparative figures for wool imports were:

1830	31,646,000lb
1840	48,421,000lb
1850	59,938,000lb
1855	69,846,000lb
1857	90,903,000lb[2]

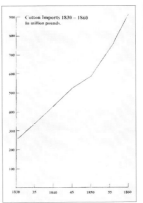
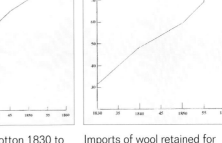

Imports of cotton 1830 to 1860.

Imports of wool retained for consumption 1830 to 1860.

Guesses for wool production in the United Kingdom were: in 1845, 157,500,000lb; in 1851, 228,950,000lb; and in 1857, 175,000,000lb, of which 15,142,881lb was exported. The cotton industry was well in the lead.

In his book published in 1832, James Montgomery included plans for a six-storey cotton mill 145ft long and 37ft wide containing 23,000 spindles. The mules would have 300 spindles each and a steam engine of 40 to 50 h.p. would be required. This was just before the impact of Richard Roberts's self-acting mule began to be felt. In the third edition published in 1836, Montgomery mentioned mules with 600 spindles and mills extended to upwards of fifty feet wide. In 1835, the New Eagley Mill, Bolton, contained 29,000 spindles and the nearby Egerton Mill 49,000 spindles. These seem to have been larger than most for the average spindleage in combined spinning and weaving mills in the Stockport area has been given as 13,983 spindles in 1832. In 1834, Clarence Mill, Bollington, was built to hold 8,640 mule spindles needing 17 h.p., 6,400 throstle spindles needing 25 h.p. and 320 looms needing 32 h.p., giving totals of 15,000 spindles and

Shaddon Mill, Carlisle, designed by William Fairbairn for the firm of Peter Dixon in 1836.

74 h.p. At the same time, Bayley Street Mill in Stalybridge was designed by Fairbairn to hold 40,000 spindles and 1,280 looms, driven by a side lever engine with two coupled cylinders, each of 110 h.p. In 1850, the average spindleage in combined Lancashire spinning and weaving factories had increased to 17,814 and in Lancashire spinning mills it was 11,818 spindles. In 1849, John Mayall of Mossley decided to embark on a hugely ambitious project to build the largest single cotton spinning mill in the world. When completed soon after 1851, his Britannia Mill contained 112 mule frames carrying the huge total of 119,000 spindles. There is no record of the source of power. It was not equalled for a very long time. More typical of larger mills around 1860 was Victoria Mill, Dukinfield, incorporated in 1861 to hold 57,414 spindles.

We have seen how in 1832 Baines summarised the number of cotton spinning mills in England and Wales at 1,000 with 27,049 h.p. from steam and 7,343½ h.p. from water (see p.66). Another survey in 1835 found that in the north of England there were 934 cotton spinning mills with 26,513 h.p. from steam and 6,094 from water. In 1850, English cotton weaving mills used 2,840 h.p. from steam and 370 h.p. from water while combined spinning and weaving mills used 37,368 h.p. from steam and 3,170 h.p. from water. The vertically integrated mills predominated before the change to greater specialisation had really begun. These figures confirm the increasing dependence on steam as the major source of power. Some figures for the worsted industry show how it also increased in the second quarter of the nineteenth century through expanding imports of merino wool from Australia and better combing machines. In 1839, there were seventy-one spinning firms in Bradford and its neighbourhood with 165,120 spindles. In 1850, there were 87 firms employing 268,653 spindles and in 1856, 88 firms with 336,618 spindles. At the same time, spindle speeds increased from 1,400 r.p.m. in 1825 to 1,800 r.p.m. in 1850. The sizes of mill engines had to increase proportionately to meet these demands.

The Self-Acting Spinning Mule

In 1824, there was a strike of mule spinners so that Mr Ashton of Stalybridge and his fellow cotton spinners asked Roberts to make their mules work by self-acting mechanisms. Roberts at first declined, claiming he knew nothing about cotton spinning. But he must have turned the challenge over in his mind and took out a patent in 1825.[3] This covered three important improvements. One was a camshaft which rotated in four stages to control the mechanisms for, first, actuating the drafting rollers, moving the carriage out and rotating the spindles. In its next move, the camshaft turned to stop the rollers and carriage but allowed the spindles to continue twisting. After these had inserted the correct amount of twist, the camshaft turned to the third position for backing off and finally, fourth, for winding on with the carriage moving back in again. During winding on, the position of the faller wire was controlled by a movable inclined plane, the second of Roberts's improvements. Then the speed of winding on was regulated by the position of a counter-faller wire which Roberts adapted for

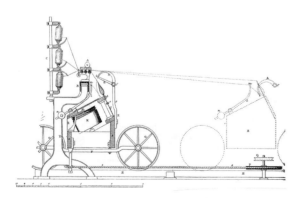

Parts of a mule carriage before the addition of Roberts's improvements.

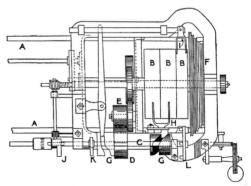

The camshaft for a late self-acting mule runs along the bottom of the drawing from J to G

this purpose as his third improvement. As devised by Roberts, the counter-faller provided the tension during winding on through its balancing weights, taking up any slack and also yielding if too much yarn was being wound on. Its height told the spinner when the winding on mechanism needed adjustment. But the method of controlling the winding on proved unsatisfactory. On our hand demonstration mule in the Museum, winding on was made much easier with the counter-faller wire.

Roberts brilliantly solved the problem of winding on in a second patent taken out in 1830.[4] The main feature was the quadrant. A nut on the main arm of the quadrant was linked by a chain wound round a drum on the carriage. The chain unwound from the drum as the carriage moved back, rotating it, which turned the spindles. The length of yarn to be wound on was the same each draw but the number of turns the spindles needed varied due to their taper as the cop was built up. The position of the nut on its arm compensated for this and was controlled by the position of the counter-faller wire. This was probably the first true self-regulating feedback mechanism to be developed, a credit to Roberts. In addition, spindle speed had to vary as the yarn was wound on first at the narrow top of the cop, down to the broadest part and back up again to the narrow top. Roberts solved this by introducing another brilliant idea through making the nut on the quadrant arm follow the arc which the movement of the quadrant described. While others tried different mechanisms, none succeeded so well as Roberts's quadrant.

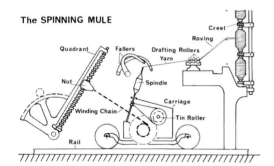
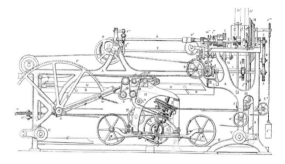

Above: Main parts of Roberts's quadrant mechanism. Above right: Vertical section through the headstock on an 1880s mule showing the complexity. The camshaft is top right, the quadrant on the left. The carriage, without spindles, is in the central position.

At the time of the introduction of the self-acting mule, a typical mule spinning 80s counts yarn would take about twenty working hours to spin one set of cops. For the spinner on manually controlled mules, this meant the strenuous putting-up or winding on each stretch of spun yarn some 2,400 times. A spinner working a pair of self-acting mules had a much easier task because he had only to adjust the quadrant nut during the period in which the cop bottom was being formed which, spinning 80s count, took a little over four hours. This involved about ninety adjustments, which was done quite simply by turning a cranked handle. For the rest of the sixteen hours, he could almost leave the self-acting mule to look after itself, making only a few minor adjustments. Various later additions, such as the nosing motion, improved even on this. Such complex mechanisms still needed the supervision of a skilled spinner who had two 'piecers' to help join up any broken yarns. At the Museum, we were grateful to our retired mule spinners, who demonstrated our mule and kept it in order.

Roberts's masterpiece was widely acclaimed as 'one of the greatest triumphs of mechanical genius that has ever been achieved, and as a display of power of the inventive faculty in man's nature surpassed anything accomplished up to that time'.[5] Those who witnessed its performance found that it exceeded 'their most sanguine expectations'.[6] Not only did the mule spinner need less skill but better cops were spun on the self-acting mule through its superior winding on. The cops contained more yarn, were firmer and a better shape. When transferred to the shuttle for weaving, there were fewer weft breakages so that looms could work at greater

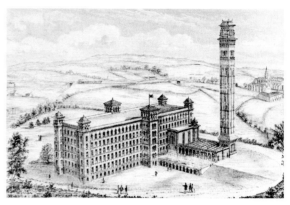

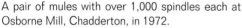

A pair of mules with over 1,000 spindles each at Osborne Mill, Chadderton, in 1972.

India Mill, Over Darwen.

speeds and produce cloth of superior quality.[7] Roberts's self-acting mule was quickly taken up by cotton spinners for coarse to medium counts. By March 1834, Sharp Roberts had made 520 with upwards of 200,000 spindles and by December 1837 there were up to half a million spindles in one hundred mills.

Because all the stages in spinning on the mule were now driven by power, the size was no longer limited by the strength of the spinner. The number of spindles on the carriage increased quickly. For example, the Ashworths' New Eagley Mill in 1828 had mules that averaged 370 spindles with their longest at 400. All these were at least fourteen per cent longer than ones sold by Dobson at that time. Between 1830 to 1833, the Ashworths were purchasing mules of over 500 spindles, the largest with 516 spindles. Replacement mules in 1854 to 1856 came with 810 spindles. These were mules for fine spinning. In 1835, Baines gave figures of mules with 'eight hundred spindles each, and some of the prodigious number of *eleven hundred* spindles each, or *two thousand two hundred* the pair – the pair being managed by one spinner'.[8] It is suspected that few were built as large as this for some years. India Mill, Over Darwen, built in 1867, had 48 pairs of mules of 708 spindles each. Then in the early 1890s, Milton Mill in Mossley had weft mules of 1,368 spindles. The technical optimum had probably been reached at that time with 1,392 spindles or 116 dozen, made possible by the introduction of lighter carriages of steel construction replacing wood.

Such long mules caused the width of cotton mills to be increased from around 99ft in 1868 to 126ft in 1875, to 134ft in 1890 and 150ft in 1905. Spindle speeds increased at the same time. The spindles on semi-powered mules in 1795 rotated at around 2,250 r.p.m. which had risen to 3,000 r.p.m by 1825. In the early days of the self-actors, this might be 4,000 r.p.m., approaching 6,000 r.p.m. in 1854. In the 1890s, spindle speeds might be 7,500 r.p.m. while the carriage was drawing out and up to 11,500 r.p.m. twisting on the head. This rise in speeds made further demands on power from the engine. Figures for the numbers of cotton mule spindles have been given as:

1832	9,000,000
1845	17,000,000
1850	21,000,000
1861	30,300,000[9]

The self-acting mule was quickly adapted for the woollen and worsted industries. It was very successful in the woollen branch when used in conjunction with the condenser carding machine to produce a softly spun weft. A couple of such mules were still at work in mills in North Wales in 2005 at Bryncir and Trefriw.

Condenser Carding

An invention for preparing rovings was introduced from America towards the end of the second quarter of the nineteenth century. It was developed between 1824 and 1826 chiefly by woollen manufacturers and machine makers in eastern Massachusetts. The web coming off the final doffer cylinder of a carding machine was not drawn into a single sliver but slit into sections which were given a false twist by being rubbed between a pair of moving leather aprons and wound into cheeses side by side on a long bobbin. The bobbin was taken to the mule for spinning. While the condenser system was adopted quickly by European manufacturers, their English counterparts were very suspicious, considering that it led to loss of quality. But by 1853 it was being mentioned with approval as eradicating many of the defects of the slubbing billy.

Carding engine with condenser apparatus. The web off the carding drum was split into ribbons which were passed between two sets of leather aprons in the centre of the picture. The smooth rollers on the left had the long bobbins for the rovings placed on top of them.

At least one Yorkshire manufacturer bought such a machine that year but it was by no means common until the later 1850s. It was introduced to the West of England woollen industry around the same time. Salter's of Trowbridge re-equipped their Home Mills after a fire in 1862 and claimed that they were one of the first mills in Great Britain to introduce condensers. In the meantime, condenser spinning of cotton waste had been developed to create woollen-type yarns. After the introduction of cotton combing machines around 1851, the amount of short staple cotton waste rose sharply. Following processing on condenser carding machines, the waste was spun on mules. The yarn was suitable for flannelette sheets, dusters and similar materials with a raised surface, creating a separate branch of the textile cotton industry.

Combing Machines

The history of machines for combing is almost as complex as the machines themselves which were finally produced. Combing is an early example of the worsted industry gaining a lead over the cotton. After his endeavours with the power loom, the Revd Edmund Cartwright turned his inventive genius to combing wool. He took out his first patent for this in August 1789[10] followed by another three before his final one in 1801.[11] He used a circular revolving comb about five feet in diameter from which the long fibres or 'tops' were carried off into a can and a smaller cylinder comb for teasing out short fibres or 'noils' which were taken off by hand. Its output equalled twenty hand combers and hence aroused much opposition. But it was only relatively successful because, while it could cope with the first six coarser grades of wool, hand combing prevailed in the six finer qualities.

The import of fine merino wool from Australia

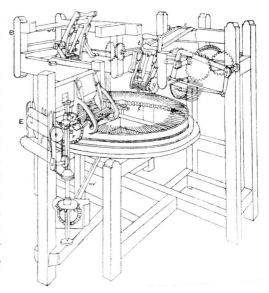

Cartwright's 'Big Ben' combing machine.

increased spectacularly during the first half of the nineteenth century and continued to do so subsequently. Spain had jealously guarded export of merino sheep renowned for the super-fine quality of their wool. After some had been introduced into France and Saxony in 1786, Sir Joseph Banks, President of the Royal Society, was able to have some presented to George III in 1787. More flocks followed, particularly during the Peninsular War around 1809, when they could be exported by sea through Portugal. In the meantime, other breeds of sheep had been introduced into New South Wales, but at first it was thought that the country was unsuitable since the early samples of wool sent back to England were of poor quality. By 1806, Spanish merinos had been introduced there and soon breeding was being carried out on a large scale, producing fine wool. A modest clip of 20,000 pounds in 1800 increased to the gigantic proportions of 500 million pounds a century later.

This may have been one stimulus which brought a number of inventors into the field of combing, the most important of whom were Josué Heilmann, a Frenchman, George Edmund Donisthorpe, a Leeds engineer, and two Bradford manufacturers, Sir Isaac Holden and Samuel Cunliffe Lister, later Baron Masham. The first of these to enter this new field was Holden, who in 1833 urged his employers, Townend Brothers of Cullingworth near Bingley, Yorkshire, to try out seven wool-combing machines of Collier's designs, but they were found to be very imperfect and brought only trouble and loss. In 1836, Holden began experimenting on them until they showed reasonable success. While Cartwright's combs contained thick teeth similar to hand combs, Holden's contained teeth finer than the finest sewing-needle, in some instances forty-eight to fifty of them being set in a lineal inch in the rows of the combs. Holden decided to concentrate entirely on developing the combing machine and in 1846 moved to Bradford to form an alliance with Lister. A joint patent in 1847[12] covered improvements to these Collier machines. The special feature was the 'square motion' which closely imitated the operations of the hand comber, giving the same characteristics to the wool with the length of fibre in the tops and noils being well preserved. Holden recommended that these machines should be introduced into France where they would be more valuable for the merino trade. He moved to France where, with Lister's help, he established mills at St Denis, Rheims and Croix near Roubaix and continued to improve his combing machines.

Donisthorpe had taken out one patent in 1842 and two in 1843 for his circular type of machine.[13] It attracted the attention of Lister who had been interested in developing a machine to comb wool through seeing the grim working conditions of the hand combers supplying his mill at Manningham. Lister was quick to perceive that Donisthorpe's invention carried sufficient promise so, in 1842, he made Donisthorpe an offer of £2,000 for half the patent right, which was accepted. In the following year, Lister purchased the other half for £10,000, by which time they were combing fine merino wool. While Donisthorpe then ceased to have any pecuniary interest in his patent, he entered into partnership with Lister and continued to patent improvements in their joint names, covering his 'nip' mechanism.[14] A gripping device, or 'nip', held one end of the wool fibres while the rest of the tuft was being combed by the circle of teeth. Lister took out further patents in 1851 and 1852[15] and was soon running nine combing mills.

By this time, the empire and monopoly which Lister was building up was challenged by another machine based on the nip mechanism. Heilmann, a native of Mulhouse, took out a British patent

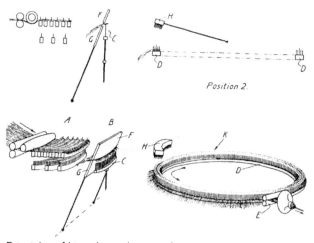

Principles of Lister's combing machine.

in 1846[16] but no machines were put to work until one was exhibited at the International Exhibition of 1851. The end of the sliver was held in the nip to allow two or more combs on cylinders to pass through the protruding fibres to comb them thoroughly. The combs were cleared of the noils by a brush cylinder and knife. The combed section was passed forward so that the part held in the nip could be combed. Then the combed fibres were joined onto the length of tops previously finished. Heilmann and Lister started litigation against each other and both were given verdicts against the other for different infringements. In the meantime, Edward Akroyd, the Halifax worsted manufacturer, and Titus Salt, the Bradford alpaca spinner, joined forces to buy Heilmann's patents for £33,000 because they knew their value to Lister if he were to establish a complete monopoly of machine-combing for wool. They sold on these rights to Lister at the same price on condition that they were allowed as many combing machines as they wanted to use for themselves. One machine cost Salt only £200 compared with the £1,200 charged by Lister.

The Heilmann machine proved to be suitable also for flax and cotton. Five firms of cotton spinners in Lancashire, including M'Connel & Co. and the machinery makers John Hetherington & Sons, both of Manchester, paid Heilmann a further £30,000 for the rights to comb cotton. Marshalls of Leeds paid £20,000 for those for flax. This made a considerable advance in spinning fine cotton because combing removed the short fibres, leaving the long, perfect ones, something beyond the capacity of the carding engine. In cotton spinning, combing machines and their attendant lap machines were usually installed within spinning mills, adding to the load demanded from the steam engine. New Eagley Mill was re-equipped between 1854 and 1866 with new combing machinery together with mules of 810 spindles at a cost of £10,573.

Back in the West Riding, James Noble took out patents in 1853[17] for a different form of combing machine consisting of a large horizontal revolving circle of vertical pins onto which the wool fibres were fed. Inside this were smaller circles of heated pins revolving at the same speed, which also caught the fibres. Combing occurred at the point where the circles separated. The Noble comb became the machine most used for wool through its mechanical simplicity and adaptability for various classes of wool. Lister again acquired the patent rights so that he controlled the three best machines, Holden's square motion, Donisthorpe's nip and

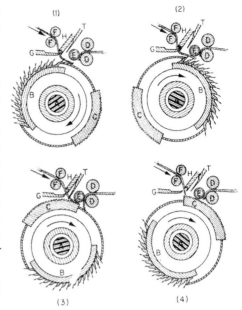

Sectional elevations of the combing stages in Heilmann's machine for cotton.

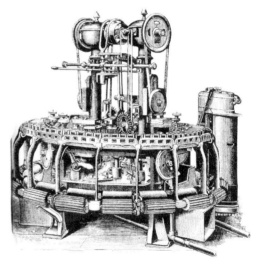

General view of the Noble wool combing machine.

Saltaire Mill.

the Noble. No single combing machine was suitable for every kind of wool but they provided a plentiful supply of noils for the woollen industry.

Lister's Manningham Mills evolved into an enormous vertically integrated concern which in the 1890s was driven by a total of over 4,000 h.p. from its various steam engines. Salt decided to build one vast complex to replace all the small mills he owned in Bradford. The result was the famous mill at Saltaire which was designed by Fairbairn (see p.95). It was opened on 26 September 1853, Salt's fiftieth birthday, with a capacity of 30,000 yards of cloth every working day. Holden returned from France and spent four years and £20,000 on further perfecting his square comb. In 1861, he built Alston Works, which became the largest establishment in Bradford devoted solely to combing on commission. It occupied fifteen acres and employed one thousand people in 1885. Long before this, combing by hand had become extinct, causing much unemployment.

The Power Loom

It took from 1774, the date of the first British patent for a power loom, until the 1840s before a really satisfactory one was developed. The person generally credited with the invention of the power loom is the remarkable Reverend Edmund Cartwright. He had been educated at University College, Oxford, before being elected a fellow of Magdalen College. He received the living of Marwood, Leicestershire, and seemed destined to remain a country parson, writing poems and making agricultural experiments. A visit to Matlock completely changed his life and introduced him to the inventions of Arkwright. He asked why weaving could not be mechanised in a similar way to spinning. Some gentlemen there from Manchester unanimously agreed this was impossible. On his return home, Cartwright built himself a loom which needed two powerful men to operate it. It had a vertical warp, 'the reed fell with the weight of at least half a hundred weight, and the springs which threw the shuttle were strong enough to throw a Congreve rocket'.[18] He patented this in April 1785.[19] He then went to see weavers at work and was surprised to discover how much easier it was to operate their hand looms than his own. So he set about totally redesigning his and took out a further patent in 1786, which has been claimed to embody the basic principles of most later power looms.[20]

To weave by hand requires a few simple repetitive movements. One hand flicks Kay's flying shuttle through the open shed in the warp. The other beats up the weft with the reed in the slay. The feet operate the pedals connected to the heddles or healds to change the shed ready for the next pick to insert the weft with the shuttle again. But a good hand-loom weaver is watching all the time, seeing that no warp threads are broken, seeing

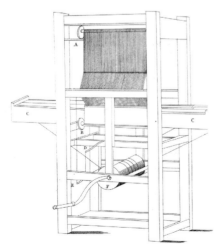

Patent drawing of 1785 for Cartwright's vertical loom.

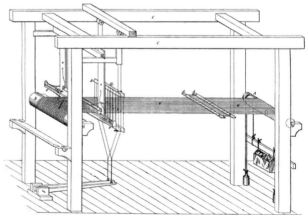

Hand loom at which the weaver sits at the left, working the foot pedals underneath to open the shed. The left hand beats up the weft with the slay while the right sends Kay's flying shuttle through the web.

that the shuttle has not run out of weft, seeing that the shuttle has passed through the shed and has not stuck in the warp, seeing when the stretcher bar or temple needs moving along the newly woven cloth to keep it at the correct width, and seeing when it is time to wind on the cloth. The weaver has to learn the knack of stopping the shuttle from bouncing back out of the box into the warp again after sending it across with the picking stick. A weaver will learn to do all this almost instinctively while retaining a feel for his actions which a power loom will never have. The eyes, body and feeling of

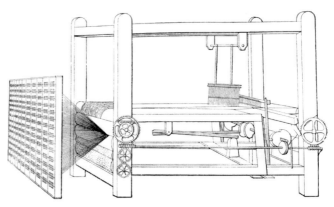

Cartwright's second loom with creel for the warp bobbins on the left.

the weaver had to be replaced with mechanisms, so we should not be surprised that it took fifty years before all these problems were successfully overcome. The power requirements of the loom varied at each stage of the weaving cycle, such as sending the shuttle across, beating up the weft and changing the healds. There was also the need to size a cotton warp to prevent the yarns fraying as they rubbed past each other in the healds and reed.

Cartwright developed a range of mechanisms to stop the loom when a fault occurred. If a warp thread broke, a hook on it dropped and disengaged the driving clutch. Likewise the shuttle had a wire and hook which fell when the weft broke or ran out. He had temples to prevent the woven cloth contracting in width. In a further patent in 1787, he added a mechanism to stop the loom should a shuttle fail to pass through the warp and enter its box.[21] The shuttles were sent across by springs which also beat up the reed and slay. He proposed drawing the warp off bobbins placed in a creel at the back of the loom and sizing it as it was drawn through rollers into the loom. He went to Manchester to seek help from experienced workmen to build his new loom, but he met little encouragement so he decided to establish his own factory at Doncaster. Twenty looms for a variety of fabrics were set to work. The motive power was at first a bull (or more likely an ox) and later horses. In 1788, he built a second factory with a Newcomen steam engine and continued with more patented inventions to improve his loom.[22]

Major John Cartwright, Edmund's elder brother, built a mill at Retford in 1788 powered by a Boulton and Watt engine. Originally it was to have over a hundred looms. Later he decided to include worsted spinning and his brother's wool combing machine but the mill was a failure and closed, probably in 1790. In 1791, the Grimshaws applied to Edmund Cartwright for a licence to build a mill at Manchester for five hundred looms. Twenty-four were set to work driven by a steam engine when anonymous letters were received threatening to destroy the mill. After operating for barely a month, it was burnt to the ground. For Cartwright, this was a bitter blow since not only did he suffer the pecuniary loss of the licence but also nobody else dared to set up another weaving mill for fear of similar arson. Therefore in 1793 he closed down his Doncaster factory, having lost £30,000 on his experiments. His patents show many ingenious mechanisms for overcoming the problems of weaving by power but it is not known how many were incorporated into the looms of subsequent inventors.

Improvements to the Power Loom

To produce an efficient power loom took the work of many people. The scene shifts to Scotland where a Mr Austin of Glasgow made his first attempt at a power loom in 1789. It was a compact design with the slay pivoted at the bottom. In 1798, one of his looms was set to work at Mr I. Monteith's spinning works at Pollokshaws near Glasgow. This performed so well that soon thirty and in 1800 two hundred were running. In 1796, Robert Miller, of Milton Printfield near Glasgow, patented an improvement called the 'Protector' which stopped the loom altogether when the shuttle failed to enter the box.[23] His looms were still working in 1808, running at 60 picks per minute, which was certainly slower than the rate of the best hand-loom weaver who might reach 120 picks. Joseph Clement, later famous for the high quality of his machine tools, started his career around 1805 in a small factory at Kirkby Stephen making parts for power looms. He moved first to Carlisle in the same line of work and then in 1807 to Glasgow, where he stayed a year. As trade was slack there, he accepted a situation with Messrs Leys, Masson & Co. of Aberdeen. His principal work consisted in designing and making power looms and fitting them up in different parts of the country.[24] Both Deanston and Catrine cotton mills were experimenting with power looms around this time, so that by 1813 there were around 1,300 power looms of various types at work in Scotland.

In the meantime, there had been an important development in England. It seems doubtful whether Cartwright's method of drawing his warp directly from a creel of bobbins and sizing it on the loom would have been satisfactory since there appears to be no method of drying it. In order

Austin's compact power loom of 1789.

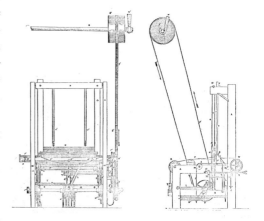

Miller's 'wiper' loom.

A sizing machine of 1862. Yarns from four beams passed through the size bath, round the steam-heated drying cylinder before being combined on a single beam ready for the loom.

to prevent the cotton warp threads chafing and to strengthen them, the hand-loom weaver applied size paste made from starch or flour to a length on the loom which had to be dried before being woven; thus his weaving became intermittent. As long as the dressing had to be carried out on the loom itself, the real economies of continuous weaving by power could not be realised. The person who first separated sizing from the loom was William Radcliffe of Stockport. He had been making small improvements to hand looms since some time after 1800 and realised how much time could be saved if the weaver did not have to dress his warps. Accordingly he first dressed the warp by hand on a separate frame and then wound it on a beam ready to be placed in a loom. Soon he invented a machine which he patented in 1803 and improvements in the following year.[25] Both patents were taken out in the name of one of his workmen, Thomas Johnson, so that they could not be traced easily. The yarns were wound from bobbins in a creel onto a beam. They were then pulled off this beam, passed through a trough of size, brushed and dried with a fan before being rolled up on another beam. Yarns from a number of beams could be combined on the final beam to give the correct number for the whole warp. While Radcliffe developed this machine to prepare warps for his hand-loom weavers, it was soon adapted for the power loom because in 1804 he persuaded Monteith to try one.

While the dressing machines enabled both hand and power looms to maintain continuous production, power looms were slow in coming into use. An estimate for England gave their numbers as 2,400 in 1803 and 12,150 in 1820. As early as 1803, William Horrocks of Stockport patented improvements for 'weaving by steam and water', using 'spiral wheels' and weights to operate the various parts. He took out a further patent in 1805 but his important one was in 1813 for using a special type of crank to beat up the weft with the slay.[26] His loom was very compact and most of the looms built before 1820 were based on it. Then Peel Williams of Manchester had made a power loom with iron framing by 1814. There is also an iron-framed power loom preserved in the silk museum at Braintree which is claimed to have been made by Courtaulds in 1820. The shuttle on it is driven across by springs, which would have given a good blow, suggesting that this may have been a problem on early power looms working at slow speed. Many small improvements were needed to make them reliable.

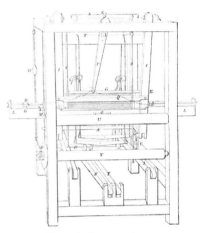

Horrocks's power loom.

The Power Loom of Richard Roberts

The Horrocks loom is said to have formed the basis for that of Roberts. One factor in the success of his loom was that production was organised in a proper system in large numbers which reduced the cost and made them competitive. Another factor may have been that his looms, being better engineered, could withstand being driven at the higher speeds made possible through Fairbairn's improved line shafting. In November 1822, Roberts patented what was probably the first power loom able to weave simple patterns with a tappet mechanism.[27] It had been developed from his loom for plain calico about which Fieldens of Todmorden had made enquiries in January that year. He placed an advertisement in the *Manchester Guardian* on 7 September. Both types had similar iron framing.

Roberts's patent drawings show a compact design, having two driving shafts with the slay pivoted at the bottom. The slay was driven by cranks from the top shaft which was geared to the lower one. This second shaft had cams or eccentrics for operating the healds and the picking stick. He may have introduced this innovation. The picker for sending the single shuttle across was jerked by a cord from a single picking stick suspended from the centre of the top of the framing which also supported the healds. If the shuttle failed to enter either of the boxes, a lever on the slay hit part of the loom framing stopping both slay and loom as well as shifting the

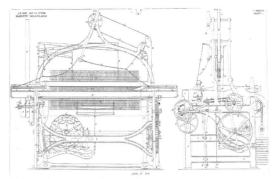

Roberts's patent of 1822 for his pattern-weaving power loom.

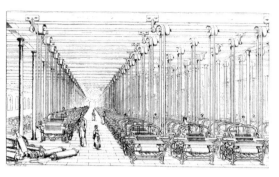

Ure's drawing of a power loom shed at Stockport in 1835.

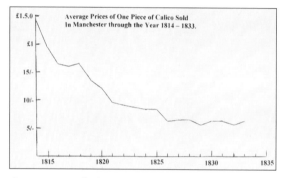

Average prices of calico, 1814 to 1833.

driving belt onto the loose pulley. It is not known whether Roberts fitted any other weft or warp stop motions. He failed to find a satisfactory method of winding the cloth onto the front beam although he proposed various ways. The diameter of the roll increased so that the cloth was taken up more quickly, leading to a more loosely woven fabric. In spite of this, Roberts's loom was accepted quickly, perhaps because its much faster speed gave improved economy.

His looms became acknowledged for the strength of their parts, resulting in few breakdowns. Once a wooden pattern had been made, many identical parts could be cast from it. By 1822, Roberts was employing his improved machine tools, such as his large lathe, his planing machine and his gear cutting machine, so he could machine parts for his looms in bulk. The Swiss industrialist, J.C. Fischer of Schaffhausen, visited Roberts's Globe Works in June 1825 and noted the high quality and large output of the concern. He recorded that power looms were being turned out at a rate of 80 a week or roughly 4,000 a year. Large orders were being received. By that time, the Oxford Road Twist Company in Manchester had opened a weaving department powered by a Boulton and Watt beam engine of 80 h.p. H.H. Birley followed their example at the nearby Chorlton Mills, where he constructed a weaving shed an acre in extent on the banks of the River Medlock. Completed around 1828, it became one of the sights of Manchester with its 600 Roberts power looms driven by an 80 h.p. Boulton and Watt side lever engine.

Numbers of power looms rose rapidly. In 1825, there were 30,000 power looms in England as against 250,000 hand looms. In 1829 there were 45,000 power looms in England and 10,000 in Scotland. These figures had risen in 1833 to 85,000 and 15,000 respectively, a total of 100,000. By 1835, there were 97,564 in England and 17,721 in Scotland, a total of 115,285. Then in the whole of England in 1850 there were 184,816 power looms in vertically integrated mills, 143,690 of them in Lancashire, compared with only 36,544 in sheds devoted to weaving with 31,875 in Lancashire, giving a total of 221,360.[28] This great increase in numbers was principally confined to coarse cotton cloth and was assisted through further refinements. The resulting expansion in production brought a fall in price by 70 to 80 per cent up to 1833. The fall in the price of calico had started well before there were any really successful power looms so it is surprising that inventors were drawn to experiment with them.[29]

Further Improvements to the Power Loom

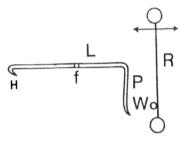

It was not long before modifications were added to the power loom. One such in 1828 was William Dickinson's 'Blackburn loom' in which he first introduced an 'over-picking' system, with a picking stick above each shuttle box. This, placed on Roberts's loom, formed the basic Lancashire loom which became the most popular type for weaving plain cotton cloth and remained in use well into the 1970s. Another addition was a weft stop motion patented by John Ramsbottom and Richard Holt of Todmorden in 1834.[30] Although somewhat crude, it contained the essence of more perfect ones such as that patented by William Kenworthy and James Bullough of Blackburn in 1841.[31] This was further improved by Dickinson in 1848[32] so that, if the weft either broke or ran out, a fork passed through a wire grid causing the loom to stop; a method which continued in use on Lancashire looms until their demise. Effec-

The prongs P of fork L will pass through the reed R when weft W is missing and so hook H will catch the stop mechanism on the loom.

tive warp stop motions came much later. Kenworthy and Bullough also patented an improved roller temple through which the cloth passed to keep it at the right width so that the loom did not have to be stopped to adjust an ordinary stretcher bar. On the hand loom this had to be repositioned after about six inches had been woven, which meant stopping weaving and so wasting time.

In 1842, Bullough patented a loose reed[33] so that, if the shuttle stuck in the warp, the reed swung backwards as the slay beat up, avoiding breaking the warp threads. But, without a doubt, the most important addition in this period was the friction or sand roller. The cloth passed partly round the front beam, the friction roller. The roller was given a rough surface to prevent the cloth slipping and was driven at a constant speed to match the output of cloth. The cloth was wound round a second beam underneath the friction roller. This lower beam was kept in contact with the friction roller by strong springs and was turned by the cloth itself being wound around it. As this lower beam was filled, the winding-on speed remained constant in spite of the increasing diameter.

In subsequent years, improvements were being continually added such as better brakes, picking motions and much more. Tape sizing and slashing machines prepared better warps. The capacity of the power loom to weave high-quality dyed and figured fabrics was extended through the use of multiple-shuttle drop-box mechanisms. In 1845, Squire Diggle of Bury, Lancashire, took out a patent for mechanising the drop box so that different types or colours of weft could be woven without the weaver himself attending to the shuttles.[34] He fitted an endless chain on which plates of different heights could be mounted to raise the shuttle boxes to the required height. Later this could be operated by either the dobby or Jacquard pattern selection mechanisms. The dobby or small Jacquard head for the control of warp shedding was not applied in the cotton industry until around 1858 although patented earlier. The full Jacquard was placed on fancy looms only between 1860 and 1890, by which time hand-loom weaving survived really only for exceptionally high-quality wool and silk fabrics, although even here the power loom was making inroads.

All these inventions enabled the speed of looms to be increased and the number of operatives reduced. Before their introduction, one power loom was as much as most weavers could manage, while the most skilful could not supervise more than two working at a speed of about 120 to 130 picks per minute. In 1850, the latest looms were described in *The Engineer and Machinist*:

The power-loom working at a speed so great that the eye can with difficulty follow its rapid movements, throwing the shuttle across the shed 220 times per minute, occupying a space of but 20 feet area, unheeded except by the occasional observations of a young boy or girl, whose attention is divided between it and one, or perhaps, two others, giving warning, by stopping its own movements, when a thread breaks or any other slight derangement takes place, and performing its duties with precision and regularity not to be surpassed by any other machine which the ingenuity of man has hitherto devised.[35]

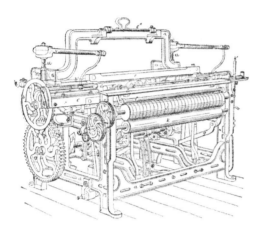 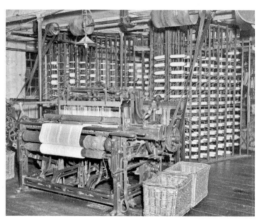

Above: An 'overpick' Lancashire loom with the friction roller above the cloth beam at the front. Above right: An 'overpick' Lancashire loom at Quarry Bank Mill, Styal, taking its warp threads directly from the creel at the back. The method of winding the cloth round the friction roller and then the cloth beam below can be seen at the front.

By the 1890s, one weaver might be responsible for up to six looms running at speeds up to 260 picks per minutes. These 'improvements rendered the loom an almost perfect automaton'.[36]

In textile industries other than cotton, the power loom was accepted first into the worsted branch. A successful worsted power loom was developed in the 1820s but, in the mid-1830s, fewer than 3,000 were in operation in Yorkshire. By 1841, their number had risen to over 11,000 and by 1850 to over 30,000. By 1850, there were some 17,642 power looms in the parish of Bradford alone when the transformation from hand-loom weaving was pretty well complete; a change brought about partly through the speed being increased by at least 100 per cent since 1839. In the woollen branch, the power loom took even longer to make headway. This was probably due to the weakness of the woollen weft. The first power looms in Gloucestershire were installed by William Stanton in 1836 at Stafford's Mill and in the same year in September Thomas and Samuel Stephens Marling installed forty-five looms in Ham Mill, the largest number for some time at any mill in that region. In the West of England, the first power looms came to Staverton in 1839 and they were soon also in use in Melksham, Westbury, Frome and Heytesbury. In Trowbridge, however, the first power looms were not purchased until some were sold at Staverton in 1847 and taken to the Castle Court Mill. Power looms were first recorded in Yorkshire woollen mills in the 1830s but fewer than 4,000 were in use by 1850. In 1840, there were still about 10,000 hand looms in the Leeds district alone. After 1850, expansion of the power loom was rapid for, by 1874, there were over 30,000 woollen power looms in operation.

Steam Power

The increasing sizes of mills and their machinery created a demand for a corresponding increase in the sizes and power of steam engines. The years before 1860 saw much discussion about the best way of doing this. One way was to use steam at higher pressures. However, Boulton and Watt had suffered two boiler explosions in Cornwall at the beginning of 1784 with loss of life. Therefore Watt decided that it was safer to use steam at low pressures because he could see no advantages with higher pressures. Many others agreed with him. Yet by the 1850s, it was being recognised that it could be more economical to use high-pressure steam expansively, which puzzled many. If the analogy of water power were followed, there appeared to be no advantage between using either a large volume of water falling through a small height or a small amount falling through a greater height. However, with a steam engine, safety pointed towards using a larger amount of low-pressure steam. But engineers could not explain why high-pressure engines could be more efficient. They were still considering the steam engine as one worked by the pressure of the fluid, in this case steam. The answer lay in the fact that, when the steam was being expanded with early cut-off and so causing its pressure/temperature to fall, they were proceeding along the right thermodynamic lines, as would become clear after 1860. In the meantime, safer boilers were being constructed.

Boilers

While most attention is paid to the development of steam engines, boilers too often are neglected, but they are an essential part of any steam-powered textile mill. The circular domed haystack boiler was the type used for the first Newcomen engines in cotton mills. It remained popular in colliery districts, where Thomas Hair sketched some in the 1830s for his illustrations in *Views of the Collieries . . . in Northumberland and Durham*. Watt soon changed to the wagon boiler, which he saw when he first went to Cornwall in 1777. This had a rectangular box for the lower part with the top shaped from half a cylinder. While the ends were flat, the bottom and sides might be concave to withstand the pressure better. The fire was situated beneath one end and the gases passed underneath before being taken in a flue right round the sides and front and so to the chimney. The tops might be covered with wooden lagging or a layer of bricks to help retain the heat. The drawings for the second engine erected by Boulton and Watt in a textile mill, that for Timothy Harris of Nottingham which started running in 1786, show a plan for a wagon boiler sketched over one for a haystack boiler. The wagon boiler retained its popularity in cotton mills for many years as long as steam pressures remained low.

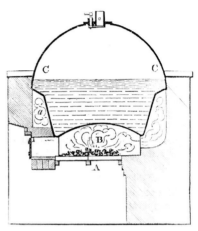

Section through a haystack boiler.

When Benjamin Hick established his own foundry at Bolton in 1833, he was offering wrought iron wagon boilers as the normal type. Some might be fitted with an internal flue running throughout their length to augment the heating surface and with additional internal stays to help withstand higher pressures. R. Armstrong wrote in 1838, 'Within the last eight or ten years, the waggon boiler may be said to have been almost universal in the cotton district around Manchester; and it is believed that four fifths of all the boilers at work in this neighbourhood at the present time are of this kind'.[37] From the 4 or 5 p.s.i. which was all that Watt had considered safe, the pressure for Lancashire mill engines nudged up to 12 p.s.i. and during the 1830s began to increase even more, making stronger designs of boilers a necessity.

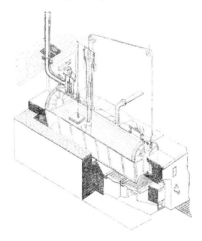

Diagram of a wagon boiler showing the water-feed apparatus.

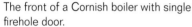

The front of a Cornish boiler with single firehole door.

An 'egg-ended' boiler being removed from Oakenholt Paper Mill, North Wales.

In Cornish mines, pressures were already much higher and during the 1840s the norm was 30 to 40 p.s.i. In the early 1800s in Cornwall, Richard Trevithick had been experimenting with cast iron boilers with pressures up to 90 or 100 p.s.i. in quite small engines. In January 1805, he experimented with a high-pressure engine that had a 10in diameter cylinder built at Coalbrookdale by placing it in a barge on the River Severn and lashing up some paddle wheels before sending it off to a cotton mill at Macclesfield. It would have been the first high-pressure engine installed in a textile mill.[38] In 1806, he proposed replacing the Boulton and Watt wagon boilers at the Dolcoath copper mine with his 'Cornish' boiler. Nothing was done so it was not until 1811 or 1812 that he had the opportunity to build his first Cornish boiler for a little pumping engine at Wheal Prosper, Gwithian. It was 6ft in diameter, 24ft long and generated steam at 40 p.s.i. These boilers were cylindrical with flat ends made from wrought iron plates. A single large tube ran through the middle and helped to stay the ends. The furnace was in one end of the tube. The gases passed through the tube where they divided before passing along either side to the front. Here they joined in a central flue under the boiler and so to the chimney. Manufacture of these boilers was improved by Arthur Woolf with better machine tools.

The basic design of the Cornish boiler was superior to either the haystack or wagon types for withstanding higher pressures; its flat end plates could be reinforced with stays. The fire being placed inside the boiler radiated its heat directly to the water and not to the brick setting. Sediment from the water fell to the bottom of the boiler from where it could be flushed out. In those boilers with fires beneath them, the circulation of water and steam kept the sediment in suspension, which could cause severe priming. In order to overcome the restricted grate size of the Cornish boiler, some mill owners in Lancashire where coal was poor turned around 1814 to the 'egg-ended' boiler which was cylindrical with hemispherical ends. It was mounted in a brick setting in the same way as the wagon boiler. While it could withstand higher pressures, it shared the same disadvantages. A variation of the Cornish boiler developed around 1811 by the Butterley Company was the 'whistle-mouth' boiler. In order to accommodate a wide grate, the lower part of the bottom by the fire was cut away and the gases passed through a central flue in the remainder. However, this caused a serious weakness in the design so that Fairbairn considered them unsafe above 12 p.s.i.

The Lancashire Boiler

In 1838, R. Armstrong noted that the ordinary Cornish boilers did not 'answer at all for the factories in this district. Those which have been found to answer best, are much wider, in proportion to their length, than in Cornwall, and with two or more flues placed as low down in the boiler, so as to leave sufficient steam room'.[39] He was describing what later became called the 'Lancashire' boiler. The advantages were a greater depth of water over the fire tubes and an increased grate area compared with the ordinary Cornish boiler. Therefore the basic Lancashire boiler with its twin fire tubes existed before William Fairbairn and John Hetherington took out their patent in 1844.[40] What they patented was not so much the type as the way the boiler was to be fired. In all probability, Fairbairn derived the idea of firing the twin fires from Charles Wye Williams, who had been experimenting with smoke consumption on board ships by dividing large furnaces with an internal partition and firing each side alternately at regular intervals. The heat from the brightly burning fuel on one side consumed the smoke from the newly charged coal on the other. Fairbairn proposed admitting more air beyond the fire and firing alternately so that the gases from the newly stoked fire would pass along the tube into the flue where the heat from the brightly burning fire in the other tube would meet them and consume the smoke. His boilers were mounted on a system of flues similar to those of wagon or Cornish boilers. A better way of admitting secondary air to ensure complete combustion was through a perforated plate covered by a 'butterfly' plate in the fire-hole door. The stoker could control the size of the holes by turning the butterfly plate and hence the volume of air being admitted.

Left: the twin firehole doors of a Lancashire boiler fitted with 'butterfly' plates. Right: section through the fire tubes showing conical water tubes.

Types and Pressures of Boilers in the Manchester Area, 1859

Type of boiler	Pressures in lbs per square inch					
	–15	15–30	30–45	45–60	60+	Total
Cylindrical with flues (Lancashire)	119	406	326	253	73	1,177
Cylindrical no flues	36	21	15	16	6	94
Galloway	4	29	36	33	1	103
Water-tube	3	14	24	43	35	119
Multiflued	-	19	19	5	1	44
Butterley	24	1	1	-	-	26
Waggon	7	-	-	-	-	7
Total	193	490	421	350	116	1,570[41]

Lancashire boilers proved to be economical steam raisers. It was claimed that, with the same thickness of plates, they could withstand four times the pressure of older types. They soon became the most popular type in Lancashire textile mills and, with steel plates and improved manufacturing techniques, were built later to withstand pressures of up to 250 p.s.i. Sometimes, the twin tubes were shortened inside the boiler to form a combustion chamber where gases from both fires could mix. One design passed the gases through a series of small diameter horizontal tubes beyond the combustion chamber, similar to those on a railway locomotive. Boilers of this design were installed by Fairbairn in the mill at Saltaire.

A more successful design was patented by William and John Galloway of Manchester in 1851.[42] The twin fire tubes united inside the boiler in a single flattened kidney-shaped tube for the rest of the length of the boiler. The flat top and bottom portions were connected and strengthened with a series of vertical conical tubes riveted between them. These conical tubes improved the circulation of water and increased the heating surface as the hot gases passed around them. Their conical shape with the greater diameter at the top assisted the steam to escape. Galloway invented special machine tools for forming these conical tubes and this boiler remained a popular type until the firm closed in about 1930. One of 1889 was used by J. Sawtell in Holt, Wiltshire, until the 1960s. It was short enough to be moved easily and so was brought back to Manchester for the North Western Museum of Science and Industry and sectioned to show the tubes and flues. When the old boiler house at Quarry Bank Mill was cleared out, it was found to contain the original boiler of 1880 by T. Oldham, Wellington Boiler Works, Stockport. It is made entirely from plates and angle iron riveted with no flanging. While it has twin fire doors, these open into a combined grate area in a kidney-shaped tube, the further end of which exits into ordinary fire tubes. Presumably this was another idea for a smoke-consuming furnace but no patent has been traced. The Lancashire boiler continued to provide steam for virtually all the last mill engines right into the 1970s through its capability of withstanding high pressures as well as the soundness of its design.

Boilers under construction at Galloway's boiler shop, Manchester. In the centre is a pair of fire tubes connected to a single kidney-shaped tube with holes for vertical conical cross tubes.

Front of the 1880 boiler by T. Oldham, Stockport, at Quarry Bank Mill, Styal.

The Economiser

One invention which enormously increased the efficiency of mill engines was the feed-water heater. The one which became virtually universal was the economiser patented by Edward Green in 1845.[43] He had experimented earlier with a circular group of thirty vertical cast iron tubes, 4in diameter by 9ft in length, connected at top and bottom to hemispherical chambers set in the flue from the boiler. Cold feed-water was introduced into the lower chamber and passed upwards through the tubes where it was heated by the exhaust gases from the boiler. The water collected in the upper chamber and was fed to the boiler. However, after being used for a little while, the temperature of the water fell off, the economy in coal dwindled while the draught was seriously impaired. It was discovered that the stack of tubes was choked with soot. After trying various expedients

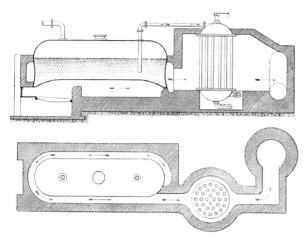

Green's 1845 patent drawings for his first economiser.

An advertisement of about 1900 for savings possible with a Green's economiser which is shown as well.

for removing the soot, Green designed mechanical scrapers which moved up and down the tubes. It was this feature which really ensured the subsequent success of the Green economiser.

The design installed in 1845 at David Illingworth's Providence Mill, Bradford, consisted of straight rows of tubes connected to flat headers. The scrapers, usually driven by their own small steam engine, alternated up and down three or four times an hour. It was important that the economisers be fed with hot water, otherwise sulphur in the smoke from the burning coal would condense on them and cause corrosion. Likewise the water in the economisers should not become hot enough to boil or steam would form in the top header which might become overheated. Therefore bypass dampers were fitted to divert the hot gases directly up the chimney when the engine was stationary and the boilers did not need water. Normally economisers were filled with water at full boiler pressure.

Green kept ahead of rivals by improving his manufacturing techniques with special tools for machining the matching tapers on the ends of the tubes as well as designing better scrapers and automatic reversing lifting apparatus for the scrapers.[44] The temperature of the feed-water was raised at first about 140°F (60°C) before it entered the boilers so the chance of cold water straining them was reduced. In 1861, Fairbairn wrote, 'It is found that when the waste gases escape at a temperature of 400° to 500°, the feed water can be heated to an average of 225°, the temperature of the gases after leaving the pipes being reduced to 250°'.[45] Figures for 1895 on later engines working at higher pressures show that the temperature of the gases was reduced from 650°F (344°C) on the boiler side of the economiser to 350°F (177°C) on the chimney side, while the temperature of the feed-water was increased on an average from 180° to 200°F (82° to 94°C). Some advantages of an economiser were that it used heat from the flues that would otherwise have passed up the chimney, that it provided a large reservoir of feed-water already approaching the temperature of that in the boiler and that feeding the boiler with hot instead of cold water prolonged the life of the boiler. In addition, the later firm of Greens claimed that the economy varied from 10 to 20 per cent of the total fuel consumed.[46] In fact, the higher the boiler pressure and hence temperature, the greater could be the fuel savings which would mean that the economiser could make savings in the same region as Watt's separate condenser.

Superheating

During this period, attempts were made to increase the efficiency of the steam engine further by superheating the steam as it passed from the boiler to the engine itself. With the Lancashire boiler, this was achieved by passing the 'wet' steam through a nest of tubes immediately to the rear of the boiler where the hottest gases passed out. Not only did this raise the temperature but it 'dried' the steam, removing any water droplets carried over. The temperature was raised without any increase in pressure. This was advantageous when the steam expanded in the cylinder as it lessened condensation. Also the extra heat gave the steam more energy which was converted into work.

The origins of superheating are unknown. A form was designed in 1826 by Mr Nevill of Shadwell Thames in which the steam was passed through a box suspended over the fire in a vertical boiler. In 1845 J.A. Detmold patented a superheater in the form of a coiled pipe exposed to 'the great heat of the furnace' through which the steam was taken, 'being by this means greatly increased in bulk and temperature'.[47] In 1848, Ernst Alban found that his high-pressure engines were much more economical, which he ascribed to the steam having greater expansive force because it contained more free caloric. He wrote that it was 'the fact of its exceedingly great subtlety and penetrating power, in which respect it is beyond comparison with any other highly compressed fluid' which brought this greater economy.[48] This led him to believe that even more beneficial results would be obtained if the steam could be 'surcharged' with this caloric.

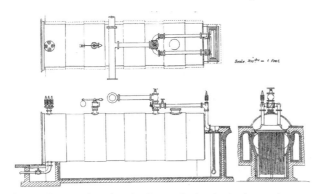

A superheater placed in the flue at the back of a Lancashire boiler.

The range of Lancashire boilers at Trencherfield Mill, Wigan, fitted with automatic stokers.

In 1858, Greens modified their economiser to form a superheater, exposed to the highest temperature of the waste gases. These gases might then pass through an economiser for greater efficiency. However, the lubricating oils then available were unable to withstand the high temperatures and the dry steam. Cylinder walls and valve faces were frequently scored and abraded while the packing of the piston and valve rod glands rapidly burnt out. Also a stronger material than wrought iron was necessary for the superheater elements. In 1861, W.J.M. Rankine thought that economies of over 15 per cent might be achieved partly because the superheating apparatus took up heat which otherwise escaped wastefully up the chimney. Fairbairn, always an advocate of high-pressure steam, wrote that 'The observation of the action of steam in expanding had led many to expect still further advantage from the use of superheated gaseous steam'.[49] But he also pointed out that the question of superheating and efficiency at higher temperatures remained unsolved and that he was carrying out experiments on this subject. Superheating was abandoned in the 1860s partly for practical reasons. In addition, its thermodynamic advantages were not understood. Fairbairn recognised that 'we must attain increased and increasing knowledge of the properties of the agent [steam] we employ under the various conditions of expansion and superheating'.[50] D.K. Clark was also puzzled about the advantages of compounding, high-pressure steam and superheating when he wrote in 1862, 'But two questions remain to be decided, – Whether the best results are to be had from two or more cylinders? and, Whether the steam should be surcharged with heat?'[51] His questions would be answered through a better understanding of thermodynamics in subsequent years when superheating would be reintroduced.

More Powerful Beam Engines

The improved textile machines necessitated the construction of more powerful steam engines to drive them in the much larger mills then being built. Fairbairn, writing in 1861, pointed out:

> It is now more than thirty years since it was found desirable to increase the power of steam engines employed in manufacture, and instead of engines of from 20 to 50 nominal horse-power, as much as 100, and in some cases 200 horse-power are required to meet the demand.[52]

The origins of the compound engine will be covered in Chapter 4. Engines with different layouts from the Watt beam engine had been introduced before 1830. These included various methods of supporting the main beam on framing independently from the engine house or the compact side lever type. Yet the traditional beam engine remained the most popular form. Such single-cylinder engines were designed regularly to produce 50 to 60 h.p. while Boulton and Watt supplied a few of 80 h.p.

In 1835, Hick sent Sharp Roberts prices of the steam engines they could supply which ranged from 10 to 60 h.p. They commented:

> For coupled engines with their cranks at right angles including the pair of first motion spur wheels, double price.
>
> We are making many 'Independent Frame' Engines with short stroke as substitutes for Marine Engines where room is an object, the cost of which is the same as for house-built engines with long strokes.[53]

The first Order Book of Benjamin Hick covered the period from October 1833 to March 1836 and in it can be seen the increasing size of engines. The total number of engines ordered was thirty-nine. In the two full years covered, there were eleven in 1834 and twenty-three in 1835. The power ranged from one at 12 h.p. to a coupled one at 160 h.p. The average size was 48 h.p. The most popular type was a pair of 30-horse engines coupled together to give a 60-horse. Five of these were ordered. Out of the thirty-nine engines, twenty-six were single and thirteen double. One of the short stroke engines has been preserved at the Armley Mill Museum in Leeds; it was used at London Road Station, now Piccadilly, in Manchester in the Manchester, Sheffield and Lincolnshire Railway warehouse, now demolished.

The comment about coupled engines referred to those consisting of a pair of engines with their connecting rods working cranks on a common crankshaft with a single flywheel keyed on the shaft in between them. Such coupled beam engines provided one solution to meeting increased demands for power. Today we would consider such paired engines as one coupled engine but frequently they were called two engines. Boulton and Watt supplied Thomas Houldsworth with two 25 h.p. side lever engines in 1834. Two more side lever engines, this time of 50 h.p., were ordered by Birley & Co. in 1837 for their Chorlton Mill. If they were coupled with their cranks at 90 degrees, such engines ran more smoothly because there were four power impulses each revolution from the double-acting cylinders. This also made it easier to start the engine and line shafting even though it was customary to disengage the textile machines at the end of the working day. Even so, the load on the engine from the line shafting and the internal friction of the engine itself might reach fifteen per cent of the total power generated.

Fairbairn began to make steam engines soon after 1832. Samuel Smiles claimed that the principles he introduced 'have been adopted wherever steam is employed as a motive power in mills'.[54] Fairbairn turned the flywheel into the main first motion wheel by casting teeth into the periphery of its rim, so saving both cost and power. Hunt had pioneered such a design around 1780. This certainly made it easier to connect a pair of beam engines to a single crankshaft because it enabled the second motion gear wheel and

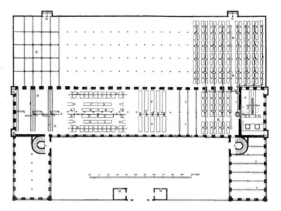

Layout of Orrell's Mill, Stockport, designed by Fairbairn with the coupled beam engines situated in the middle of the right-hand side.

shafting to be positioned clear of the cranks and also saved the expense of a separate large gear wheel. This design was featured in the coupled engine which Fairbairn supplied to the mill he designed for Mr Orrell of Stockport in 1834. Each cylinder was rated at 90 n.h.p. The upright shaft rotated at 58.8 r.p.m. while the line shafts did not exceed 120 r.p.m. The number of spindles shows that this mill was typical of the new larger mills for that period.

Throstle frames, spindles	12,948
14 pairs of mules, spindles	24,928
19 self-actors, spindles	7,984
	45,860[55]

A low weaving shed was going to be added between the multi-storey mill and the River Mersey to house 1,100 power looms.

At about the same time, Fairbairn supplied a coupled side lever engine to Messrs Bailey and Brothers of Stalybridge for their mill planned for 40,000 mule spindles, 1,280 power looms and another proposed weaving shed for 1,480 looms. Fairbairn later wrote that 'At an early period of my own practice I introduced it [the side lever engine] on an extensive scale, and there are numbers now at work . . . that are performing an efficient duty, and giving entire satisfaction'.[56] Fairbairn may have learnt about the advantages of this type through having purchased one of 20 h.p. from Boulton and Watt in 1826. Yet he had to admit that, in spite of its compactness, short stroke and regularity of motion, it did not prove as popular as the conventional beam engine. The coupled one for Bailey's mill had sturdy main framing. The condenser was not immersed in a tank of cold water so relied solely on the jet to condense the steam. The cylinders

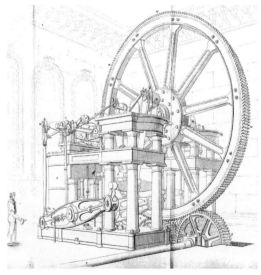

The impressive side lever engine with its two cylinders supplied to Bailey's Mill, Stalybridge.

were about 50in bore by 5ft stroke with a nominal horsepower of 110 each. With a steam pressure of around 10 p.s.i. and at 18 to 20 r.p.m., together they would have developed some 500 i.h.p.

In 1840 Fairbairn presented a paper to the Manchester Geological Society about using Cornish engines to pump water out of coalmines.[57] He had been impressed with the outstanding fuel economy shown in engines constructed by Cornish engineers through the use of steam at higher pressure than was customary in the textile industry together with a short cut-off and high expansion. The remarkably high duty of 123,300,593lb had been reported at the meeting in Glasgow of the British Association for the Advancement of Science in 1839 to 1840. Fairbairn had supplied a single-acting Cornish-type pumping engine for a mine at Verviers in Belgium. An indicator diagram for an 86in cylinder shows a boiler pressure of 30 p.s.i. and a cut-off at about 1/10 stroke.

Fairbairn determined to apply the same principles to his rotative steam engines and we see the results on the ones he installed at Salt's famous mill at Saltaire, completed in 1853, one of the greatest mills ever built for spinning and weaving alpaca wool. There were two engines, each coupled beam engines with double-acting cylinders and geared flywheels. One drove a spinning mill and the combing shed while the other drove the second mill and the weaving shed. The cylinders were 50in diameter and 7ft stroke. Each cylinder was rated at 100 n.h.p, giving a total of 1,250 i.h.p. from the engines. Instead of slide valves, he fitted double-beat drop valves based on those devised by Joseph Hornblower in Cornwall but first used there by Arthur Woolf in 1823. Woolf recognised the superiority of a valve that had been used by Samuel Moyle in an engine at Wheal Busy. The valve, known as 'Hornblowers', was the prototype of the double beat valve, but Woolf did not use it in the form suggested by Hornblower because it was not of his own contriving. Pondering on the problem, he arrived at the idea of modifying it by adding the swell portion, thereby making it more effective.

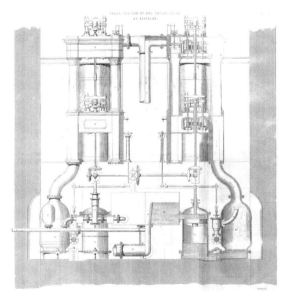

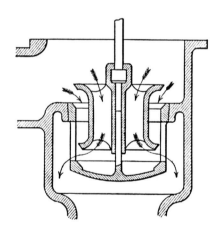

Above: The double-beat drop valve.

Left: The valve gear on Fairbairn's Saltaire engines.

On the Saltaire engines, the valves were paired at each end of the cylinder, giving separate valves for inlet and exhaust. They were operated by a vertical rotating shaft on which were mounted discs at the top and bottom of the cylinder. On the horizontal surface of the disc, three or four cams were formed to lift open the valves through roller cam followers. The cam for an exhaust valve kept that valve open for most of the exhaust stroke. The cam follower for the inlet valve could be moved onto any one of the other cams which altered the cut-off in steps to vary the expansion of steam in the cylinder from one third to one quarter or one half of the stroke. Fairbairn does not record how this change was made so it is suspected that it was done manually before the engine was started to match the average expected load.

Fairbairn strongly advocated this type of engine with steam expanded in a single cylinder instead of the two-cylinder compound engine:

> The double cylinder or compound engine, in which high pressure steam was employed, expanded through three-fourths of the stroke, appeared to effect a considerable saving of fuel; but taking both engines worked alike, with steam of the same pressure similarly expanded, as is now the case in the best single engines, there appears to be no advantage in the compound over the simple single engine. On the contrary, there is a loss in the original cost of the engine, and the complexity of one as compared with the other . . . I have therefore no hesitation in recommending the single engine worked expansively, as an efficient competitor of the compound engine.[58]

Fairbairn was probably correct as long as the steam pressure was only about 40 p.s.i., as was the case at Saltaire. The Galloway boilers installed there would have been constructed from wrought iron. On the other hand, it was argued that the slow speed of only 25 r.p.m. and the great expansion allowed the single large cylinder to cool down towards the end of the stroke, causing excessive condensation of the incoming steam.

Although Fairbairn was following many of the correct theoretical principles, there were weaknesses in his designs so that these engines at Saltaire lasted in their original form for only ten years before having the cylinders replaced by ones with Corliss valves. There were various reasons. Fairbairn's valve gear, with all its separate parts for working four drop valves, was difficult to manufacture accurately, maintain later and keep steam-tight. The valves closed through their own weight, which would have been too slow, certainly at higher engine speeds. Some method of arresting them was necessary to prevent them hitting their seats to avoid 'injurious strains'. More importantly, Fairbairn failed to make the cut-off point correspond with the demand for power as the load changed. The speed was still regulated by the governor controlling the throttle valve, thus introducing wire-drawing the steam into the system. Most of these problems were solved by the valve gear patented by the American, George H. Corliss, in 1849, which will be examined in the next chapter.

Fairbairn wrote in 1861 that the reason other types of steam engine had not supplanted the beam engine as the chief prime mover in textile mills was:

> That its simplicity of construction, and the faculty of getting to every part in case of repairs being necessary, give it a superiority over every other form, however perfect and compact . . . From these considerations, the old Boulton and Watt form of engine, strengthened and improved by being adapted to work expansively, is now the favourite, and is likely to maintain its ground as long as steam is depended on as the source of power in mills.[59]

Fairbairn's principles were followed by W.J. Yates of Blackburn, who carried out 'the engineering and mill gearing' for the India Mill, Over Darwen, completed in 1867 for Messrs Eccles, Shorrock Brothers, and Co. The engine house contained two condensing single-cylinder beam engines coupled together with cylinders of 51in diameter by 7ft 6in stroke. Cornish drop valves were fitted. The speed was only 23.1 r.p.m. Six Galloway boilers made with Bessemer steel enabled the pressure to be raised to 100 p.s.i. Greater efficiency was achieved with Green's economisers. The spindleage was 67,968. Evan Leigh stated that the mill could be 'considered as a first-class type of the engineering skill of the day'.[60] His illustration shows presumably the mill owner and his wife proudly admiring the engine in its ornate house.

But even as he praised the superb quality of the construction, Leigh doubted the expediency of employing beam engines in modern cotton mills. He used the same argument as Fairbairn had earlier for introducing lighter line shafting. With greater speeds being introduced through higher steam pressures, Leigh pointed out, 'it is found inexpedient and dangerous to transmit the power through a lever, mounted on stilts, to the main shaft'. A slow-speed engine needed massive foundations and heavy gearing. More and more weight had to be

The beam engine at India Mill, Over Darwen, in its ornate engine house.

added to the beam and other parts to counteract the shocks of higher speeds, aggravating the evil, 'struggling as it were, by brute force to overcome science and natural laws'.[61] The engine at India Mill was obsolescent at the time of its installation. It was compounded on the McNaught principle probably in 1873. It was replaced in 1890 by a 1,800 h.p. double tandem engine by J. Musgrave and Sons of Bolton.

The Horizontal Engine

One reason for the ascendancy of beam engines in textile mills may have been their evenness in running, even though Fairbairn was advocating high expansion rates which would have meant more power at the beginning of the stroke than at the end. Watt had been quick to recognise the problem of uneven power even before he and Boulton built their first engine at the Soho Manufactory on the expansive principle. This engine was nicknamed Beelzebub because it was a devil to control. In 1777, Watt sent Boulton a 'drawing of the best scheme I can at present devise for equallizing the power of Belzebub [sic] and so obliging him to save part of his youthful strength to help him forward in his old age'.[62] Watt soon realised that the mass of the reciprocating parts of the engine, or what he called the '*vis inertiae*' – strength of inertia – would help to even out the inequality of pressure within the cylinder. He calculated the dead weight of the parts of a beam pumping engine, reckoning the 'Great Beam' at two-thirds of its weight. This mass had to be accelerated at the beginning of the stroke, so absorbing energy which was given back again as it slowed down towards the end. But, although the reciprocating movement of the beam would help to even out the power, it would work best at only one power output. A heavy flywheel also helped to give steady running. Another reason for the longevity of beam engines has been given as the lack of wear in their vertical cylinders.

The American Porter–Allen engine was an early example of a high-speed horizontal engine.

It would seem that owners of textile mills were slow to take advantage of faster-running horizontal engines even though examples were introduced elsewhere. For instance, the Neath Abbey Iron Works in South Wales built a couple of horizontal engines towards the end of the 1840s, compared with 38 beam engines in that decade. But in the 1850s the positions were reversed, with thirteen horizontals and only four beam engines. Boulton and Watt supplied their last beam engine and indeed their last engine to a textile mill in 1847, a 25 h.p. side lever engine for Thomas Houldsworth in Manchester. In 1846 they had received orders for five horizontal vacuum pumping engines from the London, Croydon and Epsom Railway and from that time on continued to build more horizontal types including in 1857 what was described as a 20 h.p. horizontal high-pressure condensing engine for Rathbone Brothers and Co. The pressure is not given. In 1856, Leonard Stephenson, who had worked at Crewe locomotive works, installed a horizontal engine at John Dickinson's Apsley paper mills, suggesting that success on railway locomotives may have encouraged people to try them.

While the horizontal engine did not have the mass of reciprocating parts to help even out the force in the cylinder, this was partly compensated by the greater number of lesser power strokes per minute as it rotated more quickly. Other advantages were its compactness, so it could be built to higher standards of engineering. Because it did not take up as much space, engine houses were smaller and so cost less. The need for fewer parts, in particular dispensing with the beam and its supporting ironwork, allowed prices to be reduced. But more important was the way the engine itself was built. All the moving parts, the crankshaft, the crosshead and piston in the cylinder could be aligned on a single bedplate or sections bolted together. Not only would this give much greater accuracy but, because the bedplate could be bolted down on a single solid foundation, the engines were much more rigid.

The Durn Mill Engine

These features can be seen in the single-cylinder horizontal condensing engine built in 1864 by Earnshaw and Holt of Rochdale for A. and J. Law's Durn Mill, Littleborough, now preserved in the Museum of Science and Industry in Manchester. At a boiler pressure of 60 p.s.i. and at 63 r.p.m., it probably developed 50 n.h.p. or 250 i.h.p. from its 28in bore by 4ft stroke cylinder. This was a little more than double that of the nearby Haydock beam engine, showing the advantage of its more compact design and higher boiler pressure. On the other hand, its single short slide valve would not have been as efficient as the two short valves on the Haydock engine since the long steam passages to

The engine at Durn Mill in its original position, looking from the crank towards the cylinder.

The cylinder with its slide valve on the left at Durn Mill.

The conical condenser (right) and air pump (left) at Saxon Mill, Droylsden, were not immersed in a cold water tank.

The Durn Mill engine in course of re-erection at Liverpool Road Station.

The gearing of the Durn Mill engine showing the bevel gear for the vertical shaft drive.

the cylinder ends would have been cooled by the exhaust steam. By the 1860s, the condensing apparatus beneath the crosshead slides was no longer situated in a cold-water tank but reliance was placed solely on a jet. The upper slide bars above the crosshead were found later to be unnecessary. The massive open flywheel of 10ft diameter is a single casting, which posed some problems through its size and weight when it had to be moved. The engine drove the shafting to the rest of the mill through separate spur gears which had unequal numbers of teeth so that all would wear equally. A Lumb-type governor was added in 1921 at a cost of £300 and the engine continued in use until 1946, but remained in situ until removed for preservation in 1974.

Other Horizontal Engines

It is not known when or where the first horizontal engine was installed in a textile mill but this may not have been until into the 1860s. W.J. Yates supplied a single-cylinder horizontal engine to J. Forrest and Co., Navigation Mills, Blackburn, in 1861. The first use of a horizontal engine recorded in Yorkshire dates from around 1864 when Whetley Mills, Manningham, opened with two pairs of horizontal engines. Perhaps the best known of any early horizontal engines are the pair supplied in 1863 to W. Rylands and Co. Gidlow Mills in Wigan by Musgrave which were illustrated by Leigh in his *Science of Modern Cotton Spinning*. The three-storey mill had an unusual internal layout because it was designed so that, in case of the failure of one engine, half the mill could still be driven by the other. Each engine had two cylinders, 40in diameter by 6ft stroke, generating 60 n.h.p. per cylinder. The pistons were coupled onto a common crankshaft either side of a flywheel with geared rim. Steam was supplied from eight Lancashire boilers fired with coal from Rylands's own nearby colliery. They were undoubtedly the largest simple expansion horizontal engines in a mill for many years. In addition to all the preparatory machinery, there

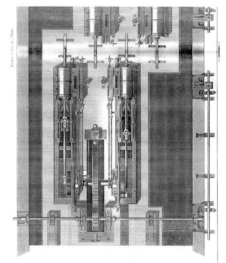

Layout of the horizontal engines by Musgrave at Gidlow Mill.

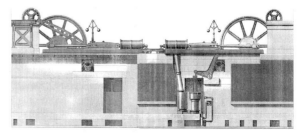

Side elevation of the Gidlow Mill engines.

were thirteen pairs of mules of 1,076 spindles, two pairs of 600 spindles, giving a total of 30,576 mule spindles and 30,800 throstle spindles, making altogether 61,376 spindles. So one engine would have driven 30,000 spindles. In addition, there was a weaving shed with 1,400 to 1,500 looms which does not appear to have been driven by these engines. After many years of successful running, both engines were converted into triple expansion engines by replacing one cylinder with two cylinders in tandem, a high-pressure, 19in bore and the intermediate 26in bore, exhausting into the other original cylinder as the low pressure. The use of multiple expansion was a portent of the next lines of development.

The Vertical Engine

Mention must be made of the true vertical engine, possibly taking its name after the beam engine where the cylinder is secured to the foundations with the piston rod working upwards. In the case of the vertical engine, the connecting rod drove a horizontal crankshaft above. The advantage in a mill was that the crankshaft might be a continuation of the line shafting with no gearing interposed. This was the case at Sunnybank Paper Mill, Darwen. The Grimes family had taken over an old cotton mill and retained the steam engine in order to drive the machinery for gluing linen onto paper for maps and similar uses. The little 10 h.p. engine with single slide-valve cylinder, 10½in diameter by 2ft stroke, ran at 70 r.p.m. with a steam pressure of 60 p.s.i. The connecting rod was forked to pass round the guide supporting the piston rod. The crank pedestal was mounted on a cast iron beam supported at its centre on a pair of thin cast iron pillars with its ends built into the mill walls. The engineer found this beam a very useful place on which to place his pots of plants where they could enjoy the light of the sun through the glass roof as well as the moist heat of steam escaping from the engine. The

General view of the vertical engine at Sunnybank Paper Mill, Darwen.

The forked connecting rod on the Sunnybank engine.

The crank and flywheel of the Sunnybank engine.

A vertical engine with Greek columns that drove the cutting machinery at a slate quarry in Nantlle, North Wales, dating from around 1840 and now at the Welsh Slate Museum, Llanberis.

flywheel had a heavy cast iron rim, held in place by six curved wrought iron spokes. A barring rack on the mill wall enabled the engineer to turn the engine round manually to the starting position. This engine could well date from before the 1850s and if so ran for about 120 years. When the mill closed in around 1971, the engine was taken out by the local authority and re-erected in an open site in Darwen.

To show an example of a vertical engine in the North Western Museum of Science and Industry, Bury Museum lent a vertical engine which could stand independently since the crankshaft bearings were supported on a pair of 'A' frames with the flywheel and eccentric situated between them. The crank overhung one end above the cylinder with the slide valve on the inside. The crosshead moved between a pair of flat vertical guides. A Watt-type governor controlled the speed through a throttle valve. The engine is still running very sweetly under steam. There is a somewhat similar engine in the sawmill of the National Trust property at Erddig near Wrexham, dating from around 1860.

Summary

The period between 1830 and 1860 perhaps saw more striking developments in textile machinery than in steam engine designs. Among the important advances in spinning were the introduction of combing machines and the self-acting spinning mule. In weaving, small but significant inventions turned the power loom into a machine that wove more evenly with less attention from the operatives. In the realm of steam engines, there were improvements to boiler design, particularly the Lancashire boiler, together with the introduction of economisers. The horizontal engine began to supersede the traditional beam engine. These inventions laid the foundations on which the next stage of developments could take place after 1860, especially on steam engines.

NOTES: CHAPTER 3

1   Farnie (1979), p. 199 and Boyson (1970), p. 25 for 1857.

2   Baines (1875), pp. 78 & 80.

3   Patent 5,138, 25 March 1825.

4   Patent 5,949, 1 July 1830.

5   Marsden (1891), p. 228.

6   Montgomery (1836), p. 198.

7   Tomlinson (1854), p. 460 and Ure (1836), Vol. 2, pp. 199–200.

8   Baines (c.1835), p. 202.

9   Farnie (1979), p. 80.

10 Patent 1,696, 3 August 1789.

11 Patent 1,747, 27 April 1790; Patent 1,787, 11 December 1790; Patent 1,876, 15 May 1792 and Patent 2,524, 25 July 1801.

12 Patent 11,896, 7 October 1847.

13 Patent 9,404, 6 July 1842; Patent 9,780, 15 June and Patent 9,966, 25 November 1843.

14 Patent 12,712, 18 July 1849 and Patent 13,009, 20 March 1850.

15 Patent 13,532, 24 February 1851 and Patent 14,135, 9 July 1852.

16 Patent 11,103, 25 February 1846.

17 Patents 890 and 894, 13 April 1853.

18 Barlow (1879), pp. 234–5.

19 Patent 1,470, 4 April 1785.

20 Patent 1,565, 30 October 1786.

21 Patent 1,616, 1 August 1787.

22 Patent 1,676, 12 November 1788; Patent 1,696, 3 August 1789 and Patent 1,876, 15 May 1792.

23 Patent 2,122, 28 June 1796.

24 Smiles (1879), pp. 239–40.

25 Patent 2,684, 28 February 1803 and Patent 2,771, 7 June 1804.

26 Patent 2,699, 20 April 1803; Patent 2,848, 14 May 1805 and Patent 3,728, 31 July 1813.

27 Patent 4,726, 14 November 1822.

28 Bythell (1969), p. 92; Parliamentary Papers, 1850 (745) XLII, pp. 456–7.

29 Baines (c.1835), p. 356. Average Prices of One Piece of Calico Sold in Manchester through the Year 1814 to 1833: 1814, £1.4.7; 1815, 19/8¾; 1816, 16/8½; 1817, 16/1; 1818, 16/8½; 1819, 13/9; 1820, 12/1½; 1821, 9/8¼; 1822, 9/3½; 1823, 8/11¼; 1824, 8/5¾; 1825, 8/5¼; 1826, 6/3¼; 1827, 6/6; 1828, 6/5¼; 1829, 5/8; 1830, 6/3¼; 1831, 6/2¼; 1832, 5/8; 1833, 6/2.

30 Patent 6,644, 12 July 1834.

31 Patent 8,790, 14 January 1841.

32 Patent 12,267, 11 September 1848.

33 Patent 9,507, 3 November 1842.

34 Patent 10,462, 11 January 1845.

35 *Engineer and Machinist*, Vol. 1 (1850), p. 274.

36 Marsden (1895), p. 95.

37 Armstrong (1838), p. 12.

38 Royal Institution of Cornwall, Trevithick Papers, R. Trevithick to D. Giddy, 10 January 1805.

39 Armstrong (1838), p. 100.

40 Patent 10,166, 30 April 1844.

41 Hills (1989), p. 135; from Kanefsky, J., 'The Diffusion of Power Technology in British Industry, 1760–1870', PhD Thesis, Exeter, 1979.

42 Patent 13,552, 11 March 1851.

43 Patent 10,986, 10 December 1845.

44 Patent 2,142, 1856 and Patent 2,184, 1866.

45 Fairbairn (1871), Vol. 1, p. 277.

46 Fowler (1895), p. 102 and *Mechanical World*, Vol. 41, p. 189, 19 April 1907.

47 Patent 10,755, 21 July 1845.

48 Alban (1848), p. 34.

49 Rankine (1861), p. 435 and Fairbairn (1871), Vol. 1, p. 188.

50 Fairbairn (1871), Vol. 1, p. 188.

51 Clark (1864), p. 358.

52 Fairbairn (1871), Vol. 1, p. 242.

53 B. Hick, 'First Order Book', 23 February 1835.

54 Smiles (1879), p. 327.

55 Ure (1836), pp. 304 & 311.

56 Fairbairn (1871), Vol. 1, p. 247.

57 Fairbairn, W., 'On the Economy of Raising Water from Coal Mines on the Cornish Principle', *Manchester Geological Society*, 29 October 1840.

58 Fairbairn (1871), Vol. 1, p. 248.

59 Ibid.

60 Leigh (1875), Vol. 1, p. 26.

61 Ibid, p. 46.

62 Boulton Papers, 348.74, J. Watt to M. Boulton, 4 August 1777.

CHAPTER 4
NEW THEORIES AND MATERIALS, 1860–1890

Growth in spite of Disruption

The Lancashire cotton industry was devastated by the American Civil War because of its heavy reliance on cotton from the southern states. Supplies were cut off. Mills were forced to work part time or close, so there was much unemployment and suffering among the operatives. It proved difficult to adapt the machines to spin the shorter-staple Surat cotton from India. But once the war was over and normality had returned, the cotton industry continued its expansion. There were boom periods of building mills around 1860, in 1873 to 1875 and again in 1880 to 1884. The average annual consumption of raw cotton rose to 1,211,000,000 pounds in 1871 to 1873. Between 1856 and 1878, the numbers of spindles increased fifty-seven per cent and power looms by seventy-two per cent. This was the period when the self-acting mule really came into its own, especially in the Oldham area, so that spindle numbers rose steadily in spite of another period of poor trade in the 1880s.

Numbers of Spindles in the Cotton Industry

1861	30,300,000
1875	37,500,000
1880	39,750,000
1885	43,000,000
1890	43,750,000

The rise in numbers of Lancashire looms was as follows:

1882	465,454
1885	546,118
1890	614,964[1]

During this period, there was a shift in weaving to north-east Lancashire where, between 1882 and 1896, its loomage increased by forty-five per cent with the addition of some 130,000 looms, or more than three times the number added in the south during the same period. In 1870, there were 1,939 woollen factories in the United Kingdom with 2,690,000 spindles and 48,140 looms needing 52,302 h.p. Wool produced at home remained about the same at 150,000,000 pounds while imports retained for home use were 140,000,000, an increase of about sixty per cent over 1857.[2]

The increase in the number of cotton spindles was accommodated in larger mills. The new cotton mills of the 1870s adopted the size of 50,000 spindles, or double the earlier size of the average Lancashire mill. Those of 1883 to 1884 had an average spindleage of 75,000 and those of 1889 to 1890 one of 90,000. The financing of the construction of these larger mills became easier after the passing of an Act in 1856 introducing limited liability for those subscribing to the capital. Until then, partners in a company were liable for the full amount of any debts in any concern which they had joined. But after the Act, shareholders were liable only to the value of their investment. This encouraged working men to join together and pool their savings to form joint-stock companies. These had their origins in co-operative companies formed during the 1850s in and around the Rossendale district of Lancashire. After the passing of the Act, they formed themselves into joint-stock companies which boomed in 1860 and 1861 under the stimulus of demand from India and rises in profits and wages. One which pioneered the creation of what became called the Oldham Limiteds was the Sun Mill, Chadderton, begun in 1858 with 60,000 spindles, or more than three times the average in local mills. This venture proved to be highly successful so that it was widely imitated. For example, Melbourne Mill, Chadderton, was built in 1860 by the Oldham Cotton Spinning Co. Another early one was Park Mill, Walkden, which was promoted in 1861 and opened in 1865. But this boom was cut short by the American Civil War and the cotton famine.

Limefield Mill, Broadbottom, a typical smaller stone-built mill of the early 1870s.

The Limited movement expanded quickly in the Oldham area in the late 1860s once more settled conditions had returned. The Limiteds challenged the private spinner because they built new mills of the largest possible size. They used loan capital to the fullest extent, encouraged by their limited liability. They built tall, wide mills and installed high-pressure horizontal engines to drive wider carding engines and longer mules, thus ensuring the triumph of the self-acting mule in the Oldham district. In addition, their machinery was operated at faster speeds, especially after 1875 when new productivity agreements were reached with the unions. In turn, this placed demands on the engine and machinery manufacturers to produce more carefully built, better-engineered machines. The results of their success were seen in the construction in 1889 of the Lion Mill at Royton with a record number of 107,472 spindles, followed by the Pearl Mill, Glodwick, in 1890 with another record of 116,352 spindles. These pale into insignificance with the largest mill in the world in 1888 at Krahnholm, Russia. In this immense establishment, there were 340,000 spindles and 2,200 looms, giving employment to some 7,000 people. The motive power came from eight water turbines on the River Marowa which generated 6,300 h.p.[3] Productivity in mills rose. Andrew commented in 1887 that, in 1837, it was estimated

> … that in a spinning mill it took seven operatives to every 1,000 spindles; in 1887 it takes only three. 2nd, taking an average length of mule spinning 40's counts, and the length turned out per spindle then and today, every man, woman and child in a cotton mill today is turning out four times the amount in hanks turned out in 1837.[4]

Introduction of Steel

As well as the change in provision of capital support for the creation of the Limiteds, the new mills and their machinery were able to expand through the introduction of a new material called at first by its inventor, Henry Bessemer, malleable iron; what today we term steel. It proved to be more homogeneous and stronger than either cast or wrought iron. In October 1855, Bessemer patented his method of turning melted pig or cast iron into steel by passing air through it to remove the carbon.[5] In the following August, he presented a paper in Cheltenham at the annual meeting of the British Association. Ironmakers showed immediate interest and agreed to take out licences. However, when they tried it they ran

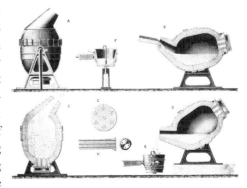

The Bessemer converter. A: in normal position; B: being filled with molten iron; C: the blowing position; D: pouring steel into ladle at E; F: emptying ladle into ingot mould.

into problems for they found their new steel was useless. Eventually Bessemer discovered that the problem lay in the presence of phosphorus which abounded in most British pig iron. In his original experiments, Bessemer by chance had used pure Swedish pig iron. Once the reason for the failure had been identified, Bessemer set up a steelworks at Sheffield and took some special bars of his steel ingots across to Galloways in Manchester. Here the workmen did not have the slightest suspicion that they were using steel made by a new process. More of Bessemer's steel was supplied to other firms in the Manchester region such as Sir Joseph Whitworth for his machine tools, to Messrs Beyer, Peacock for their railway locomotives, to Messrs Hick for their mill engines and Messrs Platt of Oldham for their textile machinery.

It was necessary to learn how to handle this new material, particularly in sheet form for boilers to prevent embrittlement. At a meeting of the Institution of Mechanical Engineers at Sheffield in the summer of 1861, Daniel Adamson exhibited 'some beautiful specimens of deep and difficult flanging in some fire-boxes for locomotive boilers' made from Bessemer steel. He had already used some two hundred tons and was about to procure more. 'He found the metal of excellent quality and of regular character throughout, and it was an admirable material for working'.[6] Adamson soon became recognised as one of the foremost authorities on boiler-making in the country and patented a range of special machine tools.[7] Instead of punching the rivet holes in flat plates and then rolling them, whereby the holes became elongated, he rolled the plates, fitted them together with a few temporary bolts and then drilled the rivet holes with radial drills with at first six and later twelve heads. The rivets were closed by machines of Adamson's own design. His steel Lancashire boilers could withstand much higher pressures so that he pioneered the introduction of triple and quadruple expansion mill engines. With steel becoming so much cheaper, it caused a revolution not only in boiler technology where it replaced wrought iron but also it replaced wood and wrought iron in mules and other textile machines (see p.108). On engines, many of the moving parts such as piston rods, slide rods, connecting rods, crossheads and guide blocks were made from it. In the mills themselves, it replaced cast iron beams, which allowed spans to be widened. This, together with thinner concrete floors replacing brick jack-arches, gave larger windows letting in more light.

Preparatory Machinery

Although the main outlines of spinning and weaving machinery had been laid down by the 1840s, inventions continued to be patented, often by machinery makers to circumvent those of their rivals. Also differences in machines were needed for different types of cotton. The tightly packed cotton taken from the bales might be broken up by the porcupine opener, in which a horizontal drum with spikes or bars beat the lumps. In 1861, William Creighton of Manchester designed a vertical conical beater in which the dirt was flung out through grids around the side and the cotton carried upwards on a draught of air to the scutcher where it was further opened and rolled into a lap.[8] The scutcher was improved in the following year with the addition of the ingenious piano-feed regulator which evened out the cotton across the width of the lap. This consisted of a series of parallel weighted levers across the scutcher which retarded lumps for more beating but allowed thinner parts past. These and other inventions so greatly improved the quality of the laps that the self-acting mule could be used to spin medium counts up to 60s whereas before the previous limit had been 50s.

The carding engine was improved as well. For wool, the system of teasing out the fibres between the main cylinder and smaller worker rollers and clearers remained unchanged. For cotton, the system of placing flat cards around the upper periphery of the main cylinder was preferred. As the cotton was teased out between the wire points on the main cylinder and those on the flats, the card clothing on the flats became choked with short fibres. Periodically the flats had to be lifted up and cleaned. In 1823, Archibald Buchanan, a partner in the Catrine Mills, invented a machine for raising each flat one after the other, turning it upside down and cleaning it with a rotary brush.[9] This does not seem to have been taken up at the time and, while a similar device

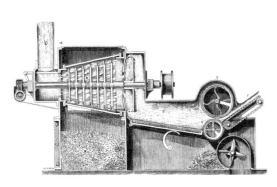

Horizontal cotton opener in which the lumps of cotton were broken up and dirt removed.

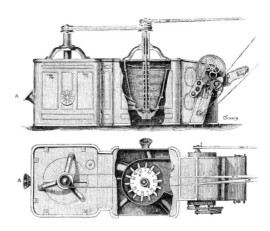

Creighton's vertical opener.

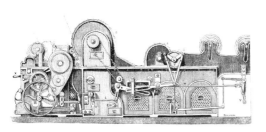

The scutching machine for further opening and cleaning the cotton. Four laps were fed in to produce one.

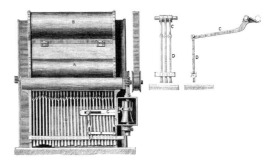

The piano feed regulator with its parallel weighted rocking bars to help hold back larger lumps of cotton.

The Wellman card where the flats were lifted and cleaned one by one.

Carding engine with an endless chain of flats which were cleaned by the rotary brush as they passed round.

was patented by Wellman in America in 1853, this also did not prove popular in Britain. Meanwhile, in 1834, James Smith of Deanston joined all the flats together and added more so that they passed in an endless chain above the main carding cylinder.[10] They were cleaned automatically as they went round one end of the loop.

As the wire points on the main cylinder had to be ground from time to time to sharpen them, the diameter of the cylinder would decrease, altering the distance between its points and those of the flats. Therefore the radius of the rails or 'bend' on which the flats travelled had to be changed to match. John Mason and George Collier patented a 'bend' in 1849.[11] But Leigh patented a more successful version, the 'flexible bend', in 1858.[12] Now the carding engine could be easily adjusted both after regrinding and also for different types of cotton. Through these and other improvements, the revolving flat card became the established machine for carding cotton during the 1880s. By this time, the wooden lagging forming the main cylinder was being replaced by an iron cylinder, giving greater accuracy.

The size of cotton-carding engines was enlarged to give greater production. Writing in 1840, James Montgomery gave the size in Scotland and England of a carding engine main cylinder for fine yarns as 18in breadth, 36in diameter and 90 to 110 r.p.m. For medium and coarse counts in England the main cylinder would be 36in breadth, 42in diameter and speed 130 to 150 r.p.m. Around 1890, the figures for medium counts would range from 38in to 45in breadth by 50in diameter. The speeds are not known but it is suspected that they would have increased.

The Ring Frame

A different type of spinning machine began to gain acceptance during this period. This was the ring frame, which was eventually to replace the mule. Leigh, writing around 1870, said, 'Notwithstanding that about forty years have elapsed since it was brought into England, not a single spinner has yet ventured to try it on a large scale'.[13] Joseph Nasmith dated its introduction to the years after 1874, 'owing to the large production possible by reason of the great speeds at which the spindles can be run'.[14] Nasmith pointed out that this impacted on the mules, which in turn had to be remodelled, using better construction such as steel replacing wood to give stronger, lighter carriages. The mules were also improved with additional motions, such as a second fast pulley on the main driving shaft which could rotate the spindles more quickly when the carriage had stopped moving out, enabling twisting on the head to be inserted faster. Then, as the carriage moved back in while winding on, the counter-faller wire tended to push the twist along the yarn so that the part near the drafting rollers became twisted more. This could be evened out by turning the drafting rollers a little to pay out more fibres which took up this extra twist. A length of only a couple of inches each draw effected a considerable gain in productivity with a thousand spindles on the carriage.

Attempts were made also to increase the speed and hence productivity of the throstle. In 1875, Baines wrote about the worsted industry, 'In the old spinning frame, called the fly frame, generally used ten years since, the spindles made 2800 revolutions per minute: in the new frame, called the bell frame, they make 6000'.[15] The limitation in speed of the fly frame or throstle was caused through the difficulty of balancing the two arms of the flyer. The flyer had to be held by a screw thread onto the top of the spindle to allow removal of the bobbin. If it were not balanced properly, it caused vibrations. One device which proved successful in worsted spinning

A doubling frame for wool at the Tan-y-grisiau Mill, Blaenau Ffestiniog, using flyers and bobbins similar to a throstle.

in the 1850s was the cap frame originating from a patent taken out by Charles Danforth in the United States in 1828 and in Britain in the following year.[16] In later versions, the flyer was replaced by a cylinder or cap with enclosed top that fitted onto the spindle. The fibres were twisted as they were fed out of the drafting rollers through rotation of the vertical spindle and cap. The yarn passed through a guide above the spindle and round the bottom of the cap to the bobbin. The drag against the edge of the cap was sufficient to cause the yarn to wind onto the bobbin. It was rapidly developed in America to operate reliably at 6,000 to 8,000 r.p.m. However, it was found unsuitable for cotton.

In the meantime in the United States, a different method was patented in 1828 by John Thorp which also dispensed with the flyer and replaced it wth a hook travelling around a stationary ring fixed on a lifting rail to guide the yarn onto the bobbin. The friction and weight of this hook, or traveller as it was called later, caused sufficient drag to wind on the yarn. Other American patentees with similar ideas were Addison and Stevens in 1829 and Jencks in 1832. Spinning by ring and traveller developed

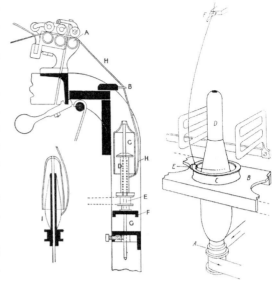

Above left: The principle of cap spinning. From the drafting rollers A, the yarn passes through guide B, round the bottom of the cap at H to bobbin D.

Above right: The principle of ring spinning. From the drafting rollers, the yarn passes through guide F, down to the traveller E on ring C from where it is wound onto tube D. Rail B moves up and down to wind the yarn on in the form of a cop.

very quickly in the United States. The travellers had a life of six to eight weeks when running at 6,000 r.p.m. The ring frame could be driven faster than either the throstle or Danforth's cap frame. Around 1890, speeds of 8,650 r.p.m. had been reached.

In Britain, Sharp Roberts purchased the rights to ring spinning from an unidentified person in 1834. Roberts patented various alternatives.[17] They sold some ring frames because Montgomery commented in 1836, 'It has, indeed, but recently been completed, and is as yet only introduced into a few Mills; but its operations, and quality of the yarn produced, are highly spoken of'.[18] Yet the ring frame did not gain acceptance at this time in Britain, perhaps through prejudice against American inventions as expressed by Montgomery:

> Though the ring throstle and eclipse roving frame, have both been introduced from America, it is but justice to the skill of British mechanics to state, that, when first introduced, they were by no means in a state fit for practical operation in this country, and that both machines had to undergo several important modifications, which were essentially necessary to render them practically useful. This remark will, indeed, apply to almost every invention imported, or communicated, from any other country whatever.[19]

Although Sharp Brothers exhibited a ring frame at the International Exhibition in 1851, their adoption by British mills took a further twenty or more years. In Oldham, Palm Mill, opened in 1884, was the first new mill in that district to be spinning wholly with rings. By that year, the combined Waterside and Bridge Mills at Hadfield had 293,000 ring spindles and 4,700 looms. Mule spinning was more suitable for finer counts but growing competition to imports of British cloth in overseas markets compelled mill owners to switch to ring frames for warp yarns. In 1887, Brookfield Mill in Dinting Vale had 28,576 mule spindles but by 1891 had reduced their mule spindles to 17,760 and installed 5,480 ring spindles. While the total number of spindles was reduced to 23,240, presumably output remained the same. Nasmith mentions ring frames with 300 to 325 spindles. Their layout followed the linear form of the waterframe and throstle. Since they were compact with no moving carriage, they took up less space than a mule. They required a less skilful operator and were quicker to 'doff'. But they required more power per spindle, with one hundred mule spindles requiring one horsepower compared with only eighty ring spindles. More could be fitted into a mill than mules so ring mills needed more powerful engines.

An 1888 ring frame made by Taylor & Lang, Stalybridge.

The Scientific Background to the Steam Engine

It is surprising to find that, even in these larger mills, entire reliance was placed on a single steam engine, perhaps reflecting Victorian pride and confidence in their achievements. Yet there were obvious advantages because the relative capital cost of both steam engine and self-acting mules became proportionately less as they became larger. As the number of spindles on a mule carriage increased, so they became proportionately cheaper because the most expensive part lay in the complex mechanisms in the central headstock. The same principle applied to steam engine valve gear and other parts with increasing size. Larger steam engines showed greater fuel economy when compared with a number of smaller ones. Running costs were also reduced in proportion with increased output. While there were many financial incentives to build larger mills and spinning machinery, the state of the understanding of the scientific principles involved in the working of the steam engine meant that designers were unable to ensure that the highest efficiencies were obtained. In 1860, the true theory of thermodynamics was only just being discovered and this applied also to theories of combustion. Once these had been formulated, steam could be generated as well as used more economically at higher pressures in more powerful engines.

The Lancashire boiler made from steel plates had the potential for higher steam pressures but many people were afraid that this would lead to disastrous boiler explosions through misconceived notions of the nature of steam. Following a series of explosions, in August 1854 a meeting was called in Manchester to discuss the formation of an 'Association for the Prevention of Boiler Explosions'. At the inaugural meeting of what became the Manchester Steam Users' Association, J.C. Dyer observed

> … that when explosions had happened, and caused a lamentable destruction of life and property, they were spoken of by the newspapers and others as if they were owing to some mysterious elastic force, generated in such a manner, and possessing such a nature, that nobody could understand it. Some said that steam confined under great heat was suddenly decomposed, and gases generated which had tremendous expansive force; others, again, said that the confined caloric of the water, by reason of sudden motion, was given out, and the sudden production of steam to a tremendous amount was the result. Now, whilst these mysterious sources of danger were darkly hinted at, people had a notion that they could do nothing about it.[20]

As long as people believed that explosions were caused by some unaccountable generation of hydrogen or sudden production of quantities of steam, they felt there was little they could do to prevent them, so they failed to take proper care of their boilers. As a way of countering these concepts, the Association carried out experiments to ascertain the validity of various theories. Instructions were issued to firemen pointing out best firing practices. Boilers were inspected regularly by competent engineers who submitted standardised reports.

The Association established the principle that every boiler explosion was due to well-understood causes and was preventable by regular examination together with correct operating procedures. In this way, confidence was gained to use steam at higher pressures.

There was still great misunderstanding about the true nature of heat. It will be noticed that Dyer included the term 'caloric', referring to heat as some sort of mysterious subtle fluid. James Hann, writing his book *The Steam Engine for Practical Men* in 1854, thought that superheating steam converted it 'into stame [*sic*], a distinct and chemical compound of heat and water'.[21] He erroneously believed that the advantage of high-pressure steam was

> … founded on the principle, *that the pressure of the steam increases in a greater ratio than its density*; whence it follows that the higher the pressure the steam is raised to, the less *proportionate* quantity of water it contains, and therefore the less fuel is consumed, since a given quantity of fuel will evaporate the same quantity of water at all temperatures.[22]

Even Wye Williams, who had put Fairbairn on the right tracks about smoke consumption, still had misconceptions about the nature of steam and heat. To give but one example, he wrote in 1860 that there were 'sufficient scientific and reasonable grounds for asserting – That vapour or steam cannot give out its heat to water, and is but mixed, *mechanically*, with it, on the true Daltonian theory'.[23] He seems to have thought that steam was distinct from water, possibly some sort of chemical combination with heat, but at least he titled his book, *On Heat in its Relations to Water and Steam*, so he was beginning to move in the right direction by recognising the importance of heat. A proper understanding of the nature of heat would explain what was happening in boilers and steam engines alike.

Much earlier, in 1824, Sadi Carnot had published in France his book *Réflections sur la Puissance Motrice du Feu et Sur les Machines Propres a Développer cette Puissance* (*Reflections on the Motive Power of Fire*), in which he pointed out that the true analogy with the steam engine had to start with the temperature of the fire in the furnace. He wrote:

> We can easily conceive a multitude of machines fitted to develop the motive power of heat through the use of elastic fluids; but in whatever way we look at it, we should not lose sight of the following principles:
>
> 1) The temperature of the fluid should be made as high as possible, in order to obtain a great fall of caloric, and consequently a large production of motive power.
>
> 2) For the same reason the cooling should be carried as far as possible.
>
> 3) It should be so arranged that the passage of the elastic fluid should be due to increase of volume; that is it should be so arranged that the cooling of the gas should occur spontaneously as the effect of rarefaction.[24]

Carnot realised that it was necessary to use the greatest possible range of heat and cold for the most efficient steam engine. There had to be a flow of heat between these extremes as well as expansion of the working fluid or steam. There should be no useless flow of heat. In other words, heat must flow smoothly and there must be no sudden falls in pressure or temperature as the fluid expanded.

Carnot pointed out that in the ordinary steam engine there was a great deal of waste because, while combustion in a fire occurred at 1,000 to 2,000°C, only a small part of this temperature range was used in the engines. At a pressure of 6 atmospheres, 90 p.s.i. in the boiler, the temperature was only 160°C (320°F), so there was a sudden fall here. Condensation in the condenser seldom took place much under 40°C (104°F). Therefore we could use only 120°C (248°F), which assumed that the steam had expanded, losing both pressure and temperature down to that of the condenser. Carnot postulated that no mechanical effect could be produced from heat if all bodies were at the same temperature. The greater the difference, the greater would be the effect. This led him to point out the advantages of the high-pressure steam engine.

> *This superiority lies essentially in the power of utilizing a greater fall of caloric* . . . A good steam-engine, therefore, should not only employ steam under heavy, but *under successive and very variable pressures, differing greatly from one another, and progressively decreasing.*[25]

Watt was not alone in failing to grasp this. From 1824 to 1834, Carnot's ideas remained forgotten until Emile Claperyon rediscovered them. He pointed out that it was solely through the use of caloric at high temperatures that improvements in the art of utilising the motive power of heat could be expected.

The Nature of Heat

However, there still remained the puzzle over what this caloric or heat actually was. Doubts had been raised whether caloric was some sort of fluid with particles or atoms through experiments carried out in 1798 by Count Rumford. He communicated the results of these to the Royal Society after he had forced a blunt boring tool at 10,000lb pressure against the rotating 'head' of a casting of a six-pounder brass cannon immersed in a trough of water. Much to the surprise of the spectators, the water boiled after two and a half hours, without any fire. Rumford was forced to ask:

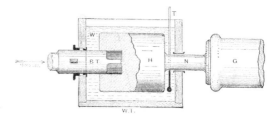

Rumford's experiment of forcing the blunt boring tool BT against the 'head' H of a cast cannon G until the water boiled.

> What is heat? Is there any such thing as an igneous fluid? Is there anything that, with propriety, can be called caloric? . . . It is hardly necessary to add that anything which an insulated body can continue to furnish without limitation, cannot possibly be a material substance; and it appears to me to be extremely difficult, if not impossible, to form any distinct idea of anything capable of being excited, and communicated in the manner heat was excited, and communicated in these experiments, except it be motion.[26]

In the following year, Humphry Davy carried out some experiments and commented, 'The immediate cause of the phenomenon of heat is motion; and the laws of its communication are precisely the same as the communication of the laws of motion'.[27]

There the matter rested for many years until James Joule in Manchester was led to consider the problems of energy conversion through an interest in electromagnetic machinery. In 1843, he published his important paper in the *Philosophical Magazine*, 'On the Caloric effects of Magneto-Electricity, and on the Mechanical Value of Heat.' Here he demonstrated that the heat caused by the passage of an electric current was not transferred from another part of the circuit which was correspondingly cooled, but was actually generated. As the result of a

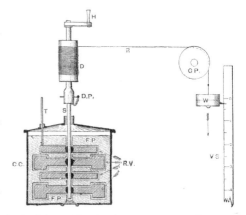

In Joule's paddlewheel experiment, the falling weight W drives the drum D which revolves the vanes RV of the paddlewheel between the fixed plates FP. A thermometer T measures the temperature.

number of experiments, Joule concluded that the mechanical value of a unit of heat was 838ft lb of work expended to raise the temperature of one pound of water by one degree Fahrenheit. He continued with a variety of experiments to determine the mechanical equivalent of heat and the principles connecting mechanical work and heat. In one of his most famous experiments in 1845, he rotated a paddlewheel to stir up a known weight of water contained in a vessel. The movement was given by a weight falling under the influence of gravity. The work done as this weight fell was measured by the increase in temperature of the water using very accurate thermometers.

After more experiments with different apparatus, Joule was able to state in 1849:

1) The quantity of heat produced by the friction of bodies, whether solid or liquid, is always proportional to the quantity of force expended.

2) The quantity of heat capable of increasing the temperature of 1 lb. of water (weighed *in vacuo*, and taken between 55°F and 60°F) by 1°F requires for its evolution the expenditure of a mechanical force represented by the fall of 772 lbs. through the space of one foot.[28]

This has been termed 'Joule's Mechanical Equivalent of Heat'. Heat was no longer seen as a substance or fluid but a form of energy in which mechanical force, energy and heat were interchangeable. From this, the first law of thermodynamics has been deduced which Rankine expressed as, 'Heat and mechanical energy are mutually convertible: and heat requires for its production, and produces by its disappearance, mechanical energy in the proportion of 772 foot-pounds for each British unit of heat.'[29] Out of this and Carnot's work would be deduced the second law of thermodynamics, which, in one of its different expressions, states that a self-acting machine cannot convey heat from one body at a lower temperature to another at a higher one.

This dynamical theory of heat startled men of science still accustomed to the caloric theory. One problem was that the caloric theory stated that heat was always conserved as heat and could not be changed into mechanical energy. For a long time it was believed that the amount of heat put into a steam engine was the same as that which could be measured in the condensate. This seemed to have been confirmed by experiments carried out by G.A. Lee during his trials on engines in Manchester at the close of the eighteenth century. His engine was never more than 2½ per cent efficient and his figures were obviously too inaccurate to distinguish between 97½ and 100 per cent of the heat reappearing in the condenser. In France, G.A. Hirn had been convinced as early as 1845 of the correctness of the dynamical theory of heat and set out to prove it at Mulhouse where he lived. In the following decade, he carried out his series of experiments to examine all aspects of the performance of a Watt engine. He reported his findings in a letter to the President of the Société Industrielle de Mulhouse, dated 21 October 1854. He was able to use steam at 200°C (392°F), which was much higher than Lee. He demonstrated that the amount of heat leaving a steam engine in the condenser was less than the amount entering it from the boiler. He succeeded in measuring the actual consumption of heat and showed that there could be a loss of between 10 and 20 per cent. He went on to show that this loss was always equal to the magnitude of the work done divided by Joule's equivalent; that is the missing heat was actually converted into work. Hirn's contribution was immediately recognised as a major advance in understanding the steam engine. As a result of his investigations, it was possible to show that what was happening was the conversion of energy into work.

In 1850, Rudolf Clausius succeeded in reconciling Carnot's arguments about the nature of heat, in which there was a transfer of heat from a hot to a cold body, with the dynamical theory in which heat was changed into energy, by showing that both processes, flow and transformation, take place. This showed that it was the heat in a steam engine which was the crucial driving force, and only secondarily the pressure. The ideas of

Carnot and the work of Joule pointed the way for the acceptance of the high-pressure steam engine and gave the correct theoretical reasons for doing so. In about 1884, T.M. Goodeve wrote:

> It is only within the last thirty years that a knowledge of the principles of the mechanical theory of heat has influenced the practice of those who are engaged in improving the construction of the steam-engine, and in seeking to obtain from it a larger amount of useful work with a given expenditure of fuel.[30]

At last, the steam engine could be developed in the most efficient way to drive the larger textile mills. This would mean increasing boiler pressures as was now possible with steel boilers, expanding steam in two or more stages and controlling the expansion through varying the point of cut-off with better valve gear and governing mechanisms.

Rope Driving

Before we look at the internal operations of the engines, we must consider an important change that occurred in the way the power from the engine was distributed to the line shafting and which affected the layout of both mills and engines. The early system of driving through gearwheels had many advantages, in that it was positive and durable if well made. It was also compact, taking up little space, but it tended to generate excessive noise and needed expensive foundations to support the vertical shaft. Speed was limited and, if a gearwheel broke, the whole mill might be put out of action until repairs could be completed. The vertical shaft was replaced by either flat belts or ropes around the periphery of the flywheel to drive pulleys on the line shafts at the various floors. By this means, gearing on the engine itself as well as the bevel gears on the vertical and horizontal shafting became redundant, reducing noise and friction levels considerably. This change was introduced in two ways, the earlier originating in America. In 1828 at the newly built Appleton Mills in Lowell, Massachusetts, flat belting replaced the gear drive from the waterwheels. Paul Moody, the millwright in charge of construction, 'did away with the heavy English-type gearing which had creaked and groaned in every American mill from 1790 on . . . [and] touched off a new American style which soon came to constitute an important distinction between English and American mills'.[31] From around a drum driven by the water-wheel, a single broad flat leather belt would be taken around guide pulleys to all the other floors of the mill where it would pass round pulleys on the line shafting. The belt ran smoothly and quietly, cost less and was more readily installed and repaired than gearing. Breakdowns were fewer and shutdown times shorter. The disadvantage was that, if the belt broke, the entire mill had to be stopped for it to be replaced and the immense weight and the difficulty in handling it were strong objections to this system.

During the 1870s, some belt drives were installed in Britain. If the mills were extensive, more than one belt might be necessary. Each floor would be driven by its own belt so that, if one broke, only that floor would be stopped until the belt could be repaired at a convenient time. In 1876, Derker Mills in Oldham were equipped with a pair of Galloway side-by-side slide-valve horizontal engines, one either side of a 22ft diameter flywheel with probably four flat belts round it. Similarly, in 1877, J. and E. Wood built a pair of tandem compound engines developing 800 i.h.p. at 46 r.p.m. for Armitage and Rigby at Warrington. This engine had a flywheel 28ft in diameter and 7ft broad, round which there were three belts, each 26in wide. Although from about 1910 a few steel belts were used which ran on rims faced with cork, flat belts were never popular to any great extent in Britain and were used mostly on small engines where the drive was taken directly from the engine to one point by a single belt.

Although Goodrich saw a rope drive at one of Strutt's mills in 1799, its use to transmit the whole power from an engine to the rest of the machinery was developed in Northern Ireland by James Combe of Combe, Barbour and Combe, Belfast.[32] In 1856, Combe applied an expanding pulley with V-shaped sides to the dif-

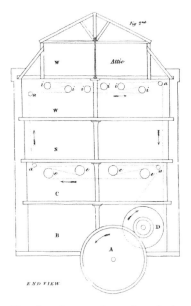

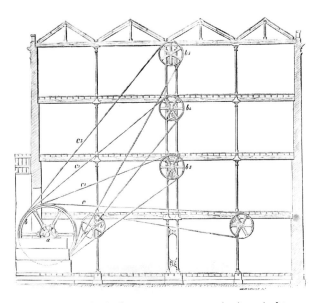

The American system of a single flat belt driving all the line shafting on different floors.

The British method of separate ropes to the line shafting on each floor.

ferential motion of flax roving frames. The pulley was driven by a round leather rope from another pulley also grooved with a V-shape. He was struck by the large amount of power obtained through round ropes working in V-shaped grooves so he decided to try their application in the transmission of larger powers. He made a series of experiments and found that grooves of 45° gave the best results. He also found that the advantages were so great that in 1863 he decided to adopt rope driving on a new engine of 200 i.h.p. which he was installing at Falls Foundry, Belfast. This was the first instance of rope driving being used for a main drive of such importance.

Rope driving transmitting 600 i.h.p. from the second motion shaft to the various line shafts in the Hilden Mills of Messrs William Barbour and Sons, Lisburn, was started in July 1864. Combe's first ropes were made from the longest possible leather strips, formed into a circular rope, but their cross-section varied and they were liable to become untwisted. Then manilla hemp ropes were tried, which were successful. Later cotton ropes were introduced which proved to be longer-lasting but more expensive. Flywheels on the engines were grooved to take the ropes. Driving with multiple ropes directly from the engine flywheel to the various line shafts on the different floors of a mill presented great advantages in a textile mill, especially where the load could be subdivided into sections and not taken all to one point. While the drive was practically noiseless, it was difficult to get equal tension on all the ropes and there could be considerable internal friction caused by the ropes bending round the pulleys. The slack side should be uppermost around the pulleys.

Combe recommended a velocity of about 3,500ft per minute and no higher than 4,000. A rope with a diameter of 1½in at a velocity of 4,700ft per min. would transmit about 40½ h.p. At much greater speeds, the effect of centrifugal force would tend to throw the ropes out of the grooves so that they slipped. Rim speeds rarely exceeded 6,000ft per min., about 70 m.p.h., because cast iron had a peculiar metallurgical property. Stresses in a wheel travelling at about 10,000ft per min. were such that instantaneous brittle fracture occurred. Malfunction of a governor caused it to happen on many occasions when the wheel would 'burst', sending pieces of cast iron flying around at 100 m.p.h.

Nasmith said that up to 1876 almost all Lancashire mills were gear-driven and that the change came after that. An early mill with rope drive was Clammerhough Mill, Farnworth, in 1873. In 1877, Galloways built a complex arrangement for a mill in Hadfield with a shaft drive on columns across a yard to the lower floors while the two higher floors were driven by ropes. More significant for future layouts was an order in the same year for a mill in Eccles where the steam engine had a 25ft diameter flywheel grooved for 17 ropes which took the drive to three different levels. In Yorkshire, at Whetley Mills, alterations in 1879 involved the installation of a new horizontal engine powering the spinning mill and combing shed by ropes. During the 1880s, ropes took over from gear drives so that by the early 1890s, 'nearly every mill was provided with rope gearing'.[33] Pike Mill near Bolton was opened in 1884 with 83,000 spindles and its rope-race greatly impressed a visitor:

> [It] is in every respect a model spinning-factory, [and] is one of the largest, handsomest, and most substantial structures of its kind in the Bolton district . . . The machinery is driven on the rope-driving principle, and thirty-four of the ropes necessary for this purpose pass over the huge fly-wheel of the mill engines, a wheel weighing ninety tons and making fifty revolutions a minute. The engines indicate about twelve hundred horse-power.[34]

Rope driving required more space so that the design of textile mills and engine houses had to be altered. The greater breadth of a flywheel with its many rope grooves meant that the crankshaft would be longer, so the engines had to be wider. Therefore engines began to be installed in separate houses on the outsides of mills. Then the rope drive itself took up more horizontal space and floor area than the previous vertical shaft drive. The engine house had to be tall to allow for the clearance that was necessary for the ropes to reach up to the highest line shaft. Sometimes the rope-race would be situated internally towards one end of the mill where its walls would separate the opening processes with their attendant risk of fire from the rest of the mill. With cotton ropes stretching the full height of the mill, the rope-races themselves were a fire hazard. Later, rope-races were built at one end of the mill, leaving the whole of the floor space on each level unobstructed.

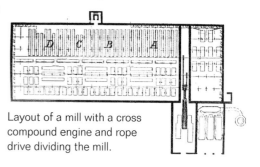

Layout of a mill with a cross compound engine and rope drive dividing the mill.

To fit a rope, the length round the pulleys would be measured and the rope spliced to the proper length at the mill round the shafts. Splicing was a very skilled job, for the rope had to remain the same thickness throughout its length or it would stick in the grooves. When the splice was finished, the rope would be levered into its correct position on the pulleys. Heat and damp could affect the tension of the ropes, and many a mill ran a hot bearing on a Monday morning because the ropes had become wet over the weekend and had shrunk. At Brooklands Mill, Leigh, should a rope start to fray, the end hit a metal bar which started a bell ringing. Each rope could transmit a known amount of power, depending upon its diameter. The power needed for all the machines on each floor had to be calculated and the number of ropes determined accordingly. For example, at the Wye No. 2 Mill, 22 ropes drove the top spinning room, 6 ropes the blowing room, 9 the carding room and 12 the bottom ring room. Should one rope break, the mill could still operate with some machines taken out of commission on that floor until a new rope could be fitted. This was not the case when a gearwheel broke.

The rope drive at Mons Mill, Todmorden. The drum is formed from three pulleys side by side.

The Compound Engine

Once it was understood that heat was the essential factor creating power in a steam engine, how to use it to the best effect became the guiding principle in engine design. Allowing steam to expand had been shown to be essential but expansion led to cooling which in turn would lead to condensation and hence waste of steam on the next charge to enter the cylinder. Herein lay the weakness of Fairbairn's promotion of his single-cylinder, high-expansion engines. The answer for more economical engines lay in expanding the steam successively in two or more cylinders. The multiple expansion engine 'acts beneficially by diminishing the range through which the temperature of any part of the cylinder metal varies'.[35]

In working as a compound engine with two cylinders, steam is first admitted at full pressure and temperature to a small high-pressure cylinder where it is cut off by closing the inlet valve before the stroke is complete. Then it expands, exerting a force on the moving piston, simultaneously losing temperature and pressure. During the exhaust stroke, the steam should pass to a receiver where it can be stored ready for use in the larger low-pressure cylinder. From the receiver, the steam will pass through separate inlet valves on that cylinder where it is again cut off to be used expansively within that cylinder before being exhausted to the condenser through another set of valves. This effectively separates the two cylinders so that their temperatures do not overlap. The hottest steam first entered the smaller cylinder which was reduced in size compared with a single cylinder on an ordinary engine. Economy was gained through the need to reheat the much smaller mass of the high-pressure cylinder, not from the combined fall in temperatures of both cylinders but only from that of the smaller pressure drop in that cylinder. Therefore wasteful condensation in a compound was considerably less than was the case with a simple engine. However, the thermodynamic advantages of the compound began only with steam pressures over 60 p.s.i. and really closer towards 100 p.s.i. At first the Manchester Steam Users' Association did not undertake the insurance of boilers working at over 60 p.s.i., so it would not be until into the 1860s that compounding began to become really economic. Nasmith said that above 70 p.s.i. compounding would pay.[36]

There were other advantages with compounding. There was less loss of steam passing round the piston rings through the pressure range in each cylinder being less. Also the pressure on the moving parts was more equal through the divided expansion being less in each cylinder. This advantage had been recognised by the first person who tried to use steam consecutively in two cylinders. Jonathan Hornblower found there was an advantage in practice 'because the combined effect of the two pistons, approaches more nearly to a uniform action, than could be done by the same extent of expansive action of the steam, when operating in only one cylinder on Mr. Watt's system'.[37] Hornblower had taken up the subject in Cornwall as early as 1776. After trials on a model in 1778, he took out a patent in 1781.[38] Then in 1782 he built a pumping engine at Radstock Colliery, Somerset, which did not perform well. After more experiments, he installed his first engine in Cornwall at the Tincroft Mine with the high-pressure cylinder 21in diameter, 6ft stroke and the low-pressure cylinder 27in diameter, 8ft stroke, followed by nine more at different mines between then and 1794. Drawings of these engines show two vertical cylinders placed together at one end of the beam of a pumping engine so that the larger cylinder was at the end furthest from the beam pivot where the stroke was longer.

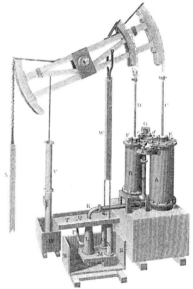

One of Hornblower's later compound engines with condensing apparatus very similar to Watt's except there is no valve in the eduction pipe between the second cylinder A and condenser L.

In order to avoid Watt's separate condenser patent, at first Hornblower used a jet of cold water to condense the steam in the bottom of the low-pressure cylinder in a way similar to Newcomen and probably with all the same disadvantages. In addition, the valves and connecting pipes appear to be too small and Hornblower did not expand the steam in his high-pressure cylinder, so gaining no thermodynamic advantage there. While later he did improve his condensing apparatus, in reality the pressure at which it was possible to generate steam at this time was far too low for there to be any thermodynamic savings in compounding and the friction of the two pistons would have been greater than Watt's single one. Trials were held to compare the performance of Watt's and Hornblower's engines. Hornblower protested that Watt's team cheated but Watt's engine seems to have been superior.[39] In the event, Hornblower was forced to abandon further progress through Watt securing injunctions to prevent the construction of any more of his compound engines but Boulton and Watt never took Hornblower to law for infringing Watt's 1769 patent probably because they realised that they could not prove he was actually condensing steam in a separate condenser.

The Woolf Compound Beam Engine

The compound engine was revived by Arthur Woolf, who took out a patent in 1804.[40] The layout he adopted was similar to Hornblower's with both cylinders together at the end of the beam. He explained his theory of the expansion of steam, which he considered to be in direct relationship to the pressure. He had ascertained the temperature of steam at different pressures and it became apparent to him that the pressure rose more quickly than the temperature. Steam at 20 p.s.i. has a temperature of 260°F (127°C) and at 70 p.s.i. one of 316°F (158°C). He stated:

> By small additions of temperature, an expansive power may be given to steam to enable it to expand to fifty, sixty . . . three hundred, or more, times its volume, without any limitation but what is imposed by the frangible nature of every material of which boilers and the other parts of steam engines have been or can be made.[41]

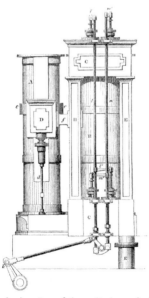

Fairbairn's drawing of the cylinders of a Woolf engine. The steam passes from the high-pressure cylinder on the left, through the passage F and up or down to the valve chests C on the low-pressure cylinder.

It is evident that Woolf was more interested in working his engines at a high pressure to obtain the greatest possible expansion from the steam rather that the greatest heat. He moved to London, where he was employed at the Griffin Brewery. He first compounded an existing 6 h.p. rotative engine made by Fenton and Murray. He then ordered a new engine fitted with cylinders high pressure 8in diameter by 3ft stroke and low pressure 30in by 5ft using steam at 40 p.s.i. When set to work in September 1805, although not as powerful as expected, its steam consumption was very small. A new larger high-pressure cylinder effected a great improvement in performance. After some trials in 1808, Trevithick calculated that he thought the consumption would be '22 million for each bushel of coal burnt in the 104 minutes', a result that was far in excess of ordinary engines of that day. However, the engine was tested by Rennie, who found that the 'comparison was as 3 to 4 in favour of Watt's engine'.[42] It would seem that Woolf failed to cut off the steam since the valves were all operated at the same time and the exhaust valve for the high-pressure cylinder also acted as the inlet valve for the low.

Woolf continued to improve his engines so that soon they performed the same work as the Watt rotatives with half the fuel consumption. He achieved this by better design, by a higher standard of engineering and by using steam at higher pressures. He formed a partnership with Humphrey Edwards but demand for his engines in London proved insufficient to sustain a manufactory there. By May 1811, the partnership had been terminated. Edwards, after continuing alone in London for a while, moved to France where he built Woolf's engines and boilers which became very successful. Fairbairn ascribed this to their using high-pressure steam with expansion though it was probably not until after 1811 that any expansive working through cut-off was adopted.

Meanwhile Woolf returned to Cornwall and placed an advertisement on 17 May 1811 in the *West Briton* stating, 'This engine is now brought to such a high degree of perfection as to require not more than one-third part of the Fuel employed in working engines on Messrs Boulton & Watt's construction'.[43] His first double-cylinder engine in Cornwall was a small one for winding at Wheal Fortune. The duty given in May 1813 was 5.3 million pounds. His first double-cylinder pumping engine at a Cornish mine was erected at Wheal Abraham. The high-pressure cylinder was 24in diameter, 4ft 3in stroke and the low-pressure 45in diameter and 7ft stroke. When first reported in October 1814, its duty was 34 million pounds. Afterwards a slight defect was discovered in some part of the castings. When this had been rectified, the very high duty of 55.9 million pounds was recorded in May 1816.

Woolf continued to erect his double-cylinder engines which at first out-performed simple engines. In 1816, the one at Wheal Abraham was loaded from 62 to 68 p.s.i. on the safety valve but his cast iron boilers were prone to cracking. Trials were held in 1824 at Wheal Alfred to settle the compound versus single engine controversy once for all. The single engine was built by Neath Abbey with a 90in diameter cylinder, 10ft stroke. The compound was by Harvey & Co., Hayle, with high-pressure cylinder 40in diameter, 6ft 6in stroke and low-pressure 70in diameter and 10ft stroke. Both engines returned similar duties, around 42 million pounds. The complexity of a compound and the problem of keeping the pistons steam-tight made people revert to single-cylinder engines in the 1820s but Woolf still considered the compound engine preferable.

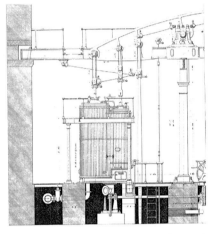

A Woolf compound beam engine of around 1880 with both cylinders together at the end of the beam.

His preference was justified through experience gained with rotative engines. It was not only on the continent that people found them to be more economical than the Watt low-pressure engines. Hick, who used the Woolf compound, pointed out to Sharp Roberts in about 1841 that a common high-pressure engine would have an estimated fuel consumption of 18lb of coal per horsepower per hour, for a condensing engine 14lb and for a compound engine 5lb. There were additional savings because the terminal pressures in Woolf's rotative engines were probably much lower than in contemporary types, which reduced the need for condensing water.

Respecting the advantages of employing Mr. Woolf's engines instead of Mr. Watt's engines, it should be kept in mind, that the quantity of cold water required for condensation by Mr. Woolf's engines is less than is required for Mr. Watt's engines, in the same proportion as the consumption of fuel is less by one than the other. In Manufacturing towns there is often great difficulty in procuring an adequate supply of cold water for Mr. Watt's engines, and in consequence of a deficiency of cold water, the condensation of the steam is very imperfectly performed, and the engines work under a great disadvantage; whereas if Mr. Woolf's engines were used in the same places, the quantity of cold water that is procured would be sufficient to effect a complete condensation.[44]

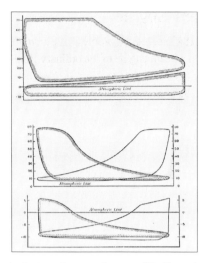

Indicator diagram from a Woolf engine showing the overlapping pressures in the cylinders compared with a receiver compound engine below.

Galloway side-by-side compound engine at the Oakenholt Paper Mill, North Wales.

How many beam engines on Woolf's principles were erected in textile mills is not known. Fairbairn said there were a few with steam pressures of 30 to 40 p.s.i. This would have been too low to gain the full advantages of compounding. Also, since the cylinders were side by side, there was no adequate receiver to contain the steam issuing out of the high-pressure cylinder. Both cylinders worked in unison so that the inlet valve to the low-pressure cylinder had to remain open for the whole of the stroke to clear the high-pressure

Galloway's erecting shop at Knott Mill, Manchester, in the 1890s with a couple of side-by-side engines being completed.

cylinder of steam. Therefore there could be no early cut-off in the low-pressure cylinder to give the advantage of expansive working in that cylinder. Through this, there was an overlap of pressures in the two cylinders which was wrong thermodynamically.

Galloways improved the Woolf engine in 1873 when they patented a side-by-side horizontal compound rotative engine which became quite popular.[45] A form of straight link gear, with the position of the valve rod in the expansion link controlled by the governor, operated the inlet valves on one side of the high-pressure cylinder so that variable cut-off could be obtained. An eccentric worked the high-pressure cylinder exhaust valves, which were also the low-pressure inlet valves. The cylinders were placed close together with very short passages between them. The low-pressure piston moved in the opposite direction to the high-pressure but, to give a little cut-off in the low-pressure cylinder, the cranks were set so that the low-pressure piston had a slight lead. More slide valves let the steam out of the low-pressure cylinder on the further side, which must have given quite a good flow of steam through the engine from the thermodynamic angle. These engines were very compact and were often fitted with a horizontal condenser driven by an extension of the low-pressure piston rod. Many were supplied to cotton and paper mills for almost thirty years, by which time the design was outmoded.

The McNaught Compound Beam Engine

The compound engine patented by William McNaught of Glasgow in 1845 solved the problem of providing an adequate receiver between the high- and low-pressure cylinders.[46] On a beam engine of the ordinary Boulton and Watt design, he placed a high-pressure cylinder between the main column supporting the beam and the crank, where the cold water pump was normally fixed. He retained the original steam cylinder. This was a simple addition which could be easily added to existing beam engines and became exceedingly popular to increase their power and efficiency. In his patent, McNaught stated that there would be:

> … the effect of increasing the power of the engine, of lessening the consumption of fuel in proportion to the power produced, and by working the steam expansively in the low-pressure cylinder a further saving of steam may be effected, and consequently a proportional saving of fuel.[47]

The situation of this extra cylinder, well away from the original one, meant that there had to be a long steam pipe connecting the two which could act as a receiver. Also there had to be two sets of valve gear so that the low-pressure cylinder could have its inlet valves set to give an appropriate cut-off. The advantages of this were recognised by McNaught stating that the steam would be worked expansively in that cylinder and savings of fuel of up to 40 per cent were being claimed by 1854.

There remained a disadvantage because, with both pistons still acting in unison, there were periods when the engine developed no power at the top and bottom of the stroke. Yet, in terms of smoothness, these engines gave a much more even power output than their single-cylinder predecessors. This was one reason for the popularity of this conversion among textile mill owners. McNaught claimed that one of his objects was to equalise the stress on the main working beam and all the parts connecting it with the framing and the engine house. To give an example of one engine:

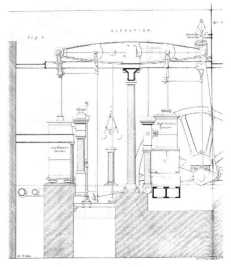

The McNaught compound beam engine with high-pressure cylinder between the connecting rod and the beam pivot and the low-pressure cylinder at the further end of the beam.

Before Compounding,	The pressure on the beam was 85,408 lbs.
	The pressure on the crank pin was 42,704 lbs.
After Compounding,	Pressure on the beam's centre reached only 656 lbs.
	Pressure on the crank pin was reduced to 40,893 lbs.[48]

Thus, although the engine was actually doing more work, the pressures in both cases were reduced. In a compound engine, the differences between the initial and final stresses in each cylinder were much reduced, especially when compared with a single cylinder. Therefore the turning moment of the crankshaft was more nearly uniform so that, in the case of the compound, the parts could be designed lighter. This applied also to the horizontal tandem compound where the high- and low-pressure cylinders were set one behind the other. Therefore mill owners had good practical, mechanical and theoretical reasons for introducing compound engines.

Examples of Compound Beam Engines

A rare survival of a McNaught single beam engine was seen at Eastburn Worsted Mill of E. & A. Matthews at Crosshill. It was installed by Bracewell in 1861. The Corliss valve high-pressure cylinder, 17in diameter, 2ft stroke, was added around 1900 to the original slide-valve cylinder, 26in diameter by 4ft stroke. A fire in 1926 caused the original wooden casing over the flywheel to be replaced with sheet metal. Otherwise the engine drove the mill until around 1956, when it was replaced by electric motors. It remained in situ until around 1970 when it was taken to the Bradford Industrial Museum. Single-cylinder beam engines might also be compounded with the addition of a horizontal high-pressure horizontal 'pusher' engine which exhausted into the original beam-engine cylinder.

The view from the crank end of the McNaughted beam engine at E.A. Matthews. The Whitehead governor and casing for the flywheel are to the right with the McNaught cylinder behind the connecting rod to the left.

Coupled beam engines could have two McNaught cylinders added, one for each side but, as boiler pressures rose, such engines might have one McNaught cylinder added as the high-pressure on one side exhausting into another larger McNaught cylinder as an intermediate cylinder on the other side. This exhausted into both original cylinders as low-pressure cylinders. This form of four-cylinder, triple-expansion beam engine evolved at Victoria Mill, Earby. The engine was installed originally in 1856 by W.J. Yates as a pair of beam engines, cylinders 40in diameter by 7ft stroke, driving a common central heavy flywheel. The gear teeth were cast in separate segments which were bolted onto the rim of the 22ft 6in diameter flywheel, enabling quick replacement should any teeth become worn or break. The engine was extensively modified by Petries of Rochdale in 1896 when increased power was required to drive a new mill erected a little distance away. A line-shaft an eighth of a mile long passed over a road and a river to the new mill. It is probable that the original cylinders were modernised with piston valves at this time and the original cast iron beams replaced with wrought iron or steel ones.

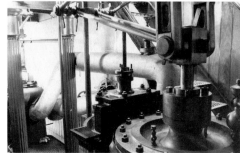

Top of the low-pressure cylinder on the E.A. Matthews engine looking across to the high-pressure cylinder behind the pillars supporting the entablature. The steam transfer pipe can be seen linking the cylinders.

To meet the extra demand, the engine was converted into a four-cylinder, triple-expansion type. The high-pressure cylinder, 29in diameter by 3ft 6in stroke, stood on a plinth in the usual McNaught position on one side. Its Corliss valves were driven from a rotating shaft which also drove the governor. The exhaust from this cylinder passed round the flywheel across to the intermediate cylinder, 46in diameter by 3ft 6in stroke, located similarly on the other side. This had piston valves and in turn exhausted into both original cylinders. The two condensers and air pumps were retained below these cylinders. Boiler pressure was 140 p.s.i. and 1,200 h.p. was indicated at 34½ r.p.m. The line shaft to the new mill had its own additional pinion below the flywheel. One day the engine seemed to be making a peculiar noise and, on investigation, the crankshaft was discovered

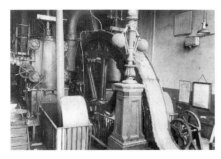

Above: Governor and flywheel of the engine at Victoria Mill with the high-pressure Corliss valve cylinder behind its connecting rod on the left.

Left: Looking along the thin section iron beam plates down to the high-pressure cylinder at Victoria Mill.

Above: The massive flywheel with bolted-on sections of rim and gearing looking across to the high-pressure cylinder at Victoria Mill.

Left: The intermediate pressure cylinder behind its connecting rod at Victoria Mill.

to have cracked. Because there were two pinions under the flywheel, the weight was taken by them and the engine appeared to be working normally. The shaft was renewed in October 1954 and in April 1958 the high-pressure cylinder was rebored and a new piston fitted. Then in 1962 the load had dropped to a quarter and, after the installation of new boilers in a nearby mill made those at the Victoria Mill redundant, the engine was stopped, having had a working life of over 100 years. It remained in situ for many years afterwards because, with a multi-storey mill on one side and a weaving shed on the other, it could not be removed until the entire mill was demolished in the early 1970s.

The last known instance of the starting of a new beam engine in Yorkshire dates from 1889 when a coupled beam engine was installed at Waterside Mill, Longfield. This was not the case in the cotton industry because the climax in the design of the beam engine must be those installed by the Preston consulting engineer, J.H. Tattersall. Soon after the India Mill beam engine was scrapped, he began advocating triple-expansion gear-drive beam engines incorporating both Woolf's and McNaught's principles. This led to something of a revival of the beam engine. Perhaps the first was a single beam engine of 230 i.h.p. built shortly before 1892 by Joseph Foster for Kent Street Cotton Mills, Preston. The high-pressure cylinder had piston valves and was placed between the centre of the beam and the connecting rod in the McNaught position. The steam was exhausted

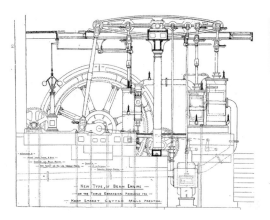

The triple-expansion beam engine designed by J.H. Tattersall for Kent Street Mills, Preston, in 1891.

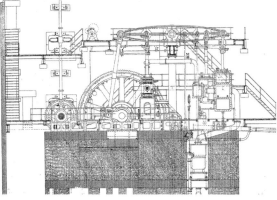

The pair of coupled triple-expansion beam engines designed by J.H. Tattersall for the Nile Mill that developed 2,500 i.h.p.

into the intermediate cylinder and from this into the low-pressure cylinder, both side by side in the Woolf position at the outer end of the beam. The heavy rim of the flywheel was plain. The power was taken off through a set of smaller geared segments bolted onto the spokes. Another was built by Buckley and Taylor at their Castleton Works, Greenacres, Oldham, for Chorley Mills.

The *Mechanical World* featured eleven of Tattersall's designs, the last in 1904. Three were built by J. Petrie and Co., Rochdale and six by Buckley and Taylor. Four were single McNaughted beam engines and three were pairs of coupled McNaught engines. Then there were three single triple-expansion engines and one pair. Earlier ones were gear drive and the last three rope. Power ranged from 230 to 2,500 i.h.p. But this does not cover all of Tattersall's engines because there were two triple-expansion engines built by Buckley and Taylor in 1898 and 1899 respectively for the Nile and Tay Mills, both in Oldham. Not only was the Nile Mill the largest mill in its day for ring spinning designed for 104,000 spindles but it was the most powerful coupled beam engine in any cotton mill at 2,500 i.h.p. The engine at Nile cost over £10,000. On each side, the high-pressure cylinder, 32in diameter by 3ft 6in stroke and Corliss valves, was placed in the McNaught position between the centre of the beam and the connecting rod. At the other end of the 30-ton beam were situated on the Woolf principle the intermediate-pressure cylinder, 38in diameter, 4ft 9in stroke, and the low-pressure cylinder, 52in diameter, 7ft stroke, both with slide valves. The speed was a stately 32 r.p.m. With steam at 160 p.s.i., coal consumption was 80 tons a week. The engine ran the mill until its closure for cotton spinning in 1960.[49]

Improved Valve Gears

Boiler pressures began to creep up after 1860. In 1850, pressures in ships' boilers of the Royal Navy rarely exceeded 10 p.s.i. and in 1860 the limit was 20 p.s.i. In 1865 it became 30 p.s.i. and in 1870 it was 60 p.s.i. But then came a sudden jump, for in 1885 triple-expansion engines were being fitted in ships with pressures of 160 p.s.i. Mill owners followed more slowly. On land, Fredrick Colyer, writing in 1886, talked about high-pressure engines with steam at 40 to 60 p.s.i. The records of J. and E. Wood show that between 1875 and 1890 boiler pressures for engines supplied by them were around an average of 70 p.s.i. to begin with, increasing towards the end up to 85 or 90 p.s.i. A pressure of 150 p.s.i. in 1876 was almost unknown while more brave souls ventured into the 100 p.s.i. range towards the end of this period.

The higher boiler pressures, the development of multiple expansion engines and the rising speed all meant that older forms of governing and valve gear became increasingly inadequate. Once it was seen that it was necessary to allow the steam to expand in the cylinder as much as possible and thereby utilise the maximum range of temperature and pressure, there was a gradual change from controlling the speed and power of the engine with the throttle valve to devising ways of allowing steam to enter the cylinder at the maximum pressure and then cutting off its entry at a suitable point to enable it to expand before the exhaust valve opened. When the flow of steam was controlled by a throttle valve, the steam passage became restricted, throttling the flow, causing a drop in pressure and hence wire-drawing.

The admission of steam should be controlled as close to the steam passages into the cylinder as possible. The ideal valve should open quickly to allow the maximum amount of steam to enter the cylinder at maximum pressure for the precise period of time necessary to generate sufficient power to drive the engine and then it should close quickly, leaving the steam to expand until towards the end of the stroke. The exhaust valve too had to open quickly to allow the steam the maximum amount of time to pass out as quickly as possible into the condenser, ideally at a pressure very little above that in the condenser. The exhaust valve should remain open for almost the duration of the exhaust stroke to keep any backpressure low until it closed just before the piston reached the end of the return stroke to create some compression to act as a cushion. When the load on the engine varied, the point of cut-off should be altered to vary the amount of steam passing through. Therefore at three points in the cycle, the timing of the valves should remain the same while the fourth (being the steam inlet) varied.

An early attempt to vary the point of cut-off was patented in 1842 by James Morris, using adjustable additional slide valves to alter the 'portion of the stroke during which the steam freely enters the cylinder by attaching the slide valves to a right and a left handed screw by which they may be placed nearer to each other, or further apart'.[50] This sounds remarkably similar to the better-known type patented in the same year by J.J. Meyer of Mulhouse. These additional valves were situated on the backs of ordinary slide valves so that, while the exhaust passed out in the usual way, these extra valves worked only on their respective inlet passages with the steam then passing through the main slide valve into the cylinder. Usually they were adjusted by hand through a wheel on the end of the screwed rod which passed through the opposite end of the valve chest to its own operating eccentric. The governor still operated the throttle valve for controlling minor speed fluctuations while the engine was running. Some form of this gear was fitted to the Gidlow Mill engines.

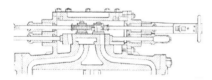

The Meyer expansion valve gear with adjustable inlet valves on the back of the main slide valve.

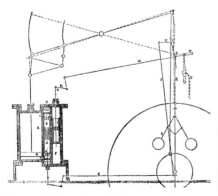

Richard Roberts's variable expansion gear worked by the governor patented in 1832.

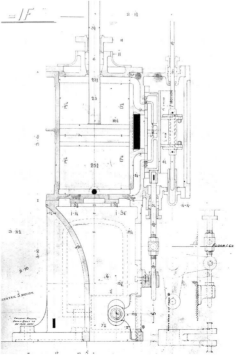

J. & W. McNaught's drawing of a McNaught cylinder with a twisting cut-off valve on the back of a slide valve.

Two pictures of the operating gear for the twist cut-off valve on the beam engine *Alexandria*. The twist motion is derived from the rod linked to the base of the gear-driven governor.

History does not tell us who in Britain first linked control of adjustable cut-off valves to the governor so that steam admission could be varied according to speed. It could have been Roberts, who in 1832 patented a variable expansion gear for a beam engine controlled by the governor, but there is doubt whether this was ever applied.[51] Another early form was that pioneered by Petrie and Co. In 1819, James Petrie had started to build mill engines in Rochdale and was joined in 1838 by William McNaught (not the McNaught of the compounding patent) who became his chief designer and superintendent for twenty years before starting his own works. It is claimed that McNaught was responsible for designing the cut-off gear patented by Petrie in 1844.[52] In this case, the cut-off valves were cylindrical and had ports with sloping faces on the admission side. As well as moving longitudinally, they could be twisted so that the sloping face gave a greater or lesser opening. This twisting motion could be connected quite easily to the governor which McNaught patented in 1850.[53] Both Petrie and then McNaught used this form of valve gear at their respective firms until well into the 1890s and other people developed variations of it. One beam engine so fitted was *Alexandria* at Buckley Mills, Rochdale, which developed 350 b.h.p.

Interest in cut-off slide valves was to continue for many years. To give but one example, the builders of the Durn Mill engine, E. Earnshaw and T. Holt, took out a patent in 1874 for 'A variable cut-off under the control of the governor . . . obtained by operating a cut-off valve on the back of the slide valve by a cam of peculiar form operated by screw gearing'.[54] Variations of this type of gear appeared subsequently but they suffered from the problems of all slide valves. Steam pressure forced them against the surface of the valve chest which caused greater friction as steam pressure increased. Another disadvantage was the comparative slowness in opening and shutting. R.S. Burn commented in 1854, 'To obtain the full efficiency of the expansive method of working, it is considered best to have the cut-off instantly effected – this the slide valve cannot do'.[55] Yet the slide valve would remain popular on low-pressure cylinders for many years where the pressure was less and a simple valve was considered to be adequate.

Corliss Valve Gear

We have seen that Fairbairn fitted four Cornish-type drop valves on his beam engines. Hick also fitted similar ones on a simple beam engine built for a cotton spinning mill in 1835. It rotated at 24 r.p.m. with a steam pressure of 30 p.s.i. He used them again in 1860 on a similar engine with the same boiler pressure but lower speed, 22½ r.p.m. The four separate valves introduced the possibility of timing each individually, especially the inlet to give variable cut-off. The type which proved to be the most popular for medium-speed engines in Britain was invented by the American George H. Corliss. Although he had started working out ideas for his engine in 1846 and had completed one for the Providence Dyeing, Bleaching and Calendering Co. in 1848, it was not until March 1849 that he obtained an American patent for 'certain new and useful improvements in Steam Engines'.[56]

The first part contained ideas for strengthening the beam of an engine with tie-rods. For his valve gear on a beam engine, he used paired slide valves which he positioned together as close as possible to the ends of the cylinder. The eccentric on the crankshaft operated a long rod to a 'wrist' plate. The movement given by an eccentric will be slowest at either end of the stroke and quickest in the middle but a steam valve should be opened quickly, i.e. the opposite to the motion actually given. Corliss made the eccentric rod oscillate the wrist plate. Four rods were attached to the circumference of the wrist plate, two operating the inlet valves and two the exhaust. The ends of the rods on the wrist plate will travel through an arc and it is possible to arrange the take-off point with such an angle that the rod moves quickly at first and then more slowly the further it leaves the tangent. The rod to the equivalent

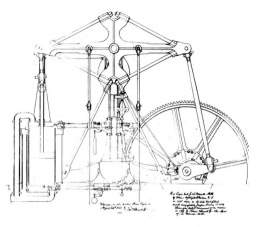

The first patent drawing by G.H. Corliss for his governor-controlled trip gear mechanism. His 1849 patent also covered tie rods to strengthen the beam.

valve at the other end of the cylinder is arranged to have the opposite movement so that one is virtually stationary, or closed, while the other is opening rapidly. It was the next part of his patent that was crucial and related

> … to the method of regulating the cut off of the steam in the main slide valves, and consists in effecting this by means of the governor, so that when the velocity of the engine is too great these cams shall be moved by the centrifugal action of the regulator that a catch on the valve rods may the sooner come in contact with them to liberate the valves and admit of their being closed by the force of weights or springs, and thus cut off the steam in proportion to the velocity of the engine this being done sooner when the velocity of the engine is to be reduced and later when it is to be increased.[57]

His mechanism acted only on the inlet valves to give them variable cut-off.

Corliss arranged for the rod operating each inlet valve to be in two parts. One part remained attached to the wrist plate and the other to the valve. To open the valve, the two parts were linked together by a catch and moved by the wrist plate. The governor set the position of cams or some other mechanism to release the catch at the appropriate point of cut-off when the valve would be shut by some form of weight or spring. More or less steam could be admitted to the cylinder by altering the point of cut-off with the governor and making the inlet valves shut sooner or later. Steam was admitted at full boiler pressure and then expanded. Very little power was needed to operate the release catches so that the governor worked more sensitively than in the older method of turning a throttle valve or some form of cut-off valves such as those by Petrie and McNaught.

The drawing in Corliss's first patent of 1849 shows that he placed his inlet and exhaust slide valves side by side at the top and bottom of the vertical cylinder. In a drawing of a cylinder for a horizontal engine supplied in 1849 to Phillip Allen & Sons, print works at Providence, Rhode Island, Corliss had placed the valves at the top and bottom ends of the cylinder. The inlet valves were at the top and the exhaust valves at the bottom. Not only would this have given much better drainage of any condensate, but, by separating the inlet and exhaust passages, the thermodynamic layout was improved. This would become the most common position of valves on Corliss engines. Equally important was the possibility of increasing the size of the ports which could lie across the cylinder and were soon enlarged to one-tenth of the area of the piston, allowing much freer movement of the steam. On this Phillip Allen engine, the wrist plate had been moved to a bracket on the middle of the cylinder, the usual place on later engines. This shortened the operating rods.

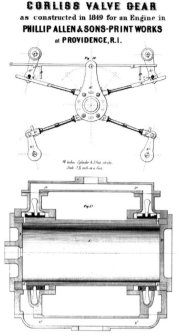

Corliss valve gear applied to a horizontal engine for Phillip Allen & Sons printworks.

In 1851, Corliss patented further improvements to the releasing mechanism and the method of closing the valves.[58] He used falling weights and in this case turned them into pistons inside cylinders or dashpots where, in their fall, they compressed the air, which acted as a cushion to prevent concussion. It would seem that these weights constituted one of the limitations to the development of the engine because, working by gravity, they did not close the valves quickly enough to allow the speed to rise above 40 r.p.m. He rectified this in a patent of 1859 by substituting springs.[59] Springs could be set with an initial compression or tension that would close the valves more quickly than gravity. The importance of this change was that closure of the inlet valves by springs enabled engine speeds to rise to 60 r.p.m. quite safely. Because Corliss valves did not close against a seat, the dashpot did not arrest the motion of the spring or weight until after the valve had closed, which could be at full speed, whereas on the drop valve the dashpot had to slow down the valve to prevent it hitting the seat, so introducing an element of wire-drawing. This patent of 1859 shows another important development which had appeared by 1850. This was the cylindrical oscillating or semi-rotary valve which is the type always associated with Corliss engines. As soon as these valves opened, the pressure differences on their surfaces were eliminated so they could be moved with very little power. At last the Corliss engine had developed far enough to start challenging other types.

The first one set to work in Britain was purchased from the Corliss Steam Engine Company in America by Alexander Pirie and erected at his Stoneywood Paper Mill near Aberdeen in 1861 or 1862. It was a horizontal type, 20in bore by 4ft stroke, and ran usually at 60 r.p.m. but sometimes at 68 r.p.m. Two continental manufacturers exhibited horizontal Corliss engines at the International Exhibition of 1862. Both engines had weight-operated valve gear and failed to impress. D.K. Clark commented:

> Another great objection is to be found in the irregularity of the cut-off, owing to want of precision of the valve gear, – varying occasionally from an admission of steam throughout the stroke, to an admission of nothing at all, – and involving a very heavy fly-wheel to neutralize those violent fluctuations of force.[60]

J.C. Bourne reflected the attitude of many others when he wrote in 1869:

> This form of engine . . . is of American design, and in some quarters its advantages have been loudly vaunted. But it is not pretended that it is able to work with greater economy than ordinary engines, while the complications of its valve gear are manifest and enormous. There are four separate valves or cocks for the admission and emission of the steam, and the gear is governed by the aid of air cushions, springs, and other rattle traps which by their complexity throw the old hand gear into the shade. Apart from these disfigurements, however, the general plan of the engine is not so good as that of some other engines now in common use. But with these additions the engine may be pronounced to be as bad a one as perverted ingenuity could easily have constructed. The American example of this engine shown at Paris in 1867 was of admirable workmanship, and was radiant with the silver in which the cylinder was enveloped. But these aids to acceptation were incapable of concealing from competent observers the inherent vices of the design, which appears to reckon complication as a merit, and which seeks to achieve no advantage in economy by a great multiplication of parts.[61]

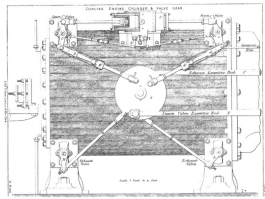

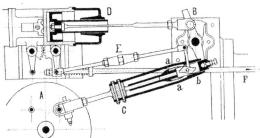

Corliss cylinder with Spencer Inglis trip gear on the inlet valves at the top.

Detail of the release mechanism of the Spencer Inglis Corliss valve gear.

Gradually prejudice was overcome, particularly through William Inglis, who had designed several Corliss marine engines for use in Canada. John Frederick Spencer persuaded Inglis to come to Britain, where he went to Edinburgh in 1863. Robert Douglas, one of the leading mill-engine builders in East Scotland, built an engine to Inglis's designs in 1863 for the papermill of David Chalmers near Edinburgh. Douglas had built or had in hand seventeen Corliss engines by 1867. Meanwhile, in 1865 Inglis moved to Manchester and linked up with Hick Hargreaves in Bolton, becoming their manager in 1868 where he promoted Corliss engines. Spencer, who came from Newcastle upon Tyne, received an order for a vertical single-cylinder engine in 1863 followed by several more.

Both he and Inglis patented improvements in the trip mechanism and springs in the dashpots. In 1865, Spencer patented additions to a release mechanism designed by Inglis in which a lever with a double foot opened a pair of flat spring catches, one on either side of the rod from the wrist plate.[62] This was both better balanced than the single spring catch of Inglis and, should one spring break, the engine could carry on with the other. It was an elegant gear to watch at work because the catches on their long flat springs looked rather like fingers. After being forced apart by the double-footed cam to release the valve, they snapped shut again as they grabbed the rod to pull the valve open once more. It was adopted by Hick Hargreaves and could still be seen on some engines a hundred years later. At the same time, Spencer patented the double-ported Corliss valve to allow more steam into or out of the cylinder without excessive movement of the valve itself. There were also improvements to the springs and the dashpots. The Spencer–Corliss valve gear was neatly laid out with a minimum of parts. It was certainly simpler than the type patented by Corliss in 1859 and was probably a great improvement which may have helped the introduction of the Corliss engine to Britain. In 1868, Inglis stated that more than sixty Corliss land engines were at work and in 1870, Spencer claimed that several hundred engines had been made in Britain.

By this time, mill-engine builders in Lancashire had started to fit Corliss or similar types of valves. J. & E. Wood had patented double-ported Corliss valves in 1867 and their archives show that they fitted Corliss valves on all their engines from 1875. Adamson patented oscillating cut-off valves within Corliss valves in 1869.[63] These valve gears worked without the wrist plate which necessitated two eccentrics, one for the inlet valves and one for the exhaust which could be timed separately. John Musgrave took out two patents in 1876 for actuating cut-off valves but it is not until 1883 that the Corliss valve is actually mentioned in one of their patents. Benjamin Goodfellow, Hyde, built their first Corliss valve engine in 1877 but it was not until after 1881 that Corliss valves became more popular than slide in their designs. Some manufacturers fitted both inlet and exhaust valves underneath the cylinder, perhaps using the American Jerome Wheelock's patents. His first British patent was taken out in 1878 when he also exhibited an engine at the Paris Exhibition. This was

When Spring Mill, Earby, needed more power for their weaving shed in 1923, they purchased a Hick Hargreaves cross compound engine built in 1899 for a mill in Levenshulme. The high-pressure cylinder, 16¾in diameter by 4ft stroke, was steam jacketed. The low-pressure cylinder was 29in diameter and at 59 r.p.m. with 160 p.s.i., 450 h.p. was developed.

The 16ft diameter flywheel at Spring Mill was grooved for ten ropes. It was fitted with a steam barring engine. When seen in November 1967, the engine was still running very quietly and smoothly with no visible play in any parts.

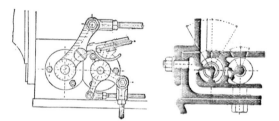

A form of Wheelock Corliss valve gear where both inlet and exhaust valves were placed together at the end of the cylinder. The steam from the inlet passed over the exhaust.

A Spencer Inglis release mechanism was fitted on the inlet Corliss valves on the high-pressure cylinder at Spring Mill. It was fascinating to watch the long finger springs releasing the catches and then snapping shut to pull the valves open again.

followed by further patents in 1885 and 1889. A steam pipe came up underneath the cylinder and divided to the inlet valves at each end. The steam was admitted by the inlet valves past the exhaust valves and into the cylinder. The incoming steam must have lost heat as it passed over the exhaust valve but this type of layout was used by Adamson, Goodfellow, Musgrave and Wood and gave a neat appearance to their engines.

Governors

With increasing speed and power, the Watt governor became more and more inadequate to control mill engines effectively where regularity of speed was so essential. It had two inherent defects. One was that, as the balls on the ends of their arms swung out and up through centrifugal force, the governing sensitivity decreased as they moved higher. Another was that the engine would settle down to a different speed when the load changed. Also such governors usually rotated at the same speed as their engines, e.g. 30 to 50 r.p.m., and the optimum range lay well below 100 r.p.m. In order to overcome friction in the joints of the rods linking the governor to the throttle valve and the friction in that valve, the balls on the governor had to be very heavy. The speed of the Watt governor could not be increased and, if the weight of the balls were increased to increase the force exerted, the inertia was increased, which slowed down the rate of response. This form of governor could require variations in speed of 15 to 40 per cent to make it work.

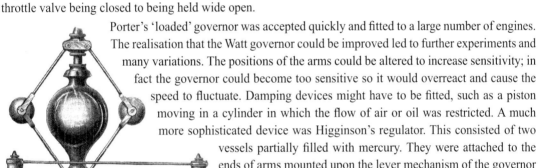

Charles T. Porter had been assisting John F. Allen of New York to produce a high-speed engine and, while trying to get the steam engine that drove a stone-dressing machine to run smoothly, he looked at its governor and patented improvements in 1858.[64] He reduced the size of the balls and increased the speed by a factor of about ten. In this way he gained a motion that was powerful. To make the device sufficiently responsive at the right speed, he balanced the centrifugal forces by a counterweight. In his patent model this counterweight was placed on a lever, but it was soon moved to the central shaft of the governor itself. He made this weight hollow so it could be filled with lead until it weighed from 60 to 175lb. The balls were only about 2½in diameter and lifted the weight at about 300 r.p.m. Balls weighing 1lb rotating at 300 r.p.m. exerted the same centrifugal force as balls of 36lb at 50 r.p.m. The counterpoise weight prevented the balls flying out until the optimum speed was reached, so the steam valves remained fully open until that point. Then the balls would react more quickly to slight variations in speed. Porter claimed that a speed variation of between three and five per cent could be achieved from the throttle valve being closed to being held wide open.

A 'loaded' governor with central weight.

Porter's 'loaded' governor was accepted quickly and fitted to a large number of engines. The realisation that the Watt governor could be improved led to further experiments and many variations. The positions of the arms could be altered to increase sensitivity; in fact the governor could become too sensitive so it would overreact and cause the speed to fluctuate. Damping devices might have to be fitted, such as a piston moving in a cylinder in which the flow of air or oil was restricted. A much more sophisticated device was Higginson's regulator. This consisted of two vessels partially filled with mercury. They were attached to the ends of arms mounted upon the lever mechanism of the governor and connected by tubes. At the correct speed, both vessels would be level, but when the speed, and therefore the position of the lever operating the control rods, altered, the levels of the vessels would change. Mercury would flow along one pipe to the lower vessel (the upper pipe allowed air to pass in the opposite direction) and its weight exercised a considerable steadying action upon the governor, preventing oscillations of a very short period.

The Higginson governor with the vessels containing the mercury at either end of the arms.

As long as the angle of the arms of the governor remained linked directly to the angle of the butterfly plate in the throttle valve, the engine would not return to the same speed as the load changed. The arms of the governor had to be at the same angle for the correct speed but, if the load dropped, less steam was needed so the butterfly plate angle had to alter to reduce the steam passage. On the Bateman and Sherratt beam engine driving Etruria Bone Mill, the solution was for the engineman to turn a knuckle with a right- and left-hand thread on the link between governor and valve so the length of the rodding was changed, thus altering the relationship between the angles of the governor arms and the butterfly plate. At first, Porter had placed his load weight on an arm which projected to one side of the governor. By sliding this weight along the arm, the effective mass could be varied. Sometimes such an auxiliary weight was fitted in addition to the central one to act similarly.

A more sophisticated version was fitted to a McNaughted beam engine built in Belfast in 1880 by Turnbull, Grant and Jack for Power's Distillery in Dublin. In this case, the weight was moved along the arm by a screw so it could be easily adjusted by the engineman while the engine was running. One of the earliest mechanisms to give an automatic variable adjusting motion was developed by W.J. Yates. They supplied an engine to Russia before 1878 on which the governor shaft was fitted with a pair of friction cones. These could drive a third cone faced with leather which remained stationary when the engine was running at its proper speed with the ordinary load. When the speed varied through a change in load, the cones on the governor shaft moved up or down into engagement with the third cone and turned it. This cone rotated the knuckle on the governor rodding and altered the length to vary the steam inlet according to the new load. When the speed had returned to its proper setting, whichever cone on the governor shaft had been in contact with the third cone disengaged and the adjustments ceased.

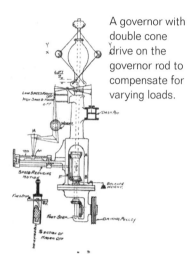

A governor with double cone drive on the governor rod to compensate for varying loads.

The Horizontal Tandem Compound Engine

The increase in boiler pressures made possible through the introduction of steel boilers encouraged the adoption of compound engines. As well as the Woolf and McNaught systems for beam engines, another layout was the horizontal tandem compound with the high- and low-pressure cylinders in line, connected to a single crank. Just as a McNaught cylinder could be inserted to improve the performance and power of an existing beam engine, so it was possible to mount an additional smaller high-pressure cylinder onto a single-cylinder horizontal engine. An example was seen at the silk mill of T. Whittles Ltd at Leek where a 7½in diameter high-pressure cylinder was bolted onto the rear cover of the 12in diameter low-pressure cylinder. This high-pressure cylinder overhung the engine bed and had no further support than the low-pressure cover. Both cylinders had slide valves. The 7ft 6in diameter flywheel had a flat belt drive. The engine at Millstead Mill, Todmorden, by Wood Bros, Sowerby Bridge, was similarly adapted. The engine may have dated from about 1870. When the high-pressure cylinder was added, possibly in 1898 by the Ebor Engineering Co., the engine house had to be extended as well. Cylinder dimensions were 14in and 28in by 3ft 6in stroke. It developed about 200 h.p. at 60 r.p.m. with 120 p.s.i. Among the fabrics made were butchers' aprons and pyjamas. The engine worked until 1972 when the mill was destroyed through an arson attack but the engine survived, only to be scrapped.

A 400 i.h.p tandem compound engine with low pressure cylinder at the rear built by Cole, Marchent and Morley in 1892.

Both cylinders on Whittles's engine had slide valves and 2ft stroke. A Pickering governor controlled the speed. The high-pressure cylinder was 7¹⁹/₃₂in and the low 12¹¹/₁₆in diameter. The steam transfer pipe can be seen above the cylinders. The engine was a neat example of the product of a local foundry.

Thomas Whittles, Wellington Mills, Leek, made embroidery silks. Their tandem compound engine was made by T. Shore & Sons in 1901 and drove the mill through a flat belt round the 7ft 6in diameter flywheel at 85 r.p.m. It indicated 32 h.p. at 80 p.s.i.

The steam transfer pipe between the cylinders can be seen at the far end of the Millstead Mill engine. The space around the additional high-pressure cylinder was too restricted to allow photography.

One advantage of the tandem layout was that the steam pipe connecting the two cylinders had to be quite long and so could act as a receiver. Each cylinder had to have its own set of valves. Very frequently those on the high-pressure cylinder were the Corliss type at each corner, which not only gave good control of the incoming steam but also any condensate could drain out easily through the horizontal position of the cylinder. It was not so critical to have variable cut off on the low-pressure cylinder so the valves were often slide which were satisfactory with the pressure of around 30 p.s.i. There was a further advantage of the tandem compound similar to that of the McNaught system for the strain on the crank pin would be less. Nasmith took the example of two engines, each developing 1,250 h.p. One was a simple engine with a 42in cylinder and the other a tandem compound with high-pressure 30in and low-pressure 50in cylinders, both using steam at 80lb. 'The initial stress on the crankpin in the simple engine is 110,836lbs and in the compound 62,248lbs.' He also pointed out that condensation in the compound would be less. If cut-off took place after 15 per cent of the stroke, the loss by condensation in a simple would be 32 and in a compound 26 per cent.[65]

The Firgrove Mill Engine

The horizontal tandem compound engine now preserved in the Museum of Science and Industry in Manchester is a classic example of the type, chosen to show a variety of technical features. It was supplied in 1907 by J. & W. McNaught, St George's Foundry, Rochdale, based on a well-tried design to replace a beam engine at the Firgrove Mill of Richard Barnes and Co. The engine was erected in a new building beside the old at the side of the Rochdale Canal and no doubt it was shipped on barges just the short distance from the foundry on the other side of the canal. This presented difficulties with its removal for preservation because there was no road access. Luckily the local Council rebuilt the original narrow road bridge over the canal just before we were due to take out the engine so that we could position a crane on the new wider bridge without blocking traffic too much. The jib of the crane was able to reach to the coal wharf where engine parts had to be assembled

Looking along the Barnes engine from the flywheel showing the narrowness of the engine house. This photo was taken while Courtaulds were filming.

The high-pressure cylinder with Corliss valve gear photographed when the cylinder end cover had been removed during the Barnes engine annual maintenance.

Front cover of the low-pressure cylinder of the Barnes engine with the Lumb compensator mechanism top right.

ready for lifting. All parts had to be dismantled, jacked up and slid out onto temporary staging on the wharf since the overhead crane in the engine room was too light to be able to lift them. The flywheel was cast in halves and one half had to be turned 180° to lift it out of the pit before sliding it outside.

The high-pressure cylinder, 15in diameter by 4ft stroke, was furthest from the crankshaft. The main steam pipe and admission valve were above the cylinder, the valve being fitted with Tate's stop motion. Should there be an emergency in the mill, a small glass panel could be broken which released a button switch, activating an electric current to close the valve. The steam pipe branched to the Corliss inlet valves at the top of either end of the cylinder. The trip gear was McNaught's own pattern, actuated by a rod from the governor and Lumb regulator. The dashpots were mounted in a plate at the bottom of the cylinder. While this allowed longer springs to be fitted, they were in a position to accumulate oil and water dripping out of the valve bonnets, which happened when the engine was not maintained so well in the Museum. A pair of eccentrics, placed near the high-pressure cylinder and driven by the same shaft as the governor, operated both inlet and exhaust Corliss valves. The exhaust valves had no trip mechanism. They exhausted into a common pipe below the cylinder which passed under the floor to the low-pressure cylinder. Some steam might be taken out at this lower pressure to heat the drying cylinders of the sizing or slashing machines preparing warps for the looms so this engine could be used as a 'pass out' engine. This was an economical way of supplying process steam. The high-pressure cylinder sat on its own feet through which long bolts passed to secure it to the foundations and was additionally bolted to the rear of the main cast iron engine bed.

Moving half the Barnes engine flywheel into position at Liverpool Road Station. There was little space to turn it the other way up to become the lower half.

The crank of the Barnes engine being lifted into position at Liverpool Road Station. Half the flywheel is already in its pit.

Twin-cylinder barring engine at Magnet Mill.

The low-pressure cylinder, 31in diameter, was bolted to the bed itself with a passage through it for the low-pressure exhaust. The securing bolts here underneath the cylinder were particularly inaccessible. The steam inlet entered the rear of the slide valve chest on the low-pressure cylinder. The two large slide valves were driven by their own eccentrics on the crankshaft. One valve gave some cut-off on the inlet and worked on the back of the main valve. In this way the exhaust could remain open much longer. The exhaust passed below floor level to the condenser situated in a pit between the low-pressure cylinder and the crank, bridged by the engine bed. The masonry foundations had to be divided to receive it. Water for the jet condenser was drawn from the canal, where excess was returned by the air pump situated alongside the condenser. The air pump bucket was driven by bell-crank levers off the crosshead. The crosshead slides were open with no upper bars. The big end on the connecting rod was fed with oil through a centrifugal drip-feed device and was surrounded with a planished steel guard to prevent oil splashing. The main bearings were lubricated from 'aquariums' by gravity with oil being returned by a small pump driven off the crankshaft. The flywheel was 15ft diameter, grooved to take ten 2in diameter ropes. It was lagged with mahogany boards to lessen the draught resulting from its rotation. This lagging gave a fine finish to many an engine. The flywheel was cast with an internal gear around the rim so it could be rotated by a small steam barring engine, a feature that became essential with increasing size of engines. With a boiler pressure of 180 p.s.i., superheated steam and a speed of 70, later 80 r.p.m., this engine gave 410, later 500 h.p. It worked in the mill for over sixty years and has continued to run for more than twenty years in the Museum, so it has reached its centenary.

Other Horizontal Tandem Compound Engines

On some other tandem compound engines, the low-pressure cylinder might be placed to the rear of the high-pressure one. This was a feature on many Musgrave engines and was the case at Eckersley's No. 1 Mill at Wigan. The tandem compound may have been chosen to reduce the width of the engine house, which was contained within the mill itself. Engine and mill were said to be contemporary with a date of 1884. The engine worked until 1967, although the 23in diameter high-pressure cylinder with Corliss valves was replaced in 1942. The low-pressure cylinder was 50¼in diameter, also with Corliss valves, and a common stroke of 6ft. The condensing apparatus was situated underneath the crosshead so that the exhaust steam passed underneath the high-pressure cylinder before being condensed. The flywheel was 26ft diameter with 26 ropes. At 52 r.p.m. and with the long stroke, the engine was impressive when running. This feeling was increased here because the engine was lit by a single large window behind the low-pressure cylinder so that the flywheel and connecting rods moved mysteriously in semi-darkness. The governor was fitted with a Higginson mercury balance regulator which maintained a steady speed. With a boiler pressure of 180 p.s.i., 1,250 h.p. was generated, high

Looking down from the rope race at the Eckersley Mill engine.

Oil pump and drive for the bearing on the line shafting at the Eckersley Mill.

Big end and crank of the Eckersley Mill engine.

Left: Low-pressure cylinder and bell crank drive off the tail rod to the air pump on the Darley Abbey engine.

Above: High-pressure cylinder and flywheel of the Musgrave engine at Darley Abbey Mill.

Left: Governor and Higginson regulator on the Darley Abbey engine.

for an engine of this configuration. The same layout of cylinders could be seen at another Musgrave engine of 1897 at Darley Abbey Mills. Here the condensing apparatus was placed at the further end of the engine beneath the rear of the low-pressure cylinder, driven by the tail rod of that cylinder. While this did not divide the foundations and was conveniently situated, it did add to the length of the engine. This was a much smaller engine, cylinders 14in and 28in by 3ft stroke, which, at 80 r.p.m., gave 250 h.p. to supplement the power from water turbines.

Pollit and Wigzell of Bank Foundry, Sowerby Bridge, had an ingenious solution for shortening the length of the engine. The firm had been founded by Timothy Bates in 1786 and were largely millwrights until 1834 when John Pollit began building mill engines. He was joined in 1865 by E. Wigzell. The idea of attaching the low-pressure cylinder to the rear of the high-pressure one was patented in 1870.[66] There was no direct connection between the two and, in order to avoid an inaccessible packing gland for a common piston rod, the high-pressure rod passed out in front to the crosshead in the usual way. Because the low-pressure piston was larger in diameter, two piston rods could be fitted near its circumference which passed either side of the high-pressure cylinder and were attached

The maze of rods on the high pressure cylinder of *Susannah Keighley* for the Corliss gear as well as the low-pressure cylinder slide valve rod and one piston rod to the low-pressure cylinder.

The metallic packing for one of the piston rods of the low-pressure cylinder of *Susannah Keighley*.

The horizontal air pump behind the low-pressure cylinder of *Susannah Keighley*.

to the crosshead. Some of Pollit and Wigzell's engines had horizontal condensers and air pumps driven off the tail rod of the low-pressure cylinder. The firm patented their own design in 1877.[67] A little engine called *Susannah Keighley* with both these features was supplied to the Habergham Room and Power Co., Burnley, in 1912. Cylinders were 16in and 30in by 3ft 6in stroke, having Corliss and slide valves respectively. The 14ft diameter flywheel with twelve ropes was driven at 71 r.p.m. The 450 h.p. provided power to a variety of small independent manufacturers who rented both space and power in the mill.

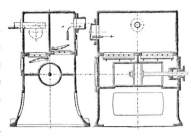

A horizontal air pump with rectangular valves.

Another Pollit and Wigzell tandem compound engine was installed at Walshaw Mill, Burnley, in 1905. It had a conventional layout with the high-pressure cylinder at the back of the low-pressure and the condensing apparatus beneath the crosshead. It remained like this until it stopped in 1975. The engine house, flywheel and crankshaft had been made large enough to take another pair of cylinders but the anticipated expansion never took place. Towards the end of its life, due to a dispute with the Electricity Board, an alternator was brought in from Elm Street Mill, Burnley, which had just closed. A pulley was fixed on the end of the crankshaft to drive the alternator. We have seen that the cycle of a power loom demanded varying power inputs, with a maximum when sending the shuttle across. Walshaw Mill sought to avoid punitive charges when the electricity maximum demand meter was tripped should too many looms pick at the same time. A steam engine would absorb this extra load through the inertia of shafting and flywheel and merely slow slightly. This was one reason for the longevity of steam power in many weaving sheds.

Had this engine been completed in the way expected, it would have become a pair of horizontal tandem compound engines. This type became very popular for mills requiring considerable power. With cranks set at 90°, the power output was smoother than that from a single tandem. Also the cylinders did not need to be excessively large. While various layouts might follow those for single tandems, most had high-pressure cylinders to the rear and condensing apparatus beneath the crossheads. These engines will be covered in more detail

The high-pressure cylinder of the Walshaw Mill engine. The bonnets of the Corliss valves give extra support to the valve rods at their outer ends.

The engine at Walshaw Mill with the high-pressure cylinder to the right.

The electric switchboard and generator from Elm Street Mill fitted to the Walshaw Mill engine.

A double horizontal tandem compound engine with rope drive by Buckley and Taylor. The slide valves on the high-pressure cylinder may have been similar to those originally fitted to the Fern Mill engine.

The narrowness of the Fern Mill engine is shown by this view overlooking the pairs of cylinders with the flywheel at the back.

The trip gear of the Corliss inlet valve release mechanism on a high-pressure cylinder at Fern Mill.

A low-pressure cylinder with its massive casing for the slide valve on the Fern Mill engine.

Gearing round the rim of the flywheel on the Fern Mill engine.

Above: A 900 h.p. cross compound engine by Musgrave in 1891 for Prospect No. 2 Mills, Bolton. Both cylinders have Corliss valves, with the high-pressure cylinder being the nearer. A feature of Musgrave's designs was the panelling on the flywheel fitted between the spokes.

in Chapter 5. While both sides were identical, except of course left-or right-handed regarding the position of the valve gear, virtually all had only one governor. This meant that when mills were gradually electrified and reduced power was required from the engine, it was possible to blank off the steam to the side without the governor, remove that connecting rod and run the engine as a single tandem. This happened to engines at Phillipshaugh Mill, Selkirk and at Ellen Road Ring Mill, New Hey, Lancashire.

An early example of a double horizontal tandem compound was the one at Fern Mill, Shaw, built in 1884. The mill was extended in 1904 with a four-storey addition which increased the spindleage to 117,292 in 1915. The engine nestled within one corner of the mill building itself and was one of Buckley and Taylor's standard gear-drive type of the 1880s. It was a surprise to find this engine still at work in 1966 since cotton spinning had ceased in 1939 under one of the Government concentration schemes and the mill had been taken over by the Ministry of Defence. The mill was purchased in 1951 by Sutcliffe, Speakman and Co. who used the engine to drive ball mills for grinding carbon black. The crankshaft broke, probably in 1969, and the engine was removed in 1981 for possible preservation. The flywheel was 21ft diameter with gearing round the rim with teeth 17½in wide. It was this narrow width that enabled the engine to be fitted inside the mill and the roof beams were short enough to carry a full load of machinery. The long connecting rods accentuated the narrowness. The crossheads carried links to operate the air pumps for the condensers underneath. It is probable that all the cylinders originally had slide valves which would have been typical of this maker's practice in the 1880s. These survived on the 48in diameter low-pressure cylinders but those on the high-pressure were Corliss. New 22in diameter high-pressure cylinders were probably installed when the mill was enlarged in 1904. Boiler pressure was increased to 160 p.s.i. to give 1,200 h.p. at a speed of either 42½ or 54 r.p.m. In its last working days, the low-pressure cylinders were blanked off and the engine exhausted to the atmosphere up a pipe beside the mill. At this slow speed with a 6ft stroke, the engine was an impressive sight when running.

Horizontal Cross Compound Engines

Another layout of the horizontal engine was the cross compound with a high-pressure cylinder driving a crank on one side of the engine and the low-pressure on the other. With cranks set at right angles, such engines were better balanced than either single-cylinder or single tandem compound engines. The horizontal cross compound was regarded by many people as one of the most reliable and versatile types that ever graced textile mills. Although most popular in medium-size mills, it was quickly adapted for larger powers. A gear-drive one of 160 h.p. by W.J. Yates was shipped in 1865 to a mill in Bombay with cylinders 37in and 56in, stroke 6ft, flywheel 23ft 8¾in diameter and speed 30 r.p.m. It was a large engine for its day but an engine of similar size with Corliss valves and rope drive built fifty years later would have been capable of at least ten times the power, running at twice the speed and using higher boiler pressure. The first horizontal engine in Preston was most likely a horizontal cross compound supplied as late as 1872 by J. & E. Wood for the Alliance Works with cylinders 22in and 34in and 4ft 6in stroke. In 1883, Astley Mill, Dukinfield, had a 1,300 h.p. horizontal cross compound built by Goodfellow.

An early horizontal cross compound by W.J. Yates was seen just before it ceased running in March 1979 at Abbey Mill, Billington, dating from around 1875 in probably original condition. It was housed within the main building and the darkness was made worse by the clouds of steam issuing from worn slide valve rods on the 16in high-pressure cylinder. This engine had retained its slide valves on both cylinders, the high-pressure on the right having cut-off slide valves set by the governor for speed control. The low-pressure cylinder was 30in diameter, both having 4ft stroke. With boiler pressure at 100 p.s.i., and at 56 r.p.m., the power was 300 h.p. The flywheel was 14ft diameter with 8ft diameter gearing bolted to it. All steam piping was below floor level with the condensing apparatus beneath the low-pressure crosshead slides. Wiseman Street Mill in the Weavers' Triangle of Burnley had another Yates engine of perhaps 1880 vintage. Here the large windows of

Looking over the low-pressure crosshead at the high-pressure slide valves. The governor mechanism at Abbey Mill was very complex with two flyball governors.

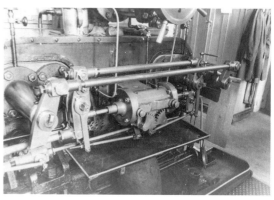

The inlet and exhaust Corliss valves placed unusually at the top of the replacement high-pressure cylinder at Wiseman Street Mill.

The wooden lagged slide valve on the low-pressure cylinder at Wiseman Street Mill.

Left high-pressure side of Brooklands Mill engine.

possibly an earlier beam engine house let the light in splendidly. The low-pressure cylinder, 30in diameter, retained its wooden lagging and its tail rod drove the horizontal condenser. The $17^5/_8$in diameter high-pressure cylinder was replaced around 1908 by Burnley Iron Works and was unusual because its Corliss valves, inlet and exhaust, were both placed at the top of the cylinder in a bad position for draining condensation. A much smaller gearwheel was bolted to the side of the 14ft diameter flywheel and engaged with a slightly larger one on the line shafting so that the engine was unusual in that, with 3ft 6in stroke at 63 r.p.m., it ran faster than the shafting.

In 1893 J. & E. Wood equipped Brooklands Mill, Leigh, with a fine horizontal cross compound engine in a spacious, tall house with marble floors. Having spent most of the day looking round the various machines in the spinning mill, at about five to five, my guide mentioned that the mill was still driven by its original steam engine. We rushed round to see it before it should stop for the day. It was most impressive with its 30ft diameter flywheel revolving at 52 r.p.m., dimly lit that winter evening by the few electric lights around the engine. The engine was still producing almost full power of 1,200 h.p. from its cylinders, 30in and 50in diameter and 6ft stroke because, while the carding room was still driven by ropes, the remainder of the 27 ropes were connected to an alternator which powered the rest of the mill. Coal was still delivered from the canal alongside which also provided the water for the condenser. The engine had many typical Wood features, such as the position of the Corliss valves together at the bottom of the cylinders. The high-pressure cylinder, *Eudora*, had

The (left) exhaust and (right) inlet Corliss valve operating rods on the high-pressure cylinder at Brooklands Mill. The release mechanism is contained in the box on the right.

The crosshead and front of the high-pressure cylinder of the Brooklands Mill engine with the low-pressure cylinder in the background.

The low-pressure side of the Brooklands Mill engine with tail rod operating the air pump bell crank.

Should a rope start to fray on the Brooklands Mill engine, the bells would ring.

trip gear on the inlet to control the speed while the tail rod of *Cecil*, the low-pressure cylinder, drove the twin-bucket air pump. The position of the valves at the bottom of the cylinders gave an uncluttered appearance and a clean curve of steel lagging over the tops of the cylinders. The sweeping lines of the castings from the crosshead slides to the fronts of the cylinders and the way in which they curved to fit the fronts added to the neatness of the general appearance besides giving greater strength. The crosshead slides had fancy curved castings and the engine beds were painted black with gold and red lining. The long stroke and slow speed combined with the tall narrow flywheel gave an air of majesty when the engine was at work. It had proved to be very reliable for seventy-four years of almost continuous use which came to an end in 1967.

The Water Turbine

From the 1850s, water power had a revival through the adoption of the turbine which reflected a more scientific approach to power generation. Waterwheels were slow-moving, of massive construction, needed inefficient gearing to be coupled to the line shafting and there was a limit to the head or fall which could be used economically. The birthplace of the water turbine was France and its early development took place on the Continent and in America. The objective was to design a wheel which would overcome the limitations of a waterwheel by turning a great deal faster so it could be smaller, lighter and cost less. In France, the Société d'Encouragement pour l'Industrie Nationale offered a prize of 6,000 francs to the inventor of a suitable machine, which was

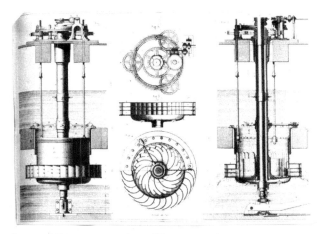

A typical Fourneyron turbine. Water was admitted to the wheel axially and directed against the moving outer ring of curved blades by a fixed inner ring of curved blades.

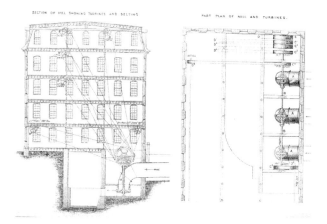

A set of three low head turbines driving Harmony No. 3 Mill, Cohoes, New York.

won by Benoit Fourneyron in 1827. On his turbine, a series of fixed curved blades in the centre guided the water onto the blades of the runner around the periphery. The volume of water passing through was controlled by raising or lowering a cylinder around the fixed blades in order to vary the size of the openings. One of 50 h.p. was installed at Catteshall Paper Mill, Godalming, in 1869. It has since been taken to the Ironbridge Gorge Museum for preservation.

Rival designs quickly appeared on the market. Perhaps the first turbines in textile mills in Britain were those based on designs by James Whitelaw, a Glasgow engineer. Details of his 'Scotch' turbine were first published in 1833 and patented in 1839. Early examples in Scotland included a cotton spinning mill near Paisley (c.1840), two woollen mills on the Shaws Water Aqueduct near Greenock (c.1840, 1841) and Culcreuch cotton mill, Stirlingshire.[68] Another type was the Thomson Vortex. James Thomson was born in Belfast and was granted a patent in 1850.[69] Thomson himself did not manufacture turbines but provided drawings and entered into licensing agreements. One important licensee was Messrs Williamson Brothers, of Kendal, who made their first turbine in 1856. They displayed one at the International Exhibition of 1862 and eventually made over 400 Vortex turbines. Their successors were Gilbert Gilkes and Gordon Ltd, a firm still making water turbines. Some thousands of Vortex turbines were built in the United Kingdom. Meanwhile, around 1850 in the United States, James B. Francis carried out careful tests on various turbines which led to his developing a well-designed inward flow turbine with a number of movable guide vanes in the surrounding casing which controlled the flow of water more efficiently. By the mid-1850s, his turbines had begun to replace the waterwheels in the textile mills at Lowell, Massachusetts. The Francis inward flow turbines soon became established as the best design for low to medium heads, say 3–160ft. They might have either vertical or horizontal shafts. Designs were improved and efficiency enhanced through James Emerson's setting up a pioneer testing station at Lowell in 1869. He published the results of all wheels tested at his flume, which were made available to anyone on request.

The amount of water power utilised in Yorkshire mills increased steadily because many waterwheels were replaced by more efficient turbines, but even so it declined in proportion to that generated by steam. Perhaps an exception was Black Rock Mill, Mossley, where a 30 h.p. steam engine was installed in 1864 for the first time but the River Tame continued to supply most of the motive power through a 40 h.p. water turbine to drive

20,000 mule spindles. The country mill particularly benefited from the more powerful turbine through reduction in costs of transporting coal. Both Glasshouses Mill at Bishopside in 1871 and Gayle Mill, Hawes, in 1879 installed new turbines which worked alongside existing waterwheels and steam engines. At Compstall in Cheshire, the spectacular 350 h.p. Fairbairn waterwheel measuring 45ft diameter and over 15ft wide was replaced by a water turbine in 1881. At New Lanark in 1852, there were nine waterwheels equal to about 400 h.p. From 1884, these were replaced gradually by turbines. There was a Jonval turbine in No. 2 mill in 1903, built by Messrs Gunter of Oldham, and at closure in 1970 there were three turbines in Nos 1 and 3 mills and in the dyehouse.

The Gilkes horizontal turbine at Quarry Bank Mill, Styal, in its original position.

Turbines brought an increase in power often at least double that of the earlier waterwheel. The seven waterwheels at Stanley Mill near Perth had already been replaced in 1878 by a 200 h.p. turbine with a system of parallel flow developed by Thomson and Co. of Dundee. This proved to be so successful that another of 400 h.p. was ordered. It was found that the mills could now run with a seven-foot flood in the River Tay whereas previously the waterwheels came to a standstill with a flood of only three feet. This saved some forty or fifty working days lost previously. At Wilson's Woollen Mill, Dunblane, the waterwheel was changed around 1880 for a Gilkes turbine that developed 200 h.p. at 178 r.p.m. It was only in 1904 that the 100 h.p. suspension waterwheel at Quarry Bank Mill, Styal, was replaced by a 200 h.p. horizontal shaft Gilkes turbine which drove the mill until it closed in 1958.

Summary

After the upheavals of the American Civil War with its cotton famine, the cotton industry continued to expand. Larger mills became possible with greater capital made available through legislation enabling limited companies to be formed. Towards the end of the period, some of these mills were filled with ring frames, a type of spinning that eventually would replace Lancashire's time-honoured mules. While in the rest of the textile machinery there were few startling innovations, this was not the case with the steam engine. Here, once ways of using the new material, steel, had been mastered, boilers capable of withstanding higher pressures could be introduced. These, together with a correct understanding of thermodynamic principles, resulted in more powerful and economic engines being built. This involved more efficient valve gears and governing systems. Compounding became worthwhile, leading to horizontal layouts replacing the traditional beam engine. Gear driving was replaced by ropes, causing the layout of mills to change. All these improvements paved the way for the continued expansion of the Lancashire cotton industry, leading to its heyday at the beginning of the twentieth century.

NOTES: CHAPTER 4

1 Farnie (1979), pp. 180 and 307.

2 Baines (1875), p. 114.

3 *Mechanical World*, Vol. 3, 25 Feb. 1888, p. 71.

4 Andrew (1887), p. 2.

5 Patent 2,321, 17 October 1855.

6 Bessemer (1905), p. 241.

7 Patent 1,820, 1862 and Patent 1,291, 1865.

8 Patent 819, 3 April 1861 and Leigh (1875), Vol. 1, pp. 59–60.

9 Patent 4,875, 4 December 1823 and Leigh (1875), Vol. 1, p. 107.

10 Patent 6,564, 17 February 1834.

11 Patent 12,535, 26 March 1849.

12 Patent 242, 9 February 1858 and Leigh (1875), Vol. 1, p. 113.

13 Leigh (1875), Vol. 2, p. 223.

14 Nasmith (c.1900), p. 10.

15 Baines (1875), p. 75.

16 Patent 5,787, 2 May 1829 in the name of George William Lee. See Jeremy (1981), p. 213 for American patent on 2 September 1828, drawing No. 5,214.

17 Patent 6,690, 8 October 1834.

18 Montgomery (1836), p. 224.

19 Ibid.

20 Manchester Steam Users' Association (1905), p. 14.

21 Hann (1854), p. 162.

22 Ibid, pp. 14–15.

23 Williams (1861), p. xviii.

24 Carnot (1824), pp. 48–9.

25 Ibid, p. 50.

26 Goodeve (1884), p. 52.

27 Ibid.

28 Ibid, p. 61.

29 Rankine (1861), p. 299.

30 Goodeve (1884), p. 1.

31 Hunter (1979–85), Vol. 1, p. 463.

32 *Mechanical World*, Vol. 20, 2 October 1896, p. 164.

33 Nasmith (c. 1900), p. 12.

34 Dale (1991), no. p.

35 Ewing (1926), p. 215.

36 Ibid, p. 216 and Nasmith (c. 1900), p. 168.

37 Farey (1971), Vol. 1, p. 390.

38 Patent 1,298, 13 July 1781.

39 Hills (2005), Vol. 2, pp. 171–9 for details of the trials.

40 Patent 2,772, 17 June 1804.

41 Ibid.

42 Harris (1966), pp. 26ff.

43 Barton (1969), p. 33.

44 Farey (1971), Vol. 2, pp. 317–8.

45 Patent 1,620, 5 May 1873.

46 Patent 11,001, 10 December 1845.

47 Ibid.

48 Rigg (1888), p, 292.

49 *Mechanical World*, Vol. 11, 8 January 1892, p. 18 for Kent Street Cotton Mill and Vol. 25, 6 January 1899, p. 6 for Nile Mill.

50 Patent 9,571, 22 December 1842.

51 Patent 6,258, 13 April 1832 and Hills (2002), p. 166.

52 Patent 10,198, 22 May 1844. See also Patent 61, 9 January 1867 for a further patent by J. Petrie.

53 Patent 12,988, 7 March 1850.

54 Patent 3,841, 7 November 1874.

55 Burn (1854), p. 110.

56 US Patent 6,192, 10 March 1849.

57 Ibid.

58 US Patent 8,253, 29 July 1851.

59 US Patent 24,618, 5 July 1859.

60 Clark (1864), p. 318.

61 Bourne (1869), p. 110.

62 Patent 82, 11 January 1865. For another patent by J.F. Spencer, see Patent 1,626, 18 May 1868. For some by W. Inglis, see patent 1,659, 20 May 1868 and patent 3,546, 23 November 1868.

63 Patent 1,337, 5 May 1869.

64 US Patent 20,894, 13 July 1858.

65 Nasmith (c.1900), pp. 167–8.

66 Patent 1,212, 27 April 1870.

67 Patent 2,878, 27 July 1877.

68 Patent 8,061, 7 May 1839 and Shaw (1984), p. 496. For a fuller account of the development of the water turbine, see Wilson, P.N., 'Early Water Turbines in the United Kingdom', *T.N.S.*, Vol. 31, 1957–8, p. 219ff.

69 Patent 13,156, 3 July 1850.

CHAPTER 5
CLIMAX AND DECLINE, 1890–1930

The Cotton Industry

During the opening years of the twentieth century, the Lancashire cotton industry enjoyed its last major mill-building boom in the years 1904 to 1908. A few more mills were erected in the euphoria after the First World War. The period 1909 to 1913 saw the last export boom when levels were reached that were never to be equalled by any other exporter. In 1913 the industry reached its peak level of consumption, production and employment. Consumption of raw cotton soared to 2,132,300,000lbs in the years around 1912. There was a steady growth in numbers of both spindles and looms until the First World War. Spindles increased from 41,6320,000 in 1893 to 60,000,000 in 1914. Likewise, after a brief fall from 614,964 looms in 1890 to 602,672 in 1893, their numbers rose to 800,000 in 1914.

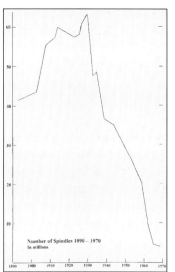

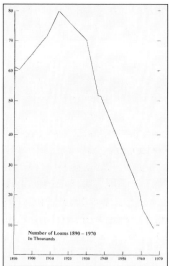

Above: The impressive mills for Leigh Spinners were built either side of the First World War. The further Number 1 was built 1914 to 1915 and the nearer Number 2 in 1925.

Numbers of spindles 1890 to 1970. Numbers of looms 1890 to 1970.

The First World War halted progress and destroyed Lancashire's hold on its Asian markets. Although there was a period of recovery after the war, there followed a lengthy recession, gradually intensifying as the years passed. Yet there was an increase in the numbers of spindles, reaching a peak of 63,200,000 in 1930. However, looms had declined to 700,000 in the same year. The real, sustained contraction began with the Great Depression of the early 1930s with little respite even during the Second World War (see graphs and Note 1 for figures). From their peak level in 1913, although declining, exports of cotton cloth continued to be the most important export from Britain until 1938 when they were overtaken by those of machinery. In 1926, eighty per cent of the cotton industry was still working for the export trade. It was not until 1957 that the value of woollen exports once again exceeded those of cotton manufactures, so restoring the former supremacy of that ancient trade in the textile sector.

Sizes of spinning mills continued to expand. In 1892–5, the Irwell Bank Spinning Co. built what was then the largest mill in all Lancashire at Stoneclough, Kearsley, with 132,408 spindles. The Oldham area was prominent in the great size of its mills which specialised in spinning medium counts. Monarch was built in 1903 to contain 132,744 spindles. In 1905 there were Durban and Laurel with 120,000 spindles and Grape with 126,324. In 1906, there was Roy with 140,000 and in 1907, Hartford with 120,000. Broadstone No. 2

Mill, Reddish, completed in 1907, was one of the largest in the industry up to that date with 138,000 spindles, to be surpassed by Times No. 2 Mill at Middleton in the following year with 160,000 spindles. Production started at Pear Mill, Stockport, in 1913 on 137,312 spindles, but here the second mill intended to be driven by the same steam engine was never built. The peak had been reached. Thereafter new mills seem to have had fewer spindles, perhaps because they were ring mills. Wye No. 2 Mill, which was the last to be completed in Shaw in 1925–6, had 96,712 ring spindles.

Most British spinners continued to prefer the mule and their confidence in it was seen in the massive investment up to 1914. For example 128 mules with 174,469 spindles were ordered in 1907 for the Times No. 2 Mill at Middleton, although only 160,000 were actually erected. It was then the largest in the world. Of the sixty million spindles in the cotton industry in 1914, 80 per cent were on mules. This percentage had barely changed by 1927 when there were still 46,851,000 mule spindles or 78 per cent. Yet the directors of Shiloh Spinners were considered to be very foolish when they built Elk Mill at Royton in 1926 as the last all-mule mill in Lancashire with 107,240 spindles. This decision was justified because mule spinning continued here until 1972 when we took out and shortened one of their mules for the North Western Museum of Science and Industry and set it to work again. It ran at Liverpool Road until 2008. Even in 1951 mules still outnumbered ring frames at 17,905,000 spindles or 64 per cent. However, by 1967 the proportion had fallen to under 15 per cent and in 1969 it was around only 2½ per cent.

Even before the First World War, some sectors of the cotton industry were meeting severe competition in Asia. This was particularly intense in the calico-printing industry exporting medium-quality cloth. The product of Waterside and Bridge Mills in the 1880s was the standard 'Printers and Shirtings' which would have been printed at the nearby Dinting Vale works of Edmund Potter and Co., the largest such works in Britain. In 1894, the Waterside Mill closed for several weeks due to shortage of orders. These mills failed to beat the foreign competition and the company went into voluntary liquidation in 1896. The receivers attempted a production run in 1898 or 1899 at Bridge Mill but the mill caught fire and was never rebuilt. In 1899 the complex was sold to Gartside and Company, Ashton-under-Lyne, a founder member of the Calico Printers' Association which was formed that year. It was a sign of the competition that Potters joined this Association in 1900. Another sign was the installation at Waterside Mill of some Northrop looms in 1905 and 1909, more suitable for this type of cloth. Economic pressures on mills saw more amalgamations in the spinning sector with firms like M'Connel joining the Fine Cotton Spinners and Doublers Association set up in 1918. The Associated Cotton Mills Trust was in operation by the same year. The Lancashire Cotton Corporation of 1929 was specifically organised with government approval to buy up obsolete spindleage and rationalise the industry.

Improvements in Spinning

Throughout this period, the ring frame continued to gain ground. Ring mills tended to be smaller than mule mills because, while their frames were more compact, their output was higher, needing more power. Iris Mill, Oldham, had 62,568 ring spindles in 1907. In Stalybridge, three new mills, Victor, completed in 1904, Premier in 1907 and Ray in 1908, were all built for ring spinning so that by 1911, 34 per cent of the spindles in that town were rings, much higher than the average elsewhere. More generally ring frames were added to or replaced mules in mills. In Glossop, the Shepley Mill Company added 5,500 ring spindles to their 43,000 mule spindles in 1908. At this date, Waterside Mill in Hadfield had 37,296 mule and 33,636 ring spindles. The proportion of ring spindles steadily increased. At Shepley Mill in 1920, mule spindles had declined to 30,000 while rings had increased to 20,000. At the Wren Nest Mills in Glossop, mule spindles declined from 139,748 spindles in 1916 to 44,748 in 1940 while ring spindles rose at the same time from 1,200 to 64,332 spindles.[2]

The attraction of the ring frame was not only that it could be supervised by less skilled operators but also that, space for space, production on it was higher. The ring frame may have been given a further advantage

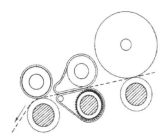

The principle of Casablancas' drafting system with aprons round the middle pair of rollers.

through the addition of the important Casablancas high draft system which could be easily included on new ring frames. In Spain in 1912, Fernando Casablancas patented his method for spinning fibres of medium length.[3] It consisted of two moving aprons round the middle pair of drafting rollers which reached almost to the front ones. The aprons lightly pressed the fibres together in the drafting zone while still allowing the quicker rotating front rollers to pull the fibres out of the aprons quite easily. It enabled slivers or rovings to be reducing in thickness more quickly and evenly with the result that some of the intermediate frames between the drawing and spinning frames could be dispensed with. His system was soon applied in both cotton and worsted industries.

Improvements in Weaving

Another important textile invention of this period was the Northrop automatic loom. Attempts had been continuing since about 1840 to develop a loom on which the shuttles were changed automatically when the weft was exhausted. In 1891, J.H. Northrop took out three British patents under the name of A.G. Brooks for methods of changing shuttles as well as changing the pirn inside a shuttle. Northrop was born at Keighley in Yorkshire but emigrated to America, where he developed his ideas. In his first patent that year, he described how the empty pirn would be pushed out through the bottom of the shuttle and through an open part of the slay to be replaced by another. In his next patent, granted the same day in June, Northrop envisaged replacing a complete shuttle with a new one already filled with weft. The full shuttles were stored in a suitable hopper. The third patent of this series described more fully the special pirns and how they would be secured in the shuttle.[4] In 1894, a further British patent was taken out concentrating on the pirn-changing loom. In one shuttle box, a feeler was pushed through a slot in the side of the shuttle each time the shuttle entered the box. As long as the pirn was full of weft, the loom carried on working normally. If lack of weft enabled the feeler to enter beyond a certain point, a device was activated which pushed down a full pirn into the place of the old one. The full pirns were contained in a rotary magazine ready for insertion.

The Northrop loom revolutionised cotton weaving in America and the Northrop system became the basis for most later automatic looms. The British Northrop Loom Co. Ltd was set up at Blackburn to manufacture them in England but they never achieved much popularity here. The length of time the shuttle remained in the box, whether the cop was changed or not, meant that the Northrop loom could not be speeded up in the same way as the Lancashire. Even so, while productivity might be a little less, one weaver could manage many more Northrop looms than Lancashires because Northrops did not have to be watched so closely. Henry Philips

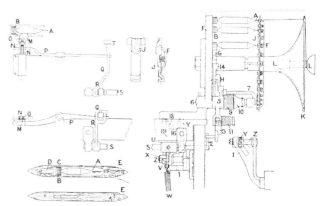

The rotary Northrop creel holding the full pirns ready for insertion into the shuttle, showing the complexity of the mechanism.

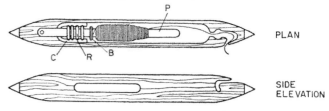

PLAN

SIDE ELEVATION

The Northrop shuttle with its special pirn and slot in the side for the feeler. Rings R on the pirn P are held by clips C.

Greg imported the first Northrops to Britain in 1902. Among the pioneers were Ashton Brothers, Hyde, who were using these looms from 1904. In 1909 Robert Alexander Greg introduced Northrops to Quarry Bank Mill, where there were 94 by 1914. Yet by this date in Britain only one or two per cent of looms were Northrops compared with 40 per cent in the United States because they were not suitable for the finer Lancashire product.

Improvements in Steam Generation

To meet competition, it was necessary to seek more and more economical power plants and the larger spinning mills called for ever larger engines. These aims could be achieved through raising boiler pressures, reintroducing superheating and increasing the speed as well as making the flow of steam through the engine smoother. This final period of the dominance of the reciprocating steam engine saw new types of engines introduced as well as better lubrication systems. Valve gears and governors were improved so that engines became even more reliable and powerful.

For the steam generating plant, the Lancashire boiler reigned supreme. Yet even here there were improvements to withstand the higher pressures being demanded. One weakness lay with the long internal fire tubes where the heat from the fire caused them to expand more than the outer shell. By 1856, Adamson connected the flat ends together with longitudinal stay bolts and fixed gusset plates to secure the flat ends to the outer shell. With these additions, his boilers could withstand pressures up to 110 p.s.i. But the expansion of the fire tubes introduced stresses in the end plates and led to stays and gussets cracking. Also these long, parallel unsupported tubes were liable to distortion and collapse. Fairbairn had provided strengthening rings at various points along the tube. A more effective way of combating the expansion caused by heat and giving strength at the same time was patented by Daniel Adamson and Leonard Cooper in 1852.[5] The ends of the sections of the tubes were flanged outwards and riveted together with a strengthening ring between them. The curvature of the flanging gave some flexibility.

In 1860, Thomas Hill patented riveting the ends of straight sections into a hooped ring in which the hoop would be compressed.[6] In 1885, James Noah Paxton formed swells or an expanded seam in the ends of the sections which were then riveted.[7] Another way of strengthening the tubes was by corrugating them, which might also increase the heating surface by fifteen to twenty per cent. Samuel Fox took out patents in 1877 for forged corrugated sections which were installed at first in marine boilers.[8] Soon they were constructed by being rolled. Flanged ends which were stronger than those made from riveted angle plates made their appearance. The boiler made by the Butterley Company for the Stretham engine in 1871 had them. Finally the ends were dished and flanged. These were introduced by John Thompson of Wolverhampton in 1905 and removed the need for both gusset plates and stay bolts.[9] Boilers with these dished ends could withstand pressures up to 250 p.s.i.

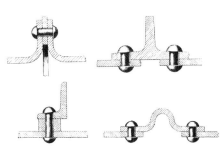

Various methods of adding strengthening rings to the fire tubes in Lancashire boilers.

The dished end of a Lancashire boiler at Cefn Coed Colliery, South Wales.

Around 1890 the practice of superheating was reintroduced. It was made possible through mineral oils replacing vegetable. Hirn pioneered their use in France and they became more general in the 1870s. A good quality mineral steam cylinder oil would have a flashpoint of 680°F (360°C), considerably higher than that of natural oils. Such oils contained no acids and did not decompose or vaporise with the increasing heat. Without them, the advent of later high-pressure steam engines would have been impossible. Towards the end of the nineteenth century, superheater elements were made from special steels rather than cast iron to prevent them burning out. The interest in superheated steam began to revive partly through the steam turbine where there were no problems with lubricants and where it was found that superheated steam produced a marked rise in efficiency through the reduction in internal friction by preventing condensation. Tests were published in 1892 for the Alsatian Society of Steam Users which showed a saving of coal of twenty per cent for superheaters installed integral with a boiler and twelve per cent where the superheaters were independently fired. The gains in economy with steam at 150 p.s.i. were stated in 1908 to be:

Degrees of superheat	50	100	150	200	250	300
Gain in economy per cent	8	14½	21½	26½	31½	34½[10]

In Britain 100 to 150°F (38–66°C) superheat was usual. In an engine using superheated steam, the effect was confined basically to the first cylinder. Prof. Johann Stumpf claimed that, in an ordinary counter-flow cylinder engine, the superheat was excessive for the first cylinder and too little in subsequent ones. The steam usually became saturated in the high-pressure cylinder before release and so entered the receiver in a wet state. While initial condensation was eliminated in the high-pressure cylinder, it occurred in subsequent ones.

The flow of steam from boilers to engines and within engines themselves was improved through taking more care with the alignment of the pipes. Normally in a horizontal cross compound, the high-pressure cylinder would be on the side closest to the boiler house to keep the steam pipe as short as possible. Early horizontal engines had the pipes tucked away neatly underneath the floor. On high-pressure cylinders with Corliss valves, the pipes hugged the side of the cylinder buried under the lagging before then dividing, running along the tops of the cylinders to reach the inlet ports. This layout caused restrictions and severe bends. On later engines, it can be seen how the pipes were given more space across the top. Later still the steam pipe would be

The tall arching steam pipe with its steel cladding to the high-pressure cylinder at Saxon Mill.

brought in overhead, through the main steam valve and divided to reach the inlet ports. A very fine example could be seen at Saxon Mill, Droylsden, where George Saxon replaced the Adamson high-pressure cylinder in 1941. Here the steam pipe rose from the floor beside the wall, swept in a graceful arch above the high-pressure cylinder and down to the main valve before branching to both ends again in sweeping curves. With its planished steel cladding, it was reminiscent of a knight in armour. Similar treatment could be seen in the piping on low-pressure cylinders.

Governors

More sophisticated control of the steam and cut-off became ever more essential as boiler pressures and speeds rose. The 'load' weights on governors suffered from the same objections as those on Corliss gears because the force of gravity was slow in operation. Therefore weights were sometimes replaced by springs, which had no inertia to overcome so their reaction was generally swifter and they could be easily adjusted for different tensions. A patent drawing of 1876 shows that Wilson Hartnell had fitted a single spring.[11] The most important of the spring-loaded governors for mill engines was the type patented in 1894 by H.F.C. Whitehead, who worked

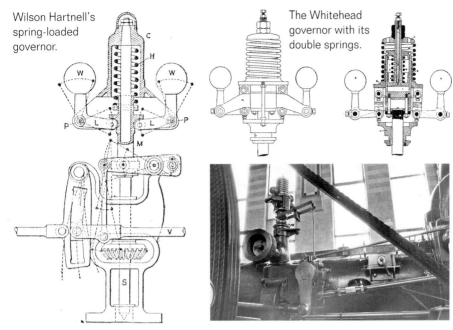

Wilson Hartnell's spring-loaded governor.

The Whitehead governor with its double springs.

The Whitehead governor on Saxon Mill engine.

for Scott and Hodgson.[12] It had a pair of springs and an oil-filled damping cylinder. At the correct speed, the force of the springs exactly balanced the centrifugal forces on the flyballs. When the speed rose, the flyballs moved out and compressed the outer spring, altering the point of cut-off. This in turn moved the piston in the damping cylinder and transferred some load to the other spring, relieving the outer spring, so bringing the flyballs back to their normal position again. The system reduced the tendency to 'hunt' and steadied the action.

Another type of governor was the shaft governor, one of which was patented by Hartnell in 1868. He gave a lecture about its origins during 1895 when he said:

> The crankshaft governor was not invented for the sake of more sensitive and prompt governing but for the sake of making it so powerful that it could act direct on the expansion valve and so simple that it could be applied to an agricultural engine . . . The governor showed itself, by comparison with other governors, extremely sensitive and prompt.[13]

Such governors became very popular in America where they were fitted inside the flywheels. Their special qualities of promptness in governing became recognised for quick-running engines for electric lighting after Hartnell's patent had expired. In the meantime, other engine builders patented their own designs.[14] On later drop valve engines in Britain, they were situated on the shaft rotating at the side of the high-pressure cylinder. Because these governors were placed horizontally, gravity could not be used, so that springs had to be fitted to give the restraining force on the weights. The important feature of shaft governors was the use of the inertia of the weights as well as the centrifugal force. At the correct speed, the position of the weights would be balanced by the centrifugal force acting against the springs, but a change in speed caused the weights to alter the steam inlet. The weights were pivoted so that, if the speed of the engine suddenly slowed down, the inertia of the weights would cause them to fly outwards, so opening the

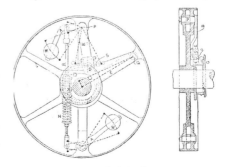

Hartnell's spring-loaded shaft governor.

Lumb governor and regulator fitted to the Barnes Mill engine.

steam valve, and vice versa when the engine speeded up. Such governors could exert great power and became popular on high-speed engines running at over 150 r.p.m. They reacted very quickly to changes in speed.

Compensation for variations in load was refined with the Lumb regulator, which was probably the most sophisticated and successful of these devices. The original patents were taken out by R. Wilby in 1886 and 1887.[15] However, the device does not seem to have become popular until after it had been improved by James Lumb in 1900.[16] A drive was taken from an oscillating shaft, such as the rod to the Corliss valves, which could turn either one of a pair of ratchet wheels. The two claws which rotated the ratchet wheels oscillated up and down all the time but were brought into engagement only when the speed of the governor varied. The ratchet wheels had teeth facing in opposite directions and were fitted onto a shaft which turned the knuckle on the governor rods through bevel wheels, thus altering their length according to load. Another linkage connected to the flyballs of the governor could be finely balanced by a small weight to bring the ratchet operating arms into and out of engagement. While the Lumb regulator still depended for its operation on a change in speed, it was reckoned that variations could be kept to less than three per cent. Most of the mill engines still running in the 1960s were fitted with these regulators because they could give such a close control of speed even when spinning machines were stopped or started. Around 1900 various devices were fitted on governors to trip out and stop the engine should the speed become too fast or too slow.

Valves and Valve Gears

Valves and valve gears also came in for scrutiny. Most makers designed their own variations of trip mechanisms to alter the cut-off. One particularly neat form was the Dobson with dashpots, trip release mechanism and operating rods to the Corliss inlet valves all in a straight line at the top of the cylinder. It was used by Yates and Thom, George Saxon and Ashton, Frost among others. That on the high-pressure cylinder would be linked to the governor while that on the low-pressure was pre-set. On the low-pressure cylinder, many manufacturers turned to Corliss instead of slide valves which would have been lighter as well as giving a better flow of steam and better drainage. A few firms adopted piston valves on the low-pressure cylinders which would have reduced friction compared with slide valves as well as enabling the ports to be enlarged. The diameter of the piston valve on Scott and Hodgson's Dee engine at Shaw was 21in compared with the 42in of the low-pressure cylinder. On the Ellen Road engine of J. & W. McNaught, the piston valve was given a twist as it moved longitudinally to help distribute the lubrication.

On high-pressure cylinders, Corliss valves could not cope with increasing speeds, higher boiler pressures and superheated steam. Their weight caused inertia when closing so that, even if the springs in the dashpots were strengthened or augmented with pistons driven by steam, the speed could not be raised much above 100 r.p.m. Their sliding surfaces became more difficult to lubricate as the heat and dryness of the incoming steam became greater. The principal alternative was a return to the drop valve in either of two forms. The double-seated drop valve was lighter than the Corliss and had a much greater port area. There was little friction on the stalk or rod which raised it off its seating. But it was difficult to keep steam-tight through different thermal expansion rates of the cylinder and the valve itself. Then, since the body of the valve came to rest on the valve seat, the dashpot mechanism had to be finely adjusted to prevent the valve smashing itself on the seat. Sulzer Brothers of Winterthur, Switzerland, were among the main exponents of this type of valve. They had fitted them on a horizontal cylinder engine in 1866 and continued to use them until production ceased in

Right: Sectioned drawing
of the Dobson Corliss
valve release mechanism.

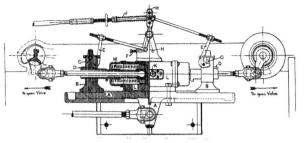

Below: The piston
valve on a low-
pressure cylinder of
the Dee Mill engine.

Right: The Dobson release
mechanism fitted to a high-
pressure cylinder at Mag-
net Mill as re-erected in the
North Western Museum of
Science and Industry.

1947. Robey of Lincoln was employing these valves by 1888 and built thousands of such engines, far more than any other British firm.

To overcome the danger of the drop valve smashing against the seat, in 1900 Van der Stegen, the Managing Director of Van den Kerchove, engine builders in Ghent, Belgium, developed the cylindrical piston drop valve. Like the Corliss valve, the piston drop valve did not shut against a seat but closed the cylindrical ports by sliding over them. Piston rings prevented escape of steam past the pistons. Such valves had all the advantages of double-beat drop valves with lightness and large port openings as well as the advantages of Corliss valves in their manner of closing. In Britain, they were adopted by Musgrave and Cole, Marchent and Morley of Bradford among others. Where double-beat or piston drop valves were used as the inlet valves, the exhaust might be some other type such as a form of slide or Corliss because precision of seating and timing of closure did not need to be so accurate. Sulzer kept their double-beat drop valves and Cole, Marchent and Morley had their piston drop valves for both inlet and exhaust. Galloway had double-beat drop valves for inlet and piston drop valves for exhaust.

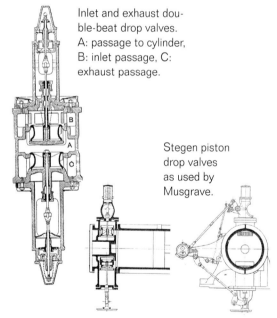

Inlet and exhaust dou-
ble-beat drop valves.
A: passage to cylinder,
B: inlet passage, C:
exhaust passage.

Stegen piston
drop valves
as used by
Musgrave.

Condensing Apparatus

Most manufacturers preferred to place the condensers below the level of the main cylinders so that condensate formed in the low-pressure cylinder could flow by gravity into the condenser. Also there would be less danger of the injection water backing up into the cylinders. In large engines, there could be multiple air pumps to remove the volume of water. There would be two sets of valves, one in the pump bucket and the second in

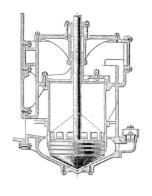

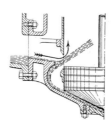

Section through an Edwards air pump.

the cover by the outlet. Rubber disc valves replaced the earlier flap valves. That on the bucket of the Firgrove engine was a single disc. There was a considerable shock when the air pump bucket descended into the condensate because the area of the valve openings was considerably less than the surface area of water in the bottom of the air pump. This meant that water had to be forced through the restricted openings. In 1894, F. Edwards patented an air pump which had valves only at the outlet.[17] Near the bottom of the pump barrel were two rings of ports. The condensate flowed through the lower ones into the bot-

tom of the air pump, which was conical. The air pump piston was a solid cone which almost fitted the cone in the barrel. In the lowest position of the piston, the condensate was forced back through the bottom ports and was flung through the higher set of ports onto the top of the piston. The piston, rising again, trapped this water on top of itself as it moved above the ports and closed them. This water was lifted and passed out of the valves in the top of the air pump in the usual way. These air pumps were claimed to draw a better vacuum than earlier ones and, with their fewer valves, were more suited for high-speed engines such as Uniflow types. Only in the 1920s did a few makers introduce rotary extraction pumps or sometimes steam ejectors on the condensers.

Large Twin Horizontal Tandem Compound Engines

The Magnet Mill Engine

There were hopes of preserving two of Courtaulds' large twin horizontal tandem compound engines but neither scheme came to fruition. The one at Magnet Mill, Chadderton, was designed by G. Saxon and ran from 1903 to 1966. In 1915, the mill contained 60,156 mule spindles and 44,680 rings. The Magnet engine was typical of earlier designs, with the steam pipes going directly into the cylinders from underneath and not entering from above in a large arch. Green was the basic colour against which the steel grey of the lagging showed up very well. A nice touch was the brass magnets on the covers of the high-pressure cylinder end covers. Corliss valves were fitted throughout, a typical Saxon feature. The inlets on both 20in high-pressure cylinders were controlled by a 'loaded' governor with a Lumb regulator. The low-pressure cylinders were 44in by 5ft stroke. The stroke of these later engines was shorter but speeds higher. Each crosshead worked an air pump underneath the engine where, as there was no top, the water could be seen splashing around. The 26ft diameter flywheel weighed 80 tons and had 35 ropes. At 60 r.p.m. the engine produced 1,700 h.p. while later the speed was increased to 64½ r.p.m., generating 2,200 h.p. The boiler pressure was raised from 160 to 180 p.s.i. Indicator diagrams taken on this engine gave practical proof of the fall in temperature of the steam between the two cylinders of a compound. The cocks on the low-pressure cylinder could just be turned by hand but a cloth was always necessary for operating those on the high-pressure one. The big ends on the connecting rods were the marine pattern where the bearing cap was bolted to the main rod.

In order to help cool the condensing water, which was drawn from the lodge beside the mill, the condensate from the engine flowed in a cascade over a cast iron fountain. Even so, the condensing water was kept at a sufficiently high temperature by the condensate for some form of semi-tropical pondweed to grow in it. A man used to buy this regularly and then sell it for aquariums, a trade which died out with the mill engines. When the engine was being scrapped, one of the men, having failed to demolish the fountain with a sledgehammer, threw a stick of dynamite into the water which totally demolished the fountain. All the water flowed out into the sewers, flooding some nearby houses. All that could be saved was the valve gear from one high-pressure

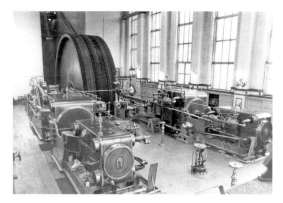

The Magnet Mill engine with high-pressure cylinders at the rear.

Crosshead with links to drive the air pump below on Magnet Mill engine.

The marine-type big end on the Magnet Mill engine.

An indicator mounted on a cylinder for taking a diagram to check the performance of the Magnet Mill engine.

cylinder, which we displayed in the Museum of Science and Industry in Manchester to show the neat Dobson layout. It has since been removed from display.

Courtaulds made a short film about the engine. It was decided that the mill engineer, who had a deep Lancashire accent, should record the commentary. I remained in Manchester while he and the film producer went to the recording studios in Altrincham. But when I saw the finished film, I realised it was not his voice. At the studio, it was discovered that he was unable to read the script, in spite of having a daily newspaper on his desk. This is a rare film about a mill engine and there is a copy in the North Western Film Archive in Manchester.

The Dee Mill Engine

The sun, pouring in through the windows and striking the colourful tiles on the walls, always made this engine very attractive. Scott and Hodgson designed this twin horizontal tandem compound engine for Dee Mill, Shaw, to drive 122,000 spindles on 48 pairs of mules. Of the 1,500 h.p., 570 h.p. was lost in friction. The engine first ran on 20 April 1907. Between the 18in high-pressure Corliss valve cylinders were the main steam valve together with valves for the barring engine and cylinder pre-heating pipes. In front of the cylinders was a double range of water cocks to let cold water into the condensers either from the mill lodge or, when that was low, from a stream running nearby. Then there were the pressure gauges mounted on a varnished wood board. One showed the boiler pressure, 160 p.s.i., two showed the pressure in the low-pressure cylinders, which at full load would have been 30 p.s.i., and another two the vacuum in the condensers. The weighted governor had no additional regulator or compensator but the engineer said that it worked very well, whatever the load.

The Dee Mill engine had ornate glazed tiling on the walls.

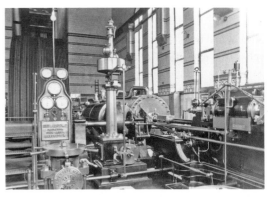

All the controls for operating the Dee Mill engine were placed centrally.

Above: The connecting rods on the Dee Mill engine had solid forged big ends. The floor was covered with heavy cloth to keep it clean from oil.

Right: Inside the twin drums of the Dee Mill engine fly-wheel.

The distance between the high- and low-pressure cylinders was quite large because the air pumps were driven by the coupling rods and placed underneath between them. The engine bed seemed to be one long casting, stretching below both cylinders and over the air pumps. A rotating shaft from the crankshaft drove both the governor and a shaft at right angles which turned the eccentrics for the Corliss valves on the high-pressure cylinders. The 42in low-pressure cylinders were only a little larger than their 21in piston valves, which had no twist in their movement. The 26ft diameter flywheel consisted of twin pulleys made from cast iron spokes with segments bolted to them. The segments were secured to each other so that it was, in effect, a single drum. The bosses of the segments where they were bolted to the spokes began to crack and show signs of fatigue. To prevent the cracks from spreading and causing the flywheel to burst, a Metalock repair was carried out. Holes were drilled either side of the crack, opened out into a channel which was filled with a special metal locking bar. An inspection later showed that the cracks were not enlarging. It was quite an experience being inside the drum of that flywheel as it was being rotated slowly by the barring engine, clambering round the spokes. Once the gap in the boarding of the wheel through which we had climbed had rotated to the bottom of the pit, the person controlling the barring engine could not hear our shouts to stop. Luckily it was not turning at its full speed of 60 r.p.m. The weight of the flywheel was probably 80 tons and the 38 ropes over 3 tons. The engine became redundant through electrification around 1968 but was retained by Courtaulds and maintained by the Northern Mill Engine Society. When the mill closed in 1980 preservation attempts failed and all was scrapped in 1984, a sad loss of a fine engine.

Multiple Expansion Engines

Since it had been shown to be advantageous to expand the steam in two stages in a compound engine, it was only to be expected that further economies would accrue if steam at higher pressures could be expanded through more cylinders of increasing size. Up to 120 p.s.i, it was found that compound engines were the best. Between 150 and 200 p.s.i, triple-expansion engines gave good results and quadruple expansion had advantages above 200 p.s.i. The temperature difference would be spread out over a greater number of cylinders so that the fall in temperature, and therefore the amount of initial condensation when the steam entered, would be less at each stage. This had to be balanced against losses in the steam pipes connecting the cylinders and also in the extra costs of the additional cylinders and the friction of their moving parts. Adamson took out a patent in 1861 for 'multiple expansion engines'.[18] His idea was to apply this either to a beam engine, in which case two cylinders could be situated at one side of the beam pivot and two the other, or to a horizontal engine in which case four cylinders would drive a common crosshead. The steam might be superheated or reheated between the various stages of expansion.[19]

In 1865 or 1866, Adamson supplied an engine with six cylinders consisting of two sets of horizontal triple-expansion engines to the Victoria Mill of the Newton Moor Spinning Co. Ltd that had 57,414 spindles. Each engine had three cylinders in line with the high-pressure one furthest from the crankshaft. Steam was supplied from Cornish boilers at 120 p.s.i. and Green's economisers were installed. When the engine was described in *Engineering* in January 1867, it was working at only half-power because not all the spinning machinery had been installed. Yet it showed 'great economy of fuel, great regularity and equality of speed allowing the self-acting mules to be run at the highest velocities at present adopted in spinning, with a remarkably small rate of breakages of thread'.[20] But this engine was not a great success because the boiler pressure was too low.

The horizontal three-in-line triple-expansion engine was never very popular through its excessive length. J. & W. McNaught built two in 1892 and another five years later. The largest developed only 650 h.p. so they were quite small. More usually horizontal triple-expansion engines had two cranks, one either side of the flywheel. On one side, there might be high and intermediate cylinders and on the other the low and the air pump. But the low-pressure cylinder became excessively large as the range of power increased. To avoid such a large cylinder and to distribute the power from three pistons more evenly, a popular layout was to divide the low-pressure cylinder into two separate ones so there were four cylinders in all. In this case, there would be normally on one side the high-pressure and one low-pressure cylinder and on the other the intermediate and the second low.

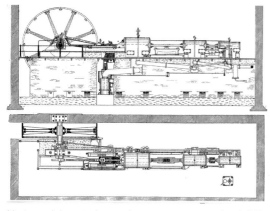

Horizontal three-in-line triple-expansion engine by J. & E. Wood with all the Corliss valves below the cylinders.

A three-cylinder triple-expansion engine with high-pressure cylinder on the right and intermediate, low-pressure and air pump on the left. It had Pollit and Wigzell's patent piston cut-off valves on the high and intermediate cylinders and their three piston rod design on the intermediate and low-pressure cylinders.

J. & E. Wood started to build horizontal triples in 1891 while Musgrave and Scott and Hodgson began in the following year. In all cases the most popular form was the horizontal four-cylinder type. One was supplied by J. & W. McNaught to Ellen Road Mill and ceremoniously named *Albert* and *Alexandra* on 21 May 1892. The 24½in high-pressure cylinder with Corliss valves on one side exhausted into the 38in intermediate cylinder in a corresponding position on the other. From there the steam passed to either of the 43½in low-pressure cylinders with piston valves. Each low-pressure cylinder had its own condenser and double air pumps driven by the crossheads. With a stroke of 6ft at 55 r.p.m., the engine developed 1,800 h.p. to drive the 99,756 mule spindles. In January 1916, a mule caught fire and set the rest of the mill ablaze. After the war, the mill was rebuilt and converted to ring spinning in 1921, so more power was needed. A new flywheel of 84 tons weight with twin pulleys was fitted by P. & R. Jackson, Salford. Clayton, Goodfellow, Blackburn, removed the high-pressure and intermediate cylinders and replaced them with two high-pressure cylinders of their own design, converting the engine into a pair of horizontal tandem compounds, retaining the front half of the engine. The Corliss valves on these new cylinders were worked in a very ingenious and neat way. Beside each cylinder was a rotating shaft with eccentrics on it. The exhaust valves were coupled directly to their eccentric, while the two inlet eccentrics were more like cams. The valve was opened by the rotation of the eccentric, while a step on the outside of the eccentric strap allowed the valve to snap shut. The angle of this step could be altered

The original layout of the Ellenroad engine. The Corliss-valve high-pressure cylinder exhausts into the piston-valve intermediate cylinder in the foreground before the steam passes to the pair of low-pressure cylinders.

Left side of Ellenroad Ring Mill engine with the later high-pressure Corliss-valve cylinder.

The unusual release mechanism for the Corliss inlet valves on the high-pressure cylinder of the Ellenroad engine. The position of the step on the eccentric sheave could be moved to adjust the cut-off.

The Mosscrop speed recorder in its box and Tate's little overspeed governor were driven off the rotary shaft to the Corliss valves on the Ellenroad engine.

by the governor to control the point of cut-off. It dispensed with many rods and links and worked very well. The engine speed was increased to 58½ r.p.m. to give 2,500 h.p. This engine has been preserved on site and is demonstrated regularly on stated weekends.

An engine that was converted the other way from a pair of horizontal tandem compounds into a four-cylinder triple was the Saxon engine at Hawthorn Mill, Chadderton. It was built originally in 1878. The low-pressure cylinders called *Samuel* and *Esther* had slide valves on the outside of the engine and, in order to work them, the cranks on the crankshaft had links bolted to them to operate reciprocating rods running along the outside of the engine bed. The connecting rods were beautifully turned and shaped and at some date had pipes strapped to them to distribute oil to the bearings. Everything behind the low-pressure cylinders was renewed in 1909 when the mill was extended to take 92,000 mule spindles. The slow speed of 53 r.p.m had to be retained although the flywheel, 26ft diameter and 5ft 6in wide, may have been renewed for rope driving. Saxon fitted their latest design of cylinders with Corliss valves and improved steam piping. On the right-hand side was the 21in high-pressure cylinder and on the left the 32in intermediate. The low-pressure cylinders were 36¼in, all with 5ft stroke. 270 h.p. was absorbed in friction and the line shafting out of 1,250 indicated. In 1967, the only electric motor in the mill was an emergency boiler pump, while in the mill itself, mules reigned supreme. It was thought to be the last rope-race steam engine-operated mill in the Oldham area when it closed down in May 1970 and the engine was scrapped.

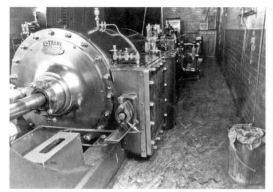

At Hawthorn Mill, the slide valves on the low-pressure cylinders were positioned on the outside of the engine.

The drive at Hawthorn Mill to the slide valves was taken off the crankpin on the outside of the big end. The movement of the valves could be adjusted by a handwheel on the near linkage

The Saxon replacement Corliss-valve high-pressure cylinder on the Hawthorn Mill engine. The pipes for the steam inlet were of ample proportions above the cylinder.

The twin-cylinder barring engine at Hawthorn Mill engaged with teeth on the outside of the flywheel drum.

A four-cylinder horizontal triple-expansion engine that has recently been extensively renovated is one called *Helen* and *Rina* at Trencherfield Mill, Wigan, supplied by J. & E. Wood in 1907. It was the most powerful they built and was still driving the mill in late 1967 when it was preserved, originally by Courtaulds Ltd. It had many typical Wood features, such as the table in the centre with the main steam valve and other controls. All the Corliss valves were underneath their cylinders. This was a powerful engine, for with the high-pressure cylinder at 25in, the intermediate at 40in and the low-pressures at 44in, 5ft stroke, boiler pressure 200 p.s.i. and 68 r.p.m., 2,500 h.p. was generated. The clean lines of the tops of the cylinders swept down to the cross-head slides where the crosshead slippers themselves were made more streamlined than those at Brooklands Mill. The cylinders were securely tied together with large tie rods but this may not have allowed for thermal expansion because the rear of the low-pressure cylinder was attached to the front of the high or intermediate on the appropriate side. There was the usual arrangement of governor-controlled trip gear on the high, and that on the intermediate was set manually. The low-pressure cylinders exhausted into a common condenser from where the condensate was removed by two air pumps, one worked by each crosshead. Water for cooling was drawn from the adjacent canal. With 54 ropes across the width of the 26ft diameter flywheel, there was plenty of room between the two sides of the engine.

The four-cylinder triple-expansion engine at Trencherfield Mill photographed when being run for filming by Courtaulds Ltd.

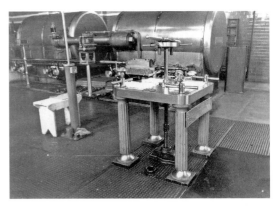

The central table with main steam valve and other controls was a feature of J. & E. Wood engines, as fitted at Trencherfield Mill.

The streamlined crosshead slides and strengthened rounded target plate of a low-pressure cylinder on Trencherfield Mill engine.

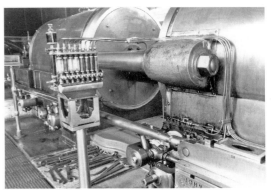

The massive rod tying together the intermediate and low-pressure cylinders at Trencherfield Mill together with the lubricators.

Quadruple-Expansion Engines

A few quadruple-expansion engines were built. One was installed by Adamson at the Albert Mill built on a contiguous site to Victoria Mill at Newton in 1873 to 1874. This mill had 48,000 spindles. Six months of trials were carried out on the engines at both mills when the coal consumption for the earlier triple was 2½lb per horsepower per hour and for the quadruple 1½lb. W.H. Uhland commented a little later that 'The mechanical action of the quadruple engine, is admirably adapted for producing a uniform power, such as is required in a cotton, woollen, or flax mill, or for the grinding of corn, the force on the crankpins being nearly the same on every portion of a revolution.'[21] Musgrave built ten quadruple-expansion engines between 1891 and 1894 to a design with triangular connecting rods. The idea seems to have originated with W.Y. Fleming and P. Ferguson in 1887 and Musgrave patented further refinements in 1893.[22] The triangle pointed downwards and the lowest point was connected to the crank. The upper two corners were connected to piston rods from a pair of cylinders. This layout gave 'no dead centre' as the engine revolved and this was the name for the type. It resulted in an engine that ran very smoothly. Some were built with four cylinders, two on either side of the flywheel, and so became quadruple-expansion engines, and there were a few with only a pair of cylinders, one of which has been preserved by the Northern Mill Engine Society in Bolton.

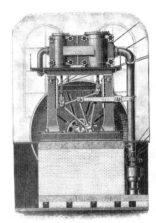

The quadruple-expansion Musgrave 'no dead centre' engine. The drawing in the middle shows the triangular connecting rod.

The Final Cross Compound Engines

In the period shortly before the First World War, there was a move away from both the four-cylinder pair of tandem compound engines and all forms of multiple expansion engines to the straight cross compound through the influence of superheating. The additional gains from expanding the steam in more than two cylinders were not matched by the additional costs of multiple cylinders and the maintenance thereof. One of the largest and most remarkable engines ever built for a cotton spinning mill was that in Yorkshire at the Hare Mill, Todmorden, later called Mons. It was even more remarkable in that the manufacturers were the Belgian firm of Carel Frères in 1908, and so was one of the few continental engines found in a British cotton mill. The intention was to have this 3,000 h.p. engine drive a pair of mills with steam supplied from seven boilers but the second mill was never built. With cylinders high-pressure 39¾in and low-pressure 72½in, stroke 4ft 7⅛in, fitted with drop valves and a high speed of 80 r.p.m., it was a very advanced design. The flywheel was assembled from three pulleys, 22ft diameter, 13ft 8in wide, grooved for 69 ropes, and weighed 130 tons with crankshaft. Steam at 200 p.s.i. was superheated to 525°F (274°C). The horizontal air pump was placed in an unusual position underneath the low-pressure cylinder, driven off the crosshead with the condenser above it.

The enormous cross compound engine at Mons Mill by Carol Frères.

Alas, photographs are all that remain now, for when the mill was visited late in 1966, at one side of the vast pit and high rope-race, all that had been left of this fine engine by the scrappers was a solitary crankshaft shorn even of its cranks.

Another good example of the final flowering of the cross compound engine was that at Ace Mill, Hollinwood. The mill building was completed as Gorse Mill No. 2 in 1914 but during the war it was taken over by the Government and used for aircraft manufacture. The boilers lay outside for the duration and the engine in packing cases until 1919 when the release of the building allowed the installation of the cotton spinning machinery to proceed under the name Ace Mill. Urmson and Thompson, Hathershaw Iron Works, Oldham, were best known for their mill gearing but built half a dozen large engines. This was a pretty engine, called *Elizabeth* and *Mary*. Steel replaced brass on all the trimmings and the flywheel sides were made from steel sheets, not wood. The four emblems, hearts, diamonds, spades and clubs, were stuck on any large flat surface.

When erection of the engine recommenced in 1919, Urmson and Thompson had ceased to use their pit in which flywheels could be machined. One pulley of the 26ft flywheel had already been completed before the

The cross compound Corliss-valve engine at Ace Mill was photographed while being filmed by Courtaulds Ltd.

The complex Corliss release gear with its supporting rods on the Ace Mill high-pressure cylinder. Note 'mill time' in the background.

The flywheel at Ace Mill was clad with planished steel sheets. The high-pressure crosshead is in the foreground.

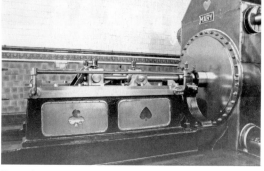

Even the guard round the tail rod slide above the air pump had ace symbols at Ace Mill.

war but the other one of the pair had to be assembled at the mill and turned and finished actually on the engine. Each pulley had 21 ropes. The total weight was 65 tons. Cylinder sizes were high-pressure 31in and a huge 62 in diameter low-pressure with Corliss valves. The stroke was 5ft. The valve gear was laid out more or less traditionally with wrist plates and sloping links to the valves. In order to make sure that the trip gear on the high-pressure inlets worked freely, rods with springs supported the boxes in which the trips were located. If the trips had stuck with a valve in the open position, the engine might have raced away and possibly caused frightful damage. The pistons were fitted with tail rods running on tail rod slides to help support their weight. The low-pressure tail rod drove the air pumps in the condensing apparatus beneath the engine house floor. Steam was delivered over the tops of the cylinders in pipes of ample size. Owing to constant hard work, the target end of the high-pressure cylinder began to fracture from the crosshead slide bed and to rock violently. Special tie rods, bolted to the top of the slides, were secured by cotters into new cylinder cover bolts with special long heads. In spite of this extra security and even when the engine had a greatly reduced load at the end of its life, this cylinder still moved when the steam shot in and even the huge casting under the crosshead slides had a little play. With superheated steam pressure of 185 p.s.i., this engine indicated 2,000 h.p. at 64 r.p.m. and at times might be overloaded 25 per cent beyond that.

Wye No. 2 Mill, Shaw, had an even more massive engine which was a fitting climax for it was not only the last engine built by Buckley and Taylor but was also the last reciprocating steam engine supplied to any British cotton spinning mill when it was started on 11 December 1926. It was an enormous cross compound called *Margaret* with a flywheel over 10ft wide, 24ft diameter for 50 ropes, weighing 90 tons to drive 96,712 ring spindles. This flywheel contrasted with that of the nearby Fern Mill which was only 17½in wide with gearing.

Wye Number 2 engine was large, as shown by the 70in diameter low-pressure cylinder on the left.

The crosshead on Wye Number 2 high-pressure side was a single huge forging running in a single slide.

The crank and big end were shielded in a casing to prevent oil splashing at Wye Number 2 engine.

The clamps securing the cracked crosshead slide casting can be seen to the right below the low-pressure cylinder on Wye Number 2 engine.

The enormous cylinders for Ferranti's 10,000 h.p. inverted vertical tandem compound engine for Deptford dwarf a horizontal cross compound engine in Hick Hargreaves's erecting shop.

Cylinder dimensions were high-pressure 32½in and low a massive 70in, both with Corliss valves and 5ft stroke. Both were fitted with tail rod slides, with that on the low-pressure cylinder working the air pump with twin buckets placed in a large well immediately to the rear.

This large hole may have caused a weakness in the foundations, because the back end of the low-pressure cylinder settled, unbeknown to the engineer. One day, just after restarting following the lunch break, the trip gear on the low-pressure cylinder began to miss. No one could find out what was wrong until an engine inspector, who happened to have called in, noticed that the vast casting under the crosshead had cracked and was moving. When the back end of the cylinder had been jacked up and packing placed underneath, clamps were put across the crack, which had affected only one side,

and no more trouble was experienced. The Corliss valve gear with its wrist plates and sloping rods retained the same characteristics as Fern Mill, and the other parts had similar massive construction, typical of this firm. The crossheads were vast blocks of metal, running in single oil troughs, not double as in most designs. Nearly all the moving parts were automatically lubricated from centrally placed oil boxes and yards of copper pipes. For such a large engine, the speed, 67 r.p.m. seemed very fast, in strange contrast to the governor which, chain-driven with Buckley and Taylor's own type of regulator, rotated quite slowly. Surprisingly this engine was not superheated but, with a boiler pressure of 200 p.s.i, some indicator diagrams showed that over 3,000 h.p. could be delivered. Production ceased at the mill in June 1967 and all was scrapped. This engine, with its associated mill-gearing, cost over £20,000.

Engines with Other Layouts

The alternators initially installed at Deptford were driven by ropes from Hick Hargreaves's inverted vertical cross compound engines.

Inverted vertical engines (hereafter called vertical engines) with cylinders supported on columns above the crankshaft were less popular than horizontals in textile mills although they were more compact and their engine houses were smaller. They might have similar layouts, such as side by side, in-line triple or cross compound. Galloway had constructed a small vertical blowing engine in 1878 but apparently no more until twenty years later. Goodfellow built only four vertical engines between 1871 and 1885. J. & W. McNaught supplied their first vertical type to Grove Mills in 1905, a side-by-side compound with Corliss valves developing 1,100 h.p. at 80 r.p.m. The later introduction of vertical engines to textile mills contrasts with their use elsewhere. Hick Hargreaves were well advanced in 1888 with building an enormous double tandem compound vertical designed to give 10,000 h.p. with a pair of cylinders either side of an alternator for Sebastian de Ferranti's Deptford power station. The height would have been nearly 50ft from the engine room floor with another 17ft below that. The weight would have been in the region of 500 tons with cylinder bores of 44in (H.P.) and 88in (L.P.). But the concessions for supplying electricity to the anticipated regions were never granted so that 1,500 h.p. vertical cross compounds were installed instead. The speed of these smaller engines at 80 r.p.m. was well above that of horizontal mill engines which was more likely to be 50 r.p.m. at this date. Musgrave became very active in supplying engines for power stations. In 1901, the Manchester Corporation Bloom Street station opened with four 1,800kW Musgrave vertical engines driving Westinghouse generators. Manchester's Stuart Street station, which came into operation the next year, had six 1,500kW Yates and Thom vertical cross compound engines. In 1905 at Stuart Street there were added a pair of engines from Wallsend Slipway, Newcastle upon Tyne, which were said to be the largest reciprocating engines in any power station in Europe, delivering 6,000 h.p. or 4,000kW at 75 r.p.m.

The Ferranti Inverted Vertical Cross Compound Engine

It proved possible to preserve a small example of a vertical electricity generating engine at the Museum of Science and Industry in Manchester. This vertical cross compound led a charmed life for it was built by S.Z. de Ferranti Ltd at Hollinwood in 1898 as one of a pair for order No. 581 to go to Lambeth Electricity Supply Company at a manufacturing cost of £3,395.2.11. It was fitted with an integral 250kW zig-zag alternator in place of the usual flywheel. This was surrounded by two rings of static electromagnets acting as the field

coils. It was one of the smallest of such engines designed by Ferranti. However, the load at Lambeth must have grown quickly because the engine was taken out and purchased in 1900 by J.H. Gillett and Son Ltd for their Brunswick Mill at Chorley to drive 850 looms. The alternator was replaced with a heavy flywheel of about 6ft diameter, grooved for ten ropes although only seven were used at the mill. At Lambeth the engine speed was about 300 r.p.m. Although this was reduced to 150 at the mill, it was still too fast and had to have a second set of pulleys to reduce the speed further to that of the existing line shafting.

Above: The team erecting the Ferranti inverted vertical cross compound engines for Lambeth at Hollinwood.

The original zig-zag alternator and crankshaft for a Ferranti engine at Lambeth.

The Ferranti engine from Lambeth installed at Brunswick Mill, Chorley.

The Ferranti engine as preserved at Hollinwood driving a later alternator.

The Ferranti engine with the Siemens alternator being installed at Liverpool Road Station.

When the mill closed in 1960, Ferranti decided to preserve the engine at Hollinwood among their other historic exhibits. There it was re-erected, still with the rope drive flywheel which was linked to an ordinary alternator and demonstrated from time to time under steam. But then notice was given in 1980 that Hollinwood Works would close and so the engine was dismantled. This coincided with our planning the proposed layout for the mill engines in the former Goods Shed at Liverpool Road Station in Manchester. I realised that here was an engine of great historic and technical interest as well as an example of an inverted vertical engine which we did not have. When I went to measure up the engine, the archivist, Charles Somers, asked if the Museum might be interested in any of the electrical test equipment which would also be scrapped. I thought not, but decided to look for the last time at a Siemens zig-zag alternator used to produce variable frequencies. I had been told that this was 18ft in diameter, which I knew was larger than the Ferranti engine. When we entered the room, I realised it was much smaller. Charles found a tape measure and we crawled over the Siemens rotor and parts of the engine. We guessed that it might be possible just to fit the alternator flywheel under the steam pipe connecting the two cylinders of the engine with a couple of inches to spare. We took the risk and designed foundations for both the Ferranti engine and the Siemens alternator.

While the crankshaft was being turned down by the Central Electricity Generating Board to fit the boss of the alternator, we temporarily erected some parts of the Ferranti engine to show Her Majesty Queen Elizabeth II when she passed through the Goods Shed to visit the Coronation Street set of Granada TV. As final erection proceeded, our assessment was correct. The rotor of the alternator fitted but brackets for a stay on the stator rings had to be removed to clear the steam pipe. So the engine now shows a very early form of alternating current generator. More than that, the engine itself has many important technical features as well as its layout occupying little space. The valves are a form of grid slide valve designed by Ferranti to give quick opening to large ports. The valve gear for the inlets is based on some form of Fink mechanism to give variable cut-off on the inlet. Cylinder bores are 15in and 30in but the stroke is only 15in for the high speed. The cranks are fitted with balance weights to give smoother running, a very early example. All the moving parts are totally enclosed to prevent the oil from the pressure lubrication system splashing everywhere. The backs of the main bearings are curved to allow for variations in the inclination of the vertical stanchions and the cross steam pipe as they warm up. The engine runs very happily in its present resting place.

Inverted Vertical Multiple Expansion Engines

High speed was a feature of most of these vertical engines. For example, the little Scott and Hodgson vertical side-by-side compound engine for Diamond Rope Works, Royton, ran at 90 r.p.m. It had cylinders of (H.P.) 14in and (L.P.) 30in with Corliss valves and the short stroke of 2ft 6in. The mill had been used for fustian cutting in 1891 before being purchased in 1898 by Hardman, Ingham and Dawson Ltd and changed to making cotton ropes, such as those fitted to mill-engine flywheels or the thin banding for driving spindles on mules. The engine with its 10ft diameter flywheel and 14 ropes was erected in 1912 and continued to supply 250 h.p. for sixty years until production ceased in 1972 after fire destroyed part of the mill. It must have been the last vertical engine running in a cotton mill and has been taken out for preservation by the Northern Mill Engine Society.

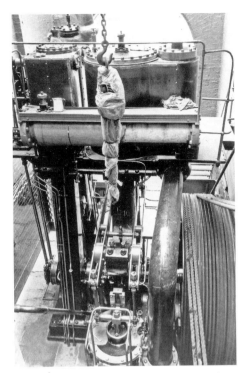

Corliss inlet valve release mechanism on the high-pressure cylinder of the Diamond Rope Works engine.

The side-by-side inverted vertical compound engine at Diamond Rope Works with flywheel on the right and high-pressure cylinder to the left.

The crankshaft of the Diamond Rope Works engine.

The column supporting the low-pressure cylinder of the Diamond Rope Works engine.

The success of the in-line vertical triple-expansion engine at sea led to its introduction into textile mills. With three connecting rods, the cranks could be set at 120° which gave an exceptionally smooth running engine even though the weights of the high- and low-pressure cylinders differed greatly. Both Buckley & Taylor and Saxon built engines of this type after 1900. A 1,200 h.p. engine was supplied by Saxon to the Cedar Mill at Ashton-under-Lyne in 1905. Cylinder bores were high-pressure 20½in, intermediate 32in and low-pressure 50in, all with Corliss valves. The stroke was 4ft. The 22ft diameter flywheel rotated at 75 r.p.m. The condenser was in the exhaust pipe which descended from the low-pressure cylinder to the ground. The air pump was placed on the floor of the engine house, worked by a lever from the low-pressure crosshead. It was totally enclosed and lifted the water up to the mill lodge which was above the floor level of the engine house.

To enter by the engine house door and look up at over twenty feet of engine towering above was an impressive sight. This engine was maintained in first-class condition and was still gleaming when it was restarted for

The upper part of the inverted vertical triple-expansion engine at Cedar Mill at the low-pressure end with the exhaust pipe in the foreground.

George Saxon inverted vertical triple-expansion engine with Corliss valves. The condenser lies below floor level, but the tops of the two air pumps can be seen on the left.

The lower part of the inverted vertical triple-expansion engine at Cedar Mill with the air pump levers to the right. The height of the engine can be judged by the men in the bottom left corner.

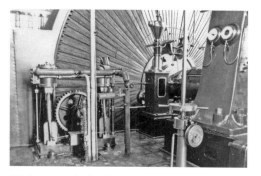

All the controls for the engine at Cedar Mill were situated by the flywheel with the handwheel for the main steam valve, barring engine, governor and pressure gauges grouped together.

Two of the stanchions supporting the cylinders at Cedar Mill with main bearings for the fabricated crankshaft. The coupling joining parts of the crankshaft can be seen in the centre.

filming by Courtaulds after it had stood for six months. Originally it was lubricated with grease but this was changed to a gravity flow oil system, with a storage tank on the cylinder floor. This meant that guards had to be fitted to stop the oil splashing out, which hid some of the moving parts. On the other hand, with the fully enclosed air pump, no water splashed onto the engine as sometimes happened on horizontal engines with open-topped air pumps. The cast ironwork was painted brown and the mahogany boarding of the flywheel was a rich red, beautifully polished. When starting the engine, the engineer had the flywheel to his left with the barring engine and governor on the same side. With his hands, he opened the main steam valve, keeping his eyes on the pressure gauges on the stanchion in front, so he could control everything from one position. Once the valves had been set correctly, this engine ran very smoothly. When it was run for filming, the engineer was apprehensive that it might be difficult to control because the ropes had been removed but it gave no trouble although it needed careful watching to prevent it running away. Some of the oil guards were removed so it was possible to watch the complex array of connecting and valve rods flashing past each other at 75 r.p.m, seemingly in confusion, yet in perfect harmony. Alas the engine was scrapped and the mill demolished.

The Manhattan Engine

Another layout, called the Manhattan, was a combination of both horizontal and vertical types. It came into prominence when Edwin Reynolds was called to New York in 1898 for consultation about some high-power engines for the Manhattan transport system. Coming to the Allis Company in 1877 from superintending the Corliss Works in Providence, Reynolds led the Milwaukee firm to first rank in the design and building of mill, mining and central generating stations of the largest capacity. He sketched out his ideas for 10,000 h.p. reciprocating engines while on the train. The originality of his design lay in the position of the four cylinders since the high-pressure ones were horizontal and the low-pressure ones vertical, compounded in pairs on either side of a flywheel alternator. The pistons on each side drove a common crank pin with the cranks set at 135° so that there were eight strokes on each revolution instead of the usual four. Vertical and horizontal pistons connected in this way had no dead position and this, together with the eight power impulses, gave an exceptionally smooth-running compact type of engine. The reciprocating forces of the vertical piston and connecting rod helped to counterbalance those of the horizontal.

The total weight of engine and alternator was 720 tons, of which the static field coils weighed 185 tons at 32ft diameter. The engines could indicate up to 11,000 h.p. These first 'Manhattan' engines were so successful that the design was copied for the New York Interborough Rapid Transport Company in 1902 with drop valves replacing Corliss on the high-pressure cylinders. Here only nine 10,000 h.p. superheated engines were installed instead of the twelve proposed. The last was scrapped in 1958. They had been chosen after careful consideration had been given to steam turbines. Yet by October 1904, when these enormous reciprocating engines had been commissioned, steam turbine design had advanced so rapidly that turbines would be considered for any future increase in generating capacity.

The Manhattan engine was copied in Britain for both textile mills and electricity generating stations. London County Council opened its Greenwich generating station in May 1906 with only four of the planned eight Manhattan engines built by Musgrave. These were rated at 3,500kW each at 94 r.p.m. with steam at 180 p.s.i. The valves were Corliss with high-pressure cylinders 33½in, low-pressure 66in bore and stroke 4ft. The two high-pressure cylinders were placed in the vertical position. These sets were magnificent examples of British engineering but were obsolete before they left the drawing board. Four 5,000kW turbo-generators were added in 1910 and the first Manhattan was scrapped in 1914 and the last by 1922.

Meanwhile Saxon had built a few for cotton spinning mills. Fox Mill, Hollinwood, should have been a double mill with two engines but the second part of the mill was never completed. The 1909 Manhattan engine had only two cylinders, high-pressure 28in and low-pressure 56in bores, 5ft 6in stroke with Corliss valves throughout. In this case, the high-pressure cylinder was again vertical and the air pump was driven off the tail rod of the low-pressure cylinder. At 75 r.p.m., the engine indicated 1,700 h.p. to drive the 57,680 mule and 49,344 ring spindles. It was scrapped in about 1964. It was dwarfed

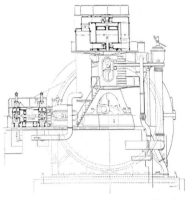

Layout of a Manhattan engine for the New York Interborough Rapid Transport Company with high-pressure cylinder horizontal on the left, low-pressure cylinder vertical at the top and condensing apparatus on the right.

One of the 10,000 h.p. Manhattan type engines with two horizontal high-pressure cylinders and two vertical low-pressure ones for the Interborough Rapid Transit Company built by Allis-Chalmers in 1904.

The Manhattan engine for Fox Mill
with the low-pressure cylinder horizontal and the high-pressure vertical, photographed in 1947.

by another Saxon Manhattan engine for the Pear Mill at Bredbury.
Here again the second projected mill was never built but the spacious
four-cylinder engine was completed in 1913. There were 140,000 mule
spindles in the finished mill which were driven from the right side of
the engine only, giving 1,850 or 2,000 h.p. at 77 r.p.m. from that single
crank. The left side was never used. Here the American layout was followed with the 30in high-pressure cylinder with drop valves horizontal
and the 60in low-pressure cylinder vertical. No information has been
found about the condensing apparatus. The 24ft diameter flywheel was
15ft wide with three separate pulleys for 76 ropes, the widest of any
British cotton mill. The engine stood 28ft high and was 41ft long. Had
it developed its full power of up to 4,000 h.p., it would have been the
most powerful of any in a British cotton spinning mill.

The Uniflow Engine

Right at the end of the reciprocating steam engine era appeared one based on scientific thermodynamic principles which enabled it to compete for a while not only with the steam turbine but also the diesel engine. It was
called in Britain the 'Uniflow' because the flow of steam from each end of the cylinder was only towards the
centre and not 'counter-flow' as in ordinary engines. This type was normally double-acting with inlet valves
at either end of the cylinder and the steam exhausted through a central ring of ports in the middle which were
closed by the movement of the piston. The piston had to be made almost as long as the length of the stroke;
about ten per cent less was customary. The steam entered at one end of the cylinder, pushed the piston along
and was cut off at the appropriate point. After expanding for the rest of the stroke, most of it escaped through
the exhaust ports and what remained was compressed as the piston returned, raising its temperature. The
attractive feature of the Uniflow engine was the good thermodynamic layout because the inlet ends always
remained hot and the centre with the exhaust stayed cold. The residual steam was reheated by compression

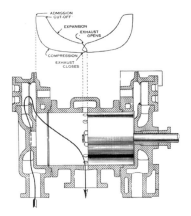

The Uniflow principle where steam
enters at one end of the cylinder and
exhausts through the central ring of
ports.

A Willans inverted vertical
tandem compound engine with
two sets of cylinders and steam
admission controlled by central
valves.

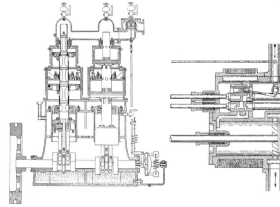

The drawing in Todd's 1885 patent
specification showing the Uniflow
cylinder and complex layout of
valves.

back to the temperature of the incoming saturated steam, thus avoiding the fresh steam having to reheat the ends of the cylinder and piston.

The Uniflow type of engine was used by Jacob Perkins in England in 1827 and patented in America by Eaton in 1857. A form of Uniflow engine was pioneered by Peter Willans in his high-speed launch engine in 1874.[23] In his first layout, there was a line of three single-acting vertical cylinders so arranged that an extension on top of one piston acted as the valve controlling steam admission to the next. In compound or triple-expansion working where the cylinders were placed one on top of the other, the piston itself uncovered ports which exhausted the steam to the next cylinder. But it is doubted whether he deliberately used any compression of steam to reheat the cylinder, a crucial concept in the Uniflow engine.

The importance of this was certainly recognised by Leonard Jennet Todd who took out a patent for a 'Terminal-exhaust' engine in 1885. He aimed:

> … to produce a double acting steam engine which shall work more efficiently, which shall produce and maintain within itself an improved gradation of temperature extending from each of its two Hot Inlets to its common central Cold Outlet, which shall cause less condensation of the entering steam, and which shall work with greater economy than has hitherto been the case.[24]

He had all the right ideas and took out further patents. It is not known how many, if any, Uniflow engines he may have built but none came into general production at this time. One problem may have been that, on condensing engines, should there be no vacuum when starting or the vacuum fail when running, the compression of a cylinder full of steam at atmospheric pressure might give rise to dangerously high pressures. The idea was not taken up at this time even though it was realised that there were advantages in closing the exhaust valve on a counter-flow engine before the end of the stroke 'in sufficient time to enable the steam filling the space... to be compressed, and thus raised to a temperature equal to or approaching that of the incoming steam. In this way the initial condensation of the steam is avoided'.[25]

There the Uniflow engine might have been left but for Professor Johann Stumpf of Charlottenburg, Germany. While he was in America in the late 1890s, he worked on steam turbine design which prompted him to wonder whether a similar unidirectional flow of steam could be achieved in a reciprocating engine. He realised that, in a turbine, the steam went in hot at one end, had its energy extracted axially, and emerged at the other end in the cold exhaust. Just as Watt, many years earlier, had pondered how to keep his cylinder hot to avoid initial condensation and his condensing chamber cold, so Stumpf became more and more convinced of the need to keep the inlet end of a reciprocating engine cylinder hot and the exhaust end cold. But this was impossible in the usual double-acting counter-flow engine of his day in which the steam, having expanded, done work and lost heat, cooled the cylinder as it was exhausted.

Stumpf found an answer by placing in effect two single-acting cylinders end to end with inlet valves at their outer ends and a ring of ports in the centre – in other words the Uniflow engine. This layout enabled Stumpf to expand the steam in one cylinder, instead of in two or three stages, so that the number of working parts was reduced and the cost of building, lubricating and maintaining Uniflow engines was less than conventional engines. But there were snags. A large ratio of expansion was necessary to produce the most work from a given quantity of steam. In some cases, this ratio could be as high as 35 or 45 to 1 in a condensing Uniflow with a good vacuum. This meant that the single cylinder had to be quite large. One way of reducing the size while maintaining the same power was to make the engine run more quickly but then the engine had to be built more strongly with forced lubrication. Because the steam was being expanded in a single stage, the inlet period was very brief. Often the cut-off at full load was only ten per cent of the stroke, compared with twenty-five to fifty per cent in an ordinary engine. Control of the cut-off valve became much more critical. Then the reciprocating parts had to be made heavier and more accurately to withstand the force of the steam from full boiler pressure down to final exhaust pressure and there was the large mass of the piston to be controlled.

Stumpf realised that the compression of the steam left in the cylinder after the piston had closed the exhaust ports was a thermodynamic advantage because, during its compression, it became hot. This could bring that end of the piston, the cylinder walls and cover back up to the temperature of the incoming steam and so avoid condensation. He also realised the potential hazard should too much steam be left in the cylinder and the compression become dangerously high. Stumpf claimed that he had been unaware of previous inventions in this field and said, 'Probably if I had advised myself fully of the work done by these gentlemen, I might have been led astray. My investigations, however, have been entirely untrammelled'.[26] No doubt Stumpf soon realised that he could not patent the basic concept of the Uniflow engine but during 1908 he had six patents sealed for improvements. In his first he applied steam-jacketing to the cylinder head or cover and part of the end of the cylinder itself.[27] This was based on his principle of keeping the hot end as hot as possible. He claimed that the extra thermodynamic gains more than justified the extra complexity of the cylinder head design and the greater difficulty in stripping the engine down for maintenance or in cases of breakdown.

Stumpf took out two patents crucial to the success of the Uniflow. They were for an improved form of valve gear and for what may be termed 'expansion chambers'.[28] The problem with the valve gear lay in the combination of higher rotating speeds and shorter valve opening periods which necessitated quick and precise closing if the engine were to be governed by cut-off. Corliss valves could not meet these conditions since this form of valve gear was not suitable for speeds much over 100 r.p.m. and cut off less than one sixth of the stroke. The greater speed of the Uniflow

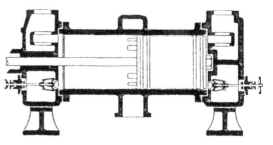

Expansion chambers at the inlet ends of a Uniflow cylinder with hand controls to open the valves.

engine and the need for the greatest possible expansion meant that the inlet valve could be open for less than a twentieth of a second. Stumpf's patent described how he would use drop valves, which were not only much lighter than Corliss but could cope both with high-pressure and high-temperature superheated steam. It was essential that the valves did not leak during the return stroke of the piston, otherwise the increased volume of the steam would cause the pressure inside the cylinder to rise too much. Nearly all Uniflow engines were fitted with various forms of these valves.

Stumpf's other patent provided a solution to the problem of excessive compression, particularly when starting a condensing engine. He proposed to make another chamber in the cylinder head which would be connected to the cylinder by a valve so it could act as an additional clearance space or expansion chamber. There could be two or three chambers, all interconnected by their own valves if necessary. Self-acting spring-loaded valves might be fitted while, in Britain, it was the job of the engine driver on starting up to turn hand-wheels and open these valves. Of course the man had to remember to close them when proper running conditions were reached. This did not solve the case when vacuum was lost while running but at least Stumpf had found solutions for making a workable Uniflow engine.

Stumpf's first engine was built in 1908 by the Erste Brunner Maschinenfabrik-gesellschaft in Brunn, then in Austria but now in Czechoslovakia. By the end of July 1911, he claimed that there were Uniflow engines with a total output of over half a million horsepower working or under construction. Most, if not all of these, would have had only a single cylinder. In Britain, Musgrave were the first to construct one in 1909. They took out a licence from Stumpf and, on 5 May 1910, supplied a single-cylinder 500 h.p. engine to J. Nuttall and Sons. Over the next ten years, they built at least 54 Uniflow engines ranging from 150 to 1,000 h.p. which was nearly half their entire output. All ran at over 100 r.p.m. with the fastest 200 r.p.m. There may have been others with different valve gear, so the total may have been 66. In 1926, Musgrave closed and their goodwill was taken over by Galloway. At least sixteen other manufacturers in Britain built Uniflows. It is not known when Robey started but Cole, Marchent and Morley and Hick Hargreaves both began in 1911. Hick Hargreaves supplied Robert Walker with a 200 h.p. one running at 75 r.p.m. and had built nine by 1914 ranging

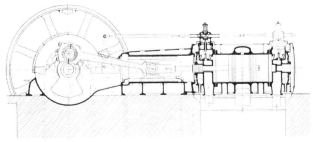

An early Uniflow engine designed by Stumpf.

from 180 to 1,000 h.p. with speeds from 47 to 130 r.p.m. They displayed a 325 h.p. example at the British Empire Exhibition at Wembley in 1924 and built their last in 1937. Galloway had entered the market by 1914 when one was supplied to a firm in London. Later they were to become leaders in this field, also exhibiting an engine at Wembley.

Superheated Steam in Uniflow Engines

While Stumpf realised that his engine was suitable for superheated steam, he did not advocate this because he claimed that 'the una-flow steam engine must give almost the same economic efficiency with superheated as with saturated steam'.[29] His reasoning may have been that, in recompressing the residual steam, the pressure could not be raised above that of the incoming steam, for this might cause the valves to lift and in any case would hinder the entry of the next charge of steam. If the steam in the cylinder remained saturated, its temperature would be in a fixed relation to that related to that pressure and would not have become superheated. Therefore if superheated steam were used, it would have been hotter than the temperature of the cylinder and there would have been heat wasted in warming up the cylinder to the superheated temperature. In practice it was found that, although losses due to initial condensation were greatly reduced in the Uniflow engine, they were still present, so that there was some advantage in using superheated steam. Musgrave's catalogue of their Uniflow engines published in 1910 stated, 'In taking up the manufacture of this Engine, our chief aim is to supply our clients with an Engine *in which highly superheated steam of high pressure can be most favourably and economically utilized*'.[30]

As boiler pressures rose and superheated steam became more common, it grew more difficult to accommodate the expansion within a single cylinder. Not only did the size of the cylinder increase in proportion but the cut-off had to be shortened. The pressure in the cylinder, and therefore the turning force on the crank, fluctuated widely from full pressure at the beginning of the stroke to very little at the end. Once again the weight of the parts needed to withstand the great pressures was acclaimed as a virtue since their inertia would help to even out the turning force on the crank. For example, there was one Uniflow piston for a 60in diameter cylinder that weighed 5 tons. F.B. Perry claimed:

> The early cut-off in a cylinder large enough to give the required ratio of expansion implies a high initial load upon the piston and consequently heavy working parts. The weight of these parts, however, is not without advantage, in as much as their inertia reduces the stresses on them and tends to equalize the turning effort throughout the revolution.[31]

It is surprising that the old argument should have surfaced once more at this late date. It was pointed out that a single-cylinder Uniflow would still have two dead points and that no advantage of inertia of the parts could get over that.

The Most Economical Reciprocating Steam Engines

To take full advantage of superheated steam, right at the end of the reciprocating mill engine era appeared a type with the most thermodynamically efficient layout that has been devised. Superheated steam entered a high-pressure counter-flow cylinder from where it passed into a Uniflow low-pressure cylinder. As well as the thermodynamic gains, this had two further advantages. In a tandem compound layout, this gave more equal forces on the crankpin and an even better balance in a cross compound. In addition, many mills needed low-pressure steam for process work which could only be obtained from a single cylinder Uniflow through special valves. It was advantageous to use a high-pressure counter-flow cylinder as a sort of reducing valve to bring the steam pressure down to that needed so that power and heat generated in this way cost very little more than raising the process steam directly. A counter-flow high-pressure cylinder could gain all the advantages of superheated steam. Then with a Uniflow low-pressure cylinder which exhausted into a condenser, this second cylinder could be designed to take maximum advantage of Uniflow principles with small clearance spaces, good compression and easy exhaust to condenser. It is interesting to note that the East Lancashire Paper Mill Company was supplied with a 1,000 h.p. single-cylinder Uniflow engine by Musgrave in 1910, one of the earliest they built. Then in 1926, this same mill received a Musgrave 2,500 h.p. tandem compound drop valve engine with counter-flow high-pressure cylinder and Uniflow low-pressure. Pass-out steam was taken off between the two cylinders for the steam drying cylinders on the paper-making machine. This engine also drove a DC dynamo on the crankshaft and the pulp-preparation beaters through shafting.

Galloway evolved their compound high-pressure counter-flow and low-pressure Uniflow cylinder engines in two stages. First they produced a tandem compound layout. The problem with the pass-out or heat extraction engine has always been that the need for power might not balance the need for process steam. Some steam might be wasted if the engine exhausted too much or more had to be added if the engine did not pass enough.

Also the steam being used for processing needed to be kept at a constant pressure however much the consumption might vary. In the tandem compound layout, the high-pressure cylinder could exhaust at a constant pressure and what was not needed for processing would go into the low-pressure cylinder and through that into the condenser. The combined power from the two cylinders would turn the single crank.

In a cross compound engine, the turning forces on the two cranks needed to be approximately equal. In the ordinary type of cross compound in a textile mill, the load for power would be fairly constant and so the inlet valves on the low-pressure side were set with a fixed cut-off suitable for driving half of that load. Changes in load were met by the governor altering the cut-off on the high-pressure cylinder which meant that the steam pressure in the transfer pipe between the cylinders would vary. This, of course, was unacceptable when steam was being taken away for other processes in a mill. Therefore a dual governing system had to be devised, one for speed against load and the other to control the speed and intermediate pressure against varying extraction of steam.

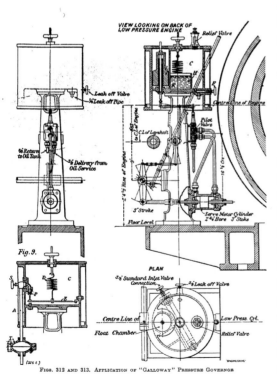

Fig. 9.

FIGS. 312 AND 313. APPLICATION OF "GALLOWAY" PRESSURE GOVERNOR

Galloway's regulator for maintaining the intermediate pressure in a pass-out engine.

For their cross compound steam extraction engine, Galloway developed a special type of pressure regulator. When the pressure in the transfer pipe between the cylinders fell through too much steam being taken off, the regulator operated a servo-motor which reduced the cut-off of the inlet valves on the low-pressure cylinder. This reduced the steam consumption of the engine and diverted it to the mill. At the same time, it also reduced the engine speed. At that point, the governor of the high-pressure cylinder operated to let more steam into the engine and so the balance was restored once more. It was claimed that overall thermal efficiencies exceeding fifty per cent might be attained, whereas in the most favourable cases, the efficiency of ordinary condensing Uniflow engines rarely exceeded twenty per cent. Steam extraction engines with counter-flow superheated high-pressure cylinders and Uniflow low-pressure cylinders may be considered the ultimate development of reciprocating mill engine designs.

The Elm Street Mill Engine, Burnley

Therefore when the 1926 Galloway engine at Elm Street Mill, Burnley, was offered to the Museum in Manchester, it was realised that it would be an excellent exhibit for not only was it probably the last new reciprocating steam engine in any cotton weaving shed but it was also the most technically advanced design. While its preservation would be a great prize, it was realised that its removal would be difficult and would require a great deal of sweat, toil and tears. Elm Street Mill was a room and power mill where the engine provided the driving force through line shafting to four separate weaving concerns. The large weaving sheds lay to one

The counter-flow high-pressure cylinder is on the left and the Uniflow low-pressure cylinder on the right of the cross compound Galloway engine at Elm Street Mill.

The low-pressure side of the Elm Street Mill engine. The big end and balanced crank are concealed under a heavy cover to prevent the oil supplied under pressure from spraying everywhere.

The drop double-beat inlet valves on the high-pressure cylinder at Elm Street Mill were operated by hydraulic pressure. The governor weights are protected by a cylindrical cover.

side of the two-storey mill block in which were situated the stores for yarn and cloth and the warp preparation machines. The engine was in the middle, with access from the road, past the boiler and up through a small hole in the wall. The crane over the engine had capacity only for the smallest parts and the site was impossible to reach with any mobile crane. Yet Galloway removed the earlier fire-damaged cross compound engine, perhaps by Roberts of Nelson, and installed theirs in six weeks, which was a major achievement.

They had to design an engine that would fit within the space in the building and onto the bed of the earlier one. The result was another cross compound with a 21in diameter counter-flow high-pressure cylinder on the left called *Brian*. On the right was the 38in diameter low-pressure cylinder called *David*, both 3ft stroke. These dimensions have been checked against those of a Galloway single-cylinder Uniflow exhibited at the Wembley Exhibition in 1924 and show that the one at Elm Street Mill was larger. Both cylinders had double-beat drop inlet valves while the exhaust valves on the high-pressure cylinder were the piston drop type. One of these caused a rare major stoppage when part of the casing broke. The agreements with the weaving companies allowed for a short period in which to rectify a breakdown after which penalties were incurred by the owner of the mill. In this instance, a repair was cobbled together to enable the engine to carry on for the rest of that day until something more permanent could be fitted during the night. Otherwise this engine ran satisfactorily for over forty years. Steam at 150 p.s.i. was superheated to 500 or 600°F (265–316°C). The speed has been given as both 114 and 125 r.p.m., generating 600 or 1,000 h.p.

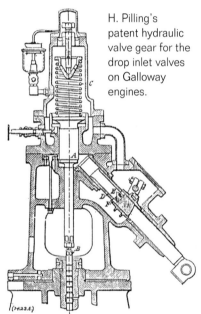

H. Pilling's patent hydraulic valve gear for the drop inlet valves on Galloway engines.

To operate the inlet valves and give short cut-off, Henry Pilling of Galloway patented a mechanism operated by hydraulic pressure.[32] On the layshaft at the side of the cylinder, an eccentric for each valve operated a plunger pump so oil pressure lifted the valve. The timing was set to give a constant point of valve opening while variable closure was achieved by the governor controlling a release valve. A spring in an oil-filled dashpot closed the valve in the usual way. This hydraulic valve gear gave remarkably effective control of the cut-off from about zero to around sixty per cent of the stroke and needed very little power to operate it. It was fitted to the Elm Street Mill engine and, after forty years in the mill, it needed no attention when erected again in the Museum. Eccentrics worked the exhaust valves in the usual way. To keep the steam extraction pressure constant, Galloway's pressure regulator controlled the cut off on the low-pressure cylinder through similar hydraulically operated inlet valves.

Different companies developed their own compression relief valves on Uniflow cylinders. For some years, Cole, Marchent and Morley engines were fitted with cam-operated, spring-loaded relief valves which had three settings. While warming up, a lever was placed in one position which kept the valves fully open so they acted as drain valves. When starting, the lever was moved to a second position which allowed the cams to hold the valves open during the return stroke but to close them during the power stroke. In the third position, the cams were inoperative for running when the vacuum was established. The valves then acted as spring-loaded relief valves which opened if the vacuum failed. But this mechanism relied on the memory of the engineer to attend to it properly. What was needed was a device that would release steam or air in starting before compression commenced. Both Robey and Galloway produced mechanisms worked by the vacuum. The Robey gear consisted of small auxiliary exhaust valves in each cylinder head, operated by cams fixed on a common shaft. There was a clutch on the end of this shaft which was engaged through a small cylinder and piston which had the underside connected to the exhaust passage and the upper side to atmospheric pressure. The necessary balance of pressure was achieved by means of a coil spring underneath the piston. When the vacuum was low, e.g. when starting or running non-condensing, the action of the spring engaged the clutch and the auxiliary exhaust valves came into action. Upon resumption of normal vacuum, the piston descended and the relief valves stopped working as the clutch was disengaged.

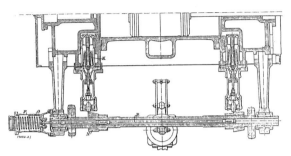

Galloway had a similar but neater arrangement. In their case, a small cylinder, with its spring-loaded piston linked up to the exhaust pipe, was placed horizontally at the end of the camshaft on which were fixed two eccentrics for the inlet valves and two cams to work auxiliary relief valves. These cams were free to slide along the camshaft and were pushed or pulled along it depending upon the degree of vacuum in the small cylinder at the end. The cams were tapered to give maximum lift at one end, for use when

The Galloway pressure relief valves for Uniflow cylinders.

there was no vacuum, to no lift at all when the vacuum had been created. On the Elm Street Mill engine, this mechanism was connected to the exhaust passage round the centre of the cylinder. Galloway had developed a compression release gear which not only gave full opening during starting but also a graduated opening related to the state of the vacuum should the vacuum begin to fail at any time during running.

At Elm Street Mill, the exhaust steam passed to a vertical condenser underneath the engine from where the condensate was extracted by an Edwards air pump driven off the tail rod of the high-pressure cylinder. Cold water came from the canal on the other side of the road and beyond a mill. The crankshaft was fitted with balance weights, the only example seen in a textile mill, to give smooth running. When we were dismantling the engine and took off the links driving the air pump bucket, the engine gave a quarter turn, so finely was it balanced. To cater for thermal expansion, the tail rod slides on both sides were supported on bearings that could slide along the tops of their pedestals. The cylinders themselves were secured rigidly at their front ends to the trunk crosshead guides but were allowed to rock at the back where they were mounted on spherical bearings.

The low-pressure cylinder was a single very complex casting with the central ports and exhaust steam passage all in one piece. On some large engines, Galloway made this cylinder from three pieces, the central ports being cast separately and bolted between the ends which were turned taper to allow for the greater expansion of the hotter outer ends. The crossheads, little ends, big ends and main bearings were totally enclosed because they were lubricated with oil at 30 p.s.i. To keep the rope speed down the 4ft wide flywheel was only 11ft

6in diameter, grooved for 16 ropes. The frictional load was 155 h.p. yet the engine and all the mill shafting could be turned by a single cylinder barring engine of 15 h.p. To start the mill, this little engine rotated the big one until an inlet valve opened when the engineer, Jim Castling, would open the main steam valve. It was an impressive sight as the engine gathered speed and away went the mill.

In 1967, two of the weaving concerns gave notice that they would close and it proved uneconomic to continue running the engine for the remaining two. The offer of the engine by the owner, Brian Melland, presented me with major

The scene in Elm Street Mill looking towards the high-pressure cylinder soon after dismantling had commenced.

problems, having no suitable storage and virtually no finance but luckily we had employed as technician a highly skilled millwright, Frank Wightman, who had suitable lifting and moving tackle of his own that he was prepared to lend. Storage was solved by the offer of space in a mill near Rochdale but we had to move the engine to two other stores before it finally reached its present home in Manchester, a soul-destroying task. Space around the engine at Elm Street was limited and soon the floor was filled with small parts which we took back to the temporary museum at Grosvenor Street in Manchester. To move the cylinders and larger parts meant taking up the chequer plating forming the floor around the engine, leaving large gaps. Working conditions were not made easier through Frank managing to set the mill on fire, which damaged the roof. During the previous weekend, a new fuel tank had been lifted over the engine and I suspect it had been cleaned out and the volatile residue dumped in the pit beneath the engine.

Small parts could be lowered through the hole in the wall onto a lorry waiting inside the mill building at the door giving access to the boiler. It was also possible to manoeuvre one of Pickford's heavy trailers into this space and build a temporary ramp on it with rails. All the large heavy parts, two cylinders, two flywheel halves, crank, two main bearing pedestals, two trunk guides, two bed plates, condenser and air pump, had to be jacked up, slid on rails to the hole in the wall and carefully lowered with block and tackle onto a succession of trailers. It was a long, slow task lowering six-ton pieces, not helped when some second-hand railway sleepers used for packing proved to be rotten inside and broke up. Special frames had to be fabricated to support the crankshaft and flywheel halves. The beams supporting the air pump were prised from their seatings with pneumatic drills. It is a great tribute to Frank that eventually all the parts were saved but it all took many weeks of hard work.

Lowering the low-pressure cylinder out of the engine room in Elm Street Mill onto Pickfords's trailer.

Erection of the high-pressure side of the Elm Street Mill engine nearly finished at Liverpool Road Station.

The barring engine, flywheel and connecting rod of the Elm Street Mill engine at Liverpool Road Station.

The Uniflow low-pressure cylinder of the Elm Street Mill engine nearly complete at Liverpool Road Station.

When at last the longed-for time came for re-erection, we were able to return to the mill and check the measurements of the engine beds. We started from the hole for one bolt and took all our measurements from that one, giving the distance in imperial units from it to all the others. The architect for Liverpool Road Station wanted metric measurements and the individual distances between each hole. The builder wanted imperial measurements. It was lucky that the final concrete beds could just be modified to fit the engine. Frank had retired before its erection but we were able to sort out all the parts and reassemble them so the engine can run once more under steam to show the final theoretical and technical development of the reciprocating steam engine.

The Steam Turbine

The early twentieth century saw three threats emerging to contest the supremacy of the reciprocating steam engine. That from internal combustion engines never developed to any great extent. The main competition came from the steam turbine and the electric motor. A year or two before 1884, Carl Gustaf Patrik de Laval designed a small reaction steam turbine on the same principle as Heron's Aeolipyle but his name is really associated with the impulse type which he had brought to a practical form by 1889. He passed the steam in a single step through a divergent nozzle from the full pressure of the supply down to the pressure of the exhaust. This gave the steam great speed so the entire capacity for work was converted into momentum with the steam hitting the blades round the periphery of the rotor. In a small de Laval turbine developing about 5 h.p., the rotor made some 30,000 r.p.m. and in one developing 600 h.p. with a mean diameter of 37in, the revolutions were 9,500. At such speeds, it was necessary to introduce gearing between the turbine and a generator, something which de Laval was the first to do. His turbine went into production in Sweden in 1893 and licences for manufacture in Britain were obtained by Greenwood and Batley of Leeds. The de Laval turbine was well suited for powering small generating sets for electric lighting in mills. No heavy foundations were necessary. The sets occupied little space, used little oil and could be started easily. Bamford Mill in Derbyshire was lit by a de Laval turbine generator set and presumably there were others elsewhere.[33]

In 1884, Charles Algernon Parsons patented a different type of steam turbine with a series of rotors set in stages with fixed blades between each.[34] There was a reaction effect as the steam acquired relative velocity and lost pressure as it passed through each ring of moving blades. Parsons was seeking to develop a high-speed motor that would be more suitable for driving electric generators than the reciprocating engines avail-

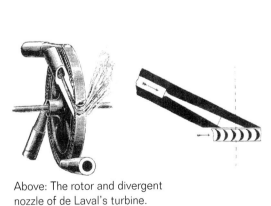

Above: The rotor and divergent nozzle of de Laval's turbine.

Right: A small de Laval turbine electric lighting set of 1895.

179

An early Parsons steam turbine coupled to a centrifugal pump.

able at that time. His first turbine on the axial flow principle was directly coupled to a generator which it turned at 18,000 r.p.m., an unheard of speed, and produced 10 h.p. Over the next years, development by Parsons was phenomenal. In 1892 he experimented with superheated steam and found it gave an exceptionally economical heat engine, with a performance equal to that of the best reciprocating engines. In 1900, two Parsons turbines were sent to Elberfeld in Germany, the first of any type in that country. At 1,000kW they were the largest constructed so far. They confirmed Parsons' prediction that, with increase in size, turbines would show greater economies.

In the same year, 1,500kW Parsons turbines were installed in the Neptune Bank Station of the Newcastle upon Tyne Electricity Supply Company which was already equipped with Wallsend Slipway marine-style four-cylinder triple-expansion reciprocating engines of the most efficient type at that period. During 1901 and 1902, numerous tests were carried out to compare the efficiency of both prime movers. At full load, the steam consumption of the triple-expansion engine was 20.7lb per kW hour and of the turbine 18.4lb in April and 18.1lb in June 1902. As a result of further tests and the performance of turbines elsewhere, 1905 may be said to have been the turning point in the education of engineers as to the efficiency of the turbine. Ferranti had commenced building inverted vertical reciprocating compound engines for driving alternators in his own factory at Hollinwood in 1895 but in July 1905 all his engine-building plant there was offered for sale by auction because the construction of his reciprocating engines had ceased through competition from the turbine. The future of power generation lay in the central electricity station with large steam turbines and not in individual reciprocating steam engines in each mill. However, some large turbines were installed in textile mills.

Gearing to reduce the turbine rotor speed down to one that could drive line shafting or generators in textile mills was essential. Parsons had carried out tests in 1897 on a small launch with a turbine at 33,000 r.p.m. which drove two propeller shafts at 1,500 r.p.m. through helical gearing. Although the machinery worked well, Parsons made no further attempts until 1909 when the tramp steamer *Vespasian*, of 4,350 tons displacement, was purchased and trials carried out on her existing triple-expansion reciprocating engines. Then these were replaced with compound turbines which drove the propeller shaft through double-helical reduction gearing. The steam consumption on a similar voyage ranged from 13½ to 19 per cent less. It was these geared turbines which proved to be suitable for driving the machinery in textile mills directly.

Ferranti's erecting shop at Hollinwood closed by 1905 through competition from the turbine.

A side-by-side compound turbine driving ropes through a gearbox.

180

An early example of a conversion to electric generation by a turbine and electric transmission was Ashworth Hadwens mill at Droylsden where, in 1907, the 1,000 h.p. beam engine and shafting with some ninety pairs of bevel wheels were replaced by a turbo-alternator and numerous motors. The type of turbine is not known. In the spinning mill, one motor was arranged to drive two floors by ropes reaching upwards and downwards. The India Mill of Messrs Kershaw, Leese and Co., Stockport, was driven through ordinary gearing and line shafting by a four-cylinder McNaughted beam engine of 2,000 h.p. In 1913, it was decided to modernise this and the old engine was replaced with a Parsons turbine with separate high- and low-pressure cylinders arranged side by side, rated at 2,300 b.h.p. but capable of developing 2,900 b.h.p. with a steam pressure of 110 p.s.i., superheated to 494°F (257°C). The turbines drove at 3,500 r.p.m. through common reduction gearing at 14 to 1 to a rope pulley turning 44 ropes at 250 r.p.m. Another similar Parsons turbine of 980 h.p. replaced a beam engine and horizontal engine at Osborne Mill, Busk, Oldham, in 1921.

One of the very few new mills to be designed for turbine and rope drive was the last steam-driven cotton spinning mill built in Britain. In 1926, Elk Mill, Royton, was equipped with a Parsons turbine of 2,600 h.p. The compound high- and low-pressure turbines lay side by side, supplied with superheated steam at 260 p.s.i. from four Daniel Adamson boilers. The rotors drove at 5,000 r.p.m. through a common gearbox to a rope pulley 5ft in diameter with fifty ropes at 333 r.p.m. While Elk Mill itself was driven in the traditional way with ropes, an additional shaft from the gearbox passed between the turbine cylinders to turn a 728kW alternator which supplied current to the nearby Shiloh Mill. The turbines and gearbox were only 16ft long and so minute compared with an equivalent reciprocating engine. It was a highly economical plant which was still driving the last spinning mules in 1972.

While Scott and Hodgson seem to have worked with Parsons, various other mill-engine builders, such as Adamson, Hick Hargreaves and Musgrave, took up construction of turbines themselves. By 1914, there was a multitude of different designs from which to choose. Turbines could be easily adapted as pass-out engines with steam being taken out at a particular section of the blading where the pressure was appropriate. Turbines continued to replace reciprocating engines either for rope drive or for electric current production. In 1927, Hick Hargreaves installed a seven-stage impulse turbine to replace horizontal engines at Birtwistle and Fielding's mill at Great Harwood. It drove the rope pulley through 18 to 1 gearing. Across in Yorkshire, in the 1930s turbines and generators were fitted easily into the engine house designed for a 2,000 h.p. reciprocating engine at Manningham Mills. At Cheapside Mills, Batley, a new house was built for a turbine in 1934–5. But more and more mill owners found it convenient to take electricity supplies from the grid, saving capital investment as well as maintenance. All that was needed was a small building or room to house transformers and switchgear.

Electricity Takes over from Steam

In the second edition of his book on mill construction, produced around 1900, Nasmith wrote:

> With regard to artificial light the most customary one is gas, but the employment of electric light is gradually being extended in this country and elsewhere. It is admittedly a better light for the purpose, and in cost is said to have proved as cheap as gas for large installations.[35]

Electricity was first introduced to mills for lighting and later for power. An early example of electric lighting was at Atlas No. 3 Mill, Bolton, where a small American-made steam engine was installed to drive an electric lighting generator in 1877.[36] Arc lamps must have been the light source at that date but they would have given an intensely bright light, hardly suitable for the comparatively low spinning rooms, so it was not until after the introduction of the incandescent lamp that electric lighting became widespread in larger mills.

By the beginning of 1887, Messrs Rhodes and Sons had equipped their mill at Hadfield with 1,500 Swan incandescent lamps in the most extensive installation of any private establishment in Britain. A pair of Edison-Hopkinson dynamos were driven by 12in wide flat belts from a 170 h.p. single-cylinder horizontal engine. The mill contained 73,566 spindles and 1,300 looms. The operatives preferred the electric light to gas and found they did not suffer as much ill-health. In 1887, Peel Spinning and Manufacturing Company, Bury, had 500 Weston lamps with current supplied from one dynamo driven by the main engine and another by a small high-speed horizontal engine of 25 i.h.p. While it appeared that electric lighting was competitive economically with gas by this time, its introduction was slow, even though the risk of fire was reduced.[37] In the Worsley area, Bridgewater Mill began to use its 170 lamps in June 1895. In the same year, Century Mill in Preston paid out just over £1,800 for its electrical installation. Here the main steam engine is known to have run an alternator.

The method which became the most usual later was to employ a small steam generator set so that lighting would be available for the workers to find their way into and out of the mill at morning and night when the main mill engine would not be running. As well as the de Laval turbine, small high-speed reciprocating engines connected directly to generators were developed for this purpose. One of the best known was the inverted vertical, in-line, double-acting compound of Belliss, Birmingham. The success of this engine has been attributed to the system of forced lubrication to all parts which was patented in 1890 and 1892 by A.C. Pain, a draughtsman in Belliss's works.[38] An oscillating pump driven from the valve eccentric supplied oil at a pressure between 10 and 30 p.s.i. The crankshaft was drilled to take the oil to the big ends and through the connecting rods up to the little ends. Pipes distributed oil to other parts. Such engines were totally enclosed to prevent oil splashing everywhere.

Alley McLellan high-speed single-acting tandem compound engine with central piston valves for both sets of cylinders now preserved in Manchester. Air buffers were fitted between the lower cylinders and crankcase.

Other manufacturers like Galloway or Browett and Lindley of Patricroft quickly followed this lead. W.M. Musgrave took out a patent in 1898. In 1901, W.A. Ashworth and W.S. Parker established a new works at Bury specifically for constructing these engines which would be coupled to generators made by Mather and Platt, Manchester, the Electric Construction Company, Wolverhampton, and others. Ashworth and Parker made engines in sizes ranging from 5 to 1,200 h.p., in compound or triple-expansion versions with three or four cylinders. One four-crank triple-expansion 500 h.p. superheated engine was installed in a woollen mill at Helmshore coupled to an alternator and a dynamo

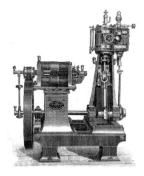

An early Browett and Lindley generating set of 1887 with single-cylinder open crank engine.

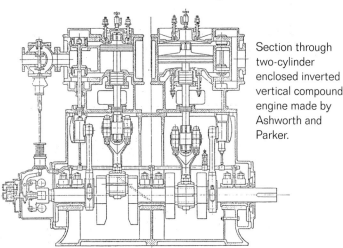

Section through two-cylinder enclosed inverted vertical compound engine made by Ashworth and Parker.

for DC current. Another drove a cotton mill at Todmorden through ropes but such installations with high-speed engines and rope drive were never common.[39]

It was not long before electricity was used to drive the spinning and weaving machinery. This was done in two ways, either through one large electric motor driving line shafting or through individual motors fitted on each machine. In 1895 individual motors were fitted to the ribbon looms and other machinery at the mill of J. Forrest and Co. at Saint-Etienne in France. The power was generated by a single-cylinder horizontal engine of 170 i.h.p. The earliest example so far discovered in Britain is a nameless large calico-printing works with individual Mather and Platt motors fitted on each printing machine in 1898. Each machine was self-contained and the speed could be varied from 5 to 60 yards or more per minute with perfect steadiness.[40] Edison-Hopkinson dynamos supplied the current but the type of engine is not known. Heasandford Shed at Burnley was an early example of electric weaving shed drive, starting in 1903 with a Belliss triple-expansion engine and alternator, which was later replaced by a turbo-alternator. William Bliss Tweed Mills, Chipping Norton, had fitted separate motors on their looms in 1907. The generators were powered by two Crossley 250 h.p. gas engines. These were replaced by a Pollit and Wigzell cross compound engine in 1918 which drove two alternators and continued to power the whole mill for many years.

The two drums of the 20ft diameter flywheel on the cross compound Pollit and Wigzell engine at William Bliss Tweed Mill were separated by one of the walls of the mill. Each side drove a generator.

The 16in high-pressure cylinder with Corliss valves and Whitehead governor at Bliss Tweed Mill. Stroke was 3ft and speed 91 r.p.m.

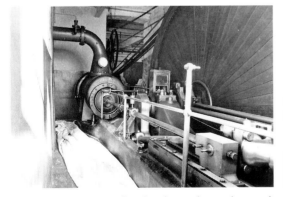

The low-pressure crosshead with coupling rod to work the horizontal air pump beyond the flywheel at Bliss Tweed Mill. The low-pressure cylinder was 32in diameter. Steam pressure was 120 p.s.i. and vacuum 28in.

One of the 375 r.p.m. 250kVA generators driven by the engine at Bliss Tweed Mill. The engine was scrapped in December 1968.

Electric driving became more common around 1906. The Kearsley Spinning Company chose steam turbines and generators to provide its electric power so it retained its boiler house and chimney. The last mill built in the Worsley area, the Walkden Spinning and Manufacturing Company's New Mill, opened in 1907, was the first there to have some machinery driven by electricity with current provided from the mill's massive steam engine. But the future trend was set perhaps as early as 1904 by the Acme Mill at Pendlebury becoming the first mill in Lancashire to adopt all-electric drive from an outside supplier, as a result of which it had no typical chimney. It was a hybrid mill of 80,000 spindles, half mule and half ring. The current was transmitted from the power station at Radcliffe three miles away at 10,000 volts and transformed at the mill to 400 volts. Separate motors were attached to each line shaft in group driving. Meanwhile in Stalybridge three-phase current was supplied to the Premier Mill, opened in 1906, directly from the nearby Stalybridge, Hyde, Mossley and Dukinfield Joint Board's main generating station, being reduced from 6,000 volts to 400 volts by three Westinghouse transformers. The mill was unusual, being only a single-storey shed containing 21,600 ring spindles and 1,017 looms. The shafts in the weaving shed were powered by nine 60 h.p. motors and the ring room by a pair of 150 h.p. motors also by the British Westinghouse Company, as were motors supplying smaller departments. The nearby Ray Mill, completed in 1908 with 66,528 ring spindles and over 9,000 doubling spindles, was also electrically driven. These two mills aggregated some 3,050 h.p. In Yorkshire, the earliest known example of a mill powered by electricity is Becks Mill, Keighley, built in 1907 with large motors placed one to each floor.

In 1912, the total electric power being used in the textile industry could not be determined as that being generated in private plant was unknown. However three power-supply companies provided about 28,000 h.p. Even so, an editorial in the *Mechanical World* stated that 'The question of electrical driving has not yet been settled.'[41] By the end of the First World War, electricity was in common use, with thousands of motors in textile factories across the country producing about two million horsepower in 1919. Country mills often added a generator driven by their water supply. One such was little Cressbrook Mill on the River Derwent. Electricity was supplied to the mill village and woe betide anyone who was not in bed by ten o'clock at night when the sluices were shut and generation ceased.

At Stanley Mill, near Perth, a new hydroelectricity system was installed in 1921. The existing lade was widened and extended to a new turbine house and power station. Swedish Boving water turbines were installed to generate 1,100 h.p. of electricity for the mills, streets and many of the houses in Stanley village. The system was abandoned in 1965. But around this time, a new hydroelectric power station was built by the English Cotton Sewing Company at Belper Mills to use water from the River Derwent.

The last traditional type of multi-storey cotton spinning mill to be built was Sir John Holden's Mill in Bolton, finished in 1927. There was no tall chimney and only a small boiler to provide heating. Its power came from the nearby Bolton Back-o-th-Bank electricity generating station. At one end of the building, the floors of the final bay were lower than the rest so that motors could be placed on them and drive the line shafting directly just under the ceilings. A portent of the future could be seen at the British Empire Exhibition at Wembley in 1924 where, in spite of mill engines being displayed by various manufacturers, the demonstration cotton spinning and weaving machines each had individual electric motors. Certainly in the mills they removed a lot of noise from the rumbling of the line shafting and the flapping of the belts, making mills much pleasanter places in which to work, but they did not have the romance or the appeal of a reciprocating steam engine.

Conclusion

Estimates have been drawn up of the amount of wind, water and steam power used in Britain between 1760 and 1907. The proportion used in the textile industry was not recorded separately. Power from steam eclipsed the combined totals of wind and water soon after 1830 and continued to rise dramatically for the rest of the nineteenth century.

	Wind h.p.	%	Water h.p.	%	Steam h.p.	%	Total h.p.
1760	10,000	11.8	70,000	82.3	5,000	5.9	85,000
1800	15,000	8.8	120,000	70.6	35,000	20.6	170,000
1830	20,000	5.7	165,000	47.1	165,000	47.1	350,000
1870	10,000	0.4	230,000	10.0	2,060,000	89.6	2,300,000
1907	5,000	-	178,000	1.8	9,659,000	98.1	9,842,000[42]

In 1880, Michael Reynolds wrote:

> England is the birth-place of the steam engine. Its invention has been a grand triumph over the material which nature has placed at our disposal. There is no limit to the sphere of its usefulness, nor can anyone measure the benefits which directly and indirectly accrue to society from its employment.[43]

The reciprocating steam engine provided most of the power for that extraordinary phenomenon, the Lancashire cotton industry, which relied on an imported raw material for its manufacturing processes and on exports for its products. The death pangs of this industry were prolonged over many years as mill after mill became uneconomic with others closed through rationalisation schemes. But in many mills, steam engines continued to perform their essential service. In 1966, even the youngest was forty years old and had led a life of hard, constant work. Most engines were sixty or more years old. Almost silently and seemingly effortlessly, these dinosaurs of the Industrial Revolution proved their reliability to the bitter end. This was achieved through the care and devotion of their engineers.

Few visitors penetrated these hallowed chapel-like precincts with their tall windows. Those who did enter the engine house were confronted by shining brass, burnished planished steel lagging and bright steel rods flashing round. Wipes would be placed around the engine to absorb any drip of oil. Walking off the matting laid around the engine onto the surrounding cleaned floors roused black looks from the staff. Yet in 1966 it was realised that modernisation must soon sweep away these old faithfuls. New ring frames driven by electric motors had greater productivity. One newly equipped mill had the productivity of three old ones. But it was never anticipated that even this truncated industry would disappear entirely from Lancashire. This has made the photographic records taken in the 1960s all the more important, together with the few engines and textile machines preserved in museums and occasionally on their original sites. The many who have seen and enjoyed the engines in their new homes may be equally impressed as was M.A. Alderson in 1834: 'The steam-engine, then we may justly look upon as the noblest machine ever invented by man – the pride of the machinist, the admiration of the philosopher'.[44]

NOTES: CHAPTER 5

1   These figures have been compiled from Farnie (1979), pp. 46 and 307, Catling (1970), p. 19 and Tippett (1969), p. 17.

Year	Spindles	Looms
1890	-	614,964
1893	41,632,000	602,672
1903	43,568,000	-
1908	55,218,024	736,325
1913	57,265,000	-
1914	60,000,000	800,000
1923	57,452,000	-
1926	58,206,000	-
1927	60,465,000	-
1930	63,200,000	700,000
1933	47,183,000	-
1935	48,200,000	530,000
1937	-	520,000
1939	36,322,000	-
1944	35,077,000	-
1951	28,252,000	-
1953	26,686,000	-
1959	20,000,000	220,000
1961	-	150,000
1962	10,469,000	-
1967	4,500,000	92,000
1969	4,000,000	-

2   Hills (2003), see tables at end.

3   UK Patents 11,783 and 12,477, 1912; Patent 11,613, 1913 and Patent 19,372, 1914.

4   Northrop loom patents were taken out in the name of A.G. Brooks. See Patents 10,633, 10634 and 10635, all 23 June 1891, and Patent 22,939, 27 November 1894. In 1895, there were further patents, Nos 6,713, 7,615, 16,432 and 24,999. There was also Patent 1,951 in 1896.

5   Patent 14,259, 12 August 1852.

6   Patent 258, 1860.

7   Patent 1,275, 29 January 1885.

8   Patent 1,097, 19 March 1887 and Patent 2,530, 30 June 1877.

9   *World's Paper Trade Review*, 28 November 1913, p. 7 for a description of a Thompson boiler at St Neot's Paper Mill, Huntingdonshire.

10 Fowler (1895), p. ii.

11 Patent 1,852, 2 May 1876.

12 Patent 20,892, 1894 and *Mechanical World*, Vol. 19, 26 June 1896, p. 306.

13 Patent by Hartnell, W. and Guthrie, S., No. 325, 30 January 1868. See *Mechanical World*, Vol. 25, 27 January 1899, p. 41.

14 Patent 3,483, 1 December 1869 by Robey, R. and Richardson, J.

15 Patent 14,431, 9 November 1886 and Patent 13,871, 13 October 1887.

16 Patent 21,847, 3 December 1900.

17 Patent 5,175, 13 March 1894.

18 Patent 52, 9 January 1861.

19 Patent 14,259, 12 August 1852.

20 *Engineering*, 4 January 1867, p. 3 and Nasmith (c.1900), p. 12.

21 Uhland (1878), p. 91.

22 Patents by Fleming, W.Y. and Ferguson, P., No. 2,605, 19 February 1887 and by Musgrave, J and Dixon, G., No. 15,395, 12 August 1893.

23 Patent 974, 19 March 1874.

24 Patent 7,301, 16 June 1885.

25 Nasmith (c. 1900), p. 169, but see *Mechanical World*, Vol. 16, 6 July 1894, p. 1 for editorial arguing that this reduced efficiency.

26 Stumpf (1912), p. iii.

27 Patent 8,371, 15 April 1908.

28 Patent 8,380, 15 April 1908 and Patent 26,020, 2 December 1908.

29 Stumpf (1912), p. 19.

30 Musgrave (1910), p. 13.

31 Perry (1922), p. 734.

32 Patent 152,863, October 1919 by Galloway Ltd. and H. Pilling.

33 *Mechanical World*, Vol. 14, 8 December 1893, p. 221; Vol. 17, 22 February 1895, p. 77; and *Encyclopaedia Britannica*, Cambridge University Press, 11th edn., 1910–11, article 'Steam Engine', p. 843.

34 Patent 6,734, 23 April 1884 and *Encyclopaedia Britannica*, 1910–11, article 'Steam Engine', p. 845.

35 Nasmith (c.1900), p. 81.

36 Williams and Farnie (1992), p. 119.

37 *Mechanical World*, Vol. 1, 29 January 1887, p. 6 and Vol. 2, 30 July 1887.

38 Patent 7,397, 1890 and Patent 11,432, 1892.

39 Ashworth and Parker, *The Parker Engine*, no date, p. 2.

40 *Mechanical World*, Vol. 17, 22 February 1895, p. 73 and Vol. 24, 28 August 1898, p. 90.

41 *Mechanical World*, Vol. 52, 27 September 1912, p. 145.

42 Kanefsky (1979), p. 338.

43 Reynolds (1885), p. 1.

44 Alderson (1834), p. 44.

APPENDIX:
SOME OF THE LAST TEXTILE MILL ENGINES

Beam Engines

Lumbhole Mill, Kettleshulme

This mill, deep in its country valley, was visited in 1967. A single-cylinder beam engine had been added to supplement the high breast suspension waterwheel, 25ft diameter by 6ft wide. Sheldon Bros commenced manufacture of candlewicks here in 1835 and used the engine for around one hundred years. It has been suggested that the engine was supplied by Sherratt's of Salford. The slide valves on the steam cylinder were renewed by J. & E. Arnfield, New Mills, at an unknown date but otherwise the engine appeared to be as originally constructed. The cylinder, 21in diameter by 4ft stroke, developed around 50 h.p. with 40 p.s.i. boiler pressure at perhaps 35 r.p.m. A gearwheel could be moved along the countershaft to engage the engine with the waterwheel.

The new slide valves supplied by J. & E. Arnfield, for the Lumbhole Mill engine.

The parallel motion on the cylinder end of the Lumbhole Mill engine beam.

Left: Looking across the Lumbhole Mill engine house beneath the beam floor from the top of the cylinder.

The crankshaft, governor, flywheel and gearing on the Lumbhole Mill engine.

Whitelees Mill, Littleborough

In November 1841, John Petrie and Co. delivered their forty-seventh beam engine to John Hurst of Whitelees Mill, Littleborough, where it worked for over one hundred years until mid-1942. With cylinder bore 25in and stroke 5ft, it developed 20 h.p. with 20 p.s.i. It cost £650 with a boiler. The original cast iron crankshaft broke and was replaced with a wrought iron one but that was the only replacement during its working life. John Holroyd and Co. Ltd preserved this engine at the end of Petrie's old works near the centre of Rochdale. When that works was demolished, the engine was re-erected at Ellenroad Ring Mill.

General view of the Whitelees Mill beam engine after re-erection in Rochdale.

The handsome slide valve casing of the Whitelees beam engine.

Manchester, Sheffield and Lincolnshire Railway Warehouse, Manchester

Around 1845, Hick Hargreaves supplied a beam engine to work the hoisting machinery in the Manchester, Sheffield and Lincolnshire Railway warehouse at London Road Station, now Piccadilly Station in Manchester. It was a short-stroke design, self-contained with the beam supported on a solid 'A' frame braced to pillars behind the cylinder. It was removed for display at the original York Railway Museum. When that was being redeveloped, the engine was offered to Manchester but we had nowhere to store it so it was taken to Armley Mill Museum in Leeds.

Above: The Hick Hargreaves beam engine originally at the Manchester Sheffield and Lincolnshire Railway warehouse in Manchester preserved at Armley Mill Museum, Leeds.

Right: The cylinder end of the Hick Hargreaves beam engine.

Single Cylinder Horizontal Engines

Warp Mill, Salford

The little engine at Warp Mill, Salford, was supplied by Daniel Adamson in 1888. It had a form of Wheelock semi-rotary valves on the 16in diameter cylinder with 3ft stroke. It generated 120 h.p. at 100 r.p.m. and drove the mill through a single 12in wide flat belt round the 10ft diameter flywheel. J. Eaton and Co. were dealers in fur and this engine ran their plant until electric motors were installed around 1960. The whole mill was demolished towards the end of 1971 when the area was being redeveloped.

The Adamson engine at Warp Mill, Salford, with flat belt drive round the flywheel.

The semi-rotary valve gear beneath the cylinder on the Warp Mill engine.

The marine-type big end on the Warp Mill engine with cross-arm governor in the background.

B. Toone, Nottingham

Little was known about this engine when it was seen in 1968 as a possible example of a Hick Hargreaves engine to be preserved in Bolton. Features such as the trunk guide and Corliss valve gear suggest that the engine could have been made by this firm. It drove through a flat belt on a separate pulley on the crankshaft.

Corliss valve cylinder and trunk guide on the Toone engine.

Crank and pedestal on the Toone engine.

Corliss valve release mechanism on the Toone engine which is the Spencer Inglis type.

Brighton and Hove Engineerium

The centrepiece of the engine displays in the Brighton and Hove Engineerium is this early Corliss-valve engine made by Crepelle and Garand, France, in 1889 when it was awarded a Grand Prix at the Universal Exposition in Paris. With its 13in by 34in cylinder, it developed 91 h.p. at 80 r.p.m. and drove a 50KvA generator. The 13ft diameter flywheel weighs four tons. The manual barring rack around the periphery of the flywheel is unusual for that is where the flat belt would have run. After the Exposition, the engine was moved to the Emile Roux Hospital in Brevannes, south of Paris.

The Crepelle and Garard Corliss-valve engine in the Brighton and Hove Engineerium.

Holmes, Mann and Co., Bradford

This little Corliss-valve engine drove a generator by a flat belt at H.D. Shaw and Co., woolcombers. Later the premises were taken over by Holmes, Mann and Co., saw millers. The engine was installed by Newton Bean and Mitchell around 1921. It was fitted with a 'Bee' governor which controlled the speed to 1%. It was designed for 100 i.h.p. but sometimes developed over twice that.

Above: The 'Bee' governor in the foreground with an open flywheel behind on the little engine at Holmes, Mann and Co.

Right: The Corliss cylinder on the Newton, Bean and Mitchell engine at Holmes, Mann and Co. The generator was situated behind the engine.

Horizontal Tandem Compound Engines

Hartley, Spencer and Co., Burnley

Hartley, Spencer made reeds and healds for looms. Space must have been at a premium when Burnley Iron Works designed this engine in 1895. This little tandem compound had cylinders 8¾in and 17¾in by 2ft stroke. Pollit and Wigzell three-rod design was used so the slide valve cylinders were placed back to back. Also the condensing apparatus was placed alongside the crank. The flywheel was outside the engine room. 90 h.p. was produced at 100 r.p.m with 120 p.s.i. The engine was still working in May 1970 but ceased soon afterwards.

Hartley, Spencer's engine looking towards the end of the high-pressure cylinder with part of the condensing apparatus on the right.

The eccentrics and shapely curved crank on the Hartley, Spencer engine. The pedestal for the main bearing was cast integral with the engine bed.

Queen Street Manufacturing Co., Harle Syke, Burnley

Peace was built by William Roberts, Nelson, in 1895. As it exists today, new Corliss-valve cylinders, 16in and 32in bore by 4ft stroke, were fitted after a fire in 1914. The engine is coupled directly to the line shafting of the weaving shed with a very heavy 14ft diameter flywheel so steps have to be climbed to reach the engine. The colours of the tiling together with the rich brown paintwork and grey planished steel lagging are attractive. The engine and mill with its looms are preserved by the Lancashire County Council.

The barring engine, flywheel and engine at Queen Street Mill.

End of the high-pressure cylinder Peace at Queen Street Mill.

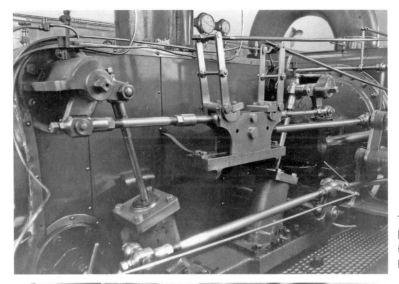

The inclined dashpots on the high-pressure cylinder were a feature on Robert's engines as here at Queen Street Mill.

The Corliss inlet valve gear on the low-pressure cylinder with vertical dash pots at Queen Street Mill.

The front of the low-pressure cylinder at Queen Street Mill with Whitehead governor on the left and arching steam transfer pipe to the right.

Primrose Mill, Harle Syke, Burnley

The Pollit and Wigzell engine at Primrose Mill was another of their three-rod designs supplied in 1905. With cylinders 17in and 35in diameter by 4ft stroke it produced 700 h.p. at 80 r.p.m. with superheated steam at 150 p.s.i. The 20ft diameter flywheel was grooved for 16 ropes to drive 1,700 looms so the engine was heavily loaded for most of its life. The engine bed on the low-pressure cylinder had swellings around the exhaust valve gear probably to give additional strength. It was one of the last steam engines to work in the area for it stopped late in 1975 and was scrapped the following year.

The advantage of Pollit and Wigzell's three-rod design with the cylinders back to back was that the engine was more compact, even with a horizontal air pump behind the low-pressure cylinder as was the case at Primrose Mill.

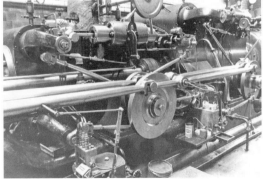

The disadvantage of the three-rod design was that the drive to the Corliss gear might have to be placed further away from the cylinders. On the high-pressure cylinder at Primrose Mill, two rods worked the wrist plates for the valve gear. Behind them is one low-pressure piston rod. The high pressure piston rod is just off the photograph to the left while beyond that was the second low-pressure piston rod.

The low-pressure cylinder of the Primrose Mill engine showing how the engine bed was strengthened over the exhaust valve levers.

Bamford Mill, Derbyshire

The mill of Robert Marsland and Son at Bamford, Derbyshire, had just ceased cotton doubling when visited in November 1965. Rain was pouring down and already causing the river to rise and back up the tail race. That night, as the rain washed the rest of the snow off the hills, the river poured through the mill, flooding the turbines and lowest rooms although the engine house was not affected. This shows the hazards of these country mills and water power. At Bamford, an 18ft diameter waterwheel was assisted by a beam engine. When more power was needed in 1907, water turbines were installed as well as this tandem compound engine by Musgrave.

The engine was a modern design with Stegen drop piston valves on both cylinders. With cylinders 16in and 32in bore by 3ft stroke, 400 h.p. was produced at the fast speed of 100 r.p.m. with steam at 170 p.s.i. super-heated to 550°F. Trouble was experienced with the crosshead and a new one was made and fitted to the original dimensions. On restarting, the engine would not run properly and the bearings overheated. It was discovered that, over the years, the trunk guides on the low-pressure cylinder had shifted or warped slightly out of their proper alignment. A little easing and scraping on one side of the crosshead, and a little burning of midnight oil, put the engine in running order for the following day. Carbolite, the next occupiers of the mill, preserved the engine on site where it still remains even though the mill has been turned into apartments.

Looking down at the Bamford Mill engine from the rope race. The 15ft diameter flywheel is grooved for 14 ropes.

One side of the high-pressure cylinder with the encased governor and Higginson regulator on the right at Bamford Mill.

The other side of the low-pressure cylinder showing the Stegen drop piston valves worked by eccentrics on the rotary shaft at Bamford Mill.

Above: A water turbine at Bamford Mill, now scrapped. The maker was not recorded.

The trunk guide for the crosshead looking towards the oil shield round the crank and typical Musgrave boarding on the flywheel at Bamford.

E. and P. Riley, Walk Mill, Nelson

There were two engines in the engine house at Walk Mill, both by Roberts. They replaced an earlier beam engine in 1908 and drove separate weaving sheds. The smaller 350 h.p. was a tandem compound engine with Corliss valves on the 13½in diameter high-pressure cylinder and slide valves on the 26in diameter low-pressure cylinder, with 3ft stroke running at 75 r.p.m. The mill closed around 1970.

The tandem compound Roberts engine at Riley's Mill with low pressure cylinder closer to the flywheel.

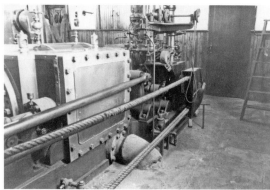

The slide valve cover on the low pressure cylinder at Riley's Mill. The ropes drove the governor which had a cone system to regulate the speed.

The Corliss valve gear and release mechanism on Riley's Mill engine with typical Roberts inclined dashpot.

Shawclough Mill, Rochdale

This was another example of McNaught's small engines similar to the one at Barnes Mill with a few alterations. In 1908, this engine also replaced an earlier one, probably a beam engine, although here the engine house was lengthened. The former engine was probably gear-driven because the main shafting taking the power to the rest of the mill ran on the other side of the engine house wall. If the flywheel had been placed at the inner end in the customary position, the ropes would have been very short. Accordingly, the engine was placed the other way round with its 15ft diameter flywheel beside the window. The ropes ran across the engine house at head level and returned under the floor. The 15in diameter high-pressure cylinder had Corliss valve gear while the 30in diameter low-pressure cylinder, 4ft stroke, had piston valves. At 75 r.p.m. and 160 p.s.i., the engine developed 500 h.p. to drive the mules spinning cotton waste.

The Corliss valve gear on the high-pressure cylinder of Shawclough Mill engine. McNaught retained the under-floor dashpot.

The piston valve on the low-pressure cylinder of the Shawclough Mill engine.

The link to twist the piston valve rod on the Shawclough Mill engine to give better oil distribution.

McNaught's type of barring engine with horizontal cylinder at Shawclough Mill.

John Pilley and Sons, Bradford

A small tandem compound engine built in 1910 by Cole, Marchent and Morley, Prospect Foundry, Bradford. Both cylinders were fitted with Morley's patent piston drop valves on inlet and exhaust.

Left: The cover of the low-pressure cylinder with its piston drop valves on Pilley's engine.

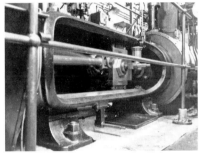

Trunk guide and crosshead on Pilley's engine

Above: The piston drop valve on the high-pressure cylinder of Pilley's engine and on the right the governor with its complex links.

Twin Horizontal Tandem Compound Engines

Dawn Mill, Shaw

George Saxon built many fine twin horizontal tandem compound engines similar to this one at Dawn with high-pressure cylinders to the rear and condensers and air pumps below the crosshead slides. The left side of the red and grey Dawn Mill engine was called *Venus* and the right *Mars*. The high-pressure cylinders were 20½in diameter and the low 40½in with 5ft stroke. Dawn Mill was built in 1901/2 and in 1915 it had 91,000 mule and 8,000 ring spindles. 1,400 h.p. was required to drive them with the engine running at 60 r.p.m. with 140 p.s.i. The 26ft diameter flywheel was 7ft 10in wide, grooved for 35 ropes. The engine was stopped in May 1965 but remained in situ at least until June 1967 when these photos were taken.

The width of the engine room of these large twin horizontal tandem compound engines is well illustrated by Dawn Mill.

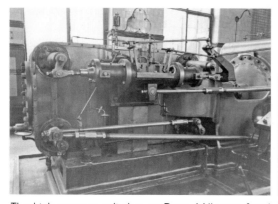

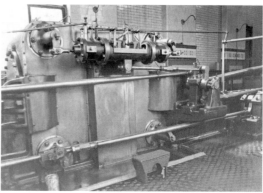

The high-pressure cylinders at Dawn Mill were fitted with Saxon's standard Corliss valve release mechanism controlled by the governor.

The Corliss valve release mechanism on the low pressure cylinders at Dawn Mill was pre-set so much simpler.

The massive flywheel and governor at Dawn Mill.

Philiphaugh Mill, Selkirk

The sources of power for this woollen mill underwent many alterations, starting with multiple waterwheels which were merged into one large wheel. This was replaced in 1878 with water turbines which themselves were replaced in 1920. In 1911, the twin horizontal tandem compound engine by J. Petrie and Co. of Rochdale replaced a beam engine. Cylinders were 12in and 24in bore by 2ft 6in stroke. Corliss valves were fitted on the high-pressure and piston valves on the low-pressure cylinders. At 80 to 100 r.p.m. and 75 p.s.i., the engine gave an additional 500 h.p. for the mill. The crankshaft was linked directly through a clutch to the shaft drive to the mill from the turbine. When seen in June 1969, only the right side of the engine was in use but it was always well kept with the brass beading bright over the planished steel lagging.

The 7-ton flywheel and left side of the Philiphaugh engine with the connecting rod lying on the floor alongside.

The disused left side of the Philiphaugh engine with the main steam pipe crossing to the high-pressure cylinder.

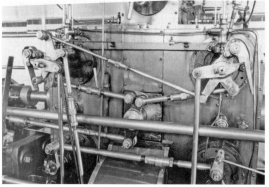

The Corliss valve gear on the right-hand high-pressure cylinder at Philiphaugh Mill.

The rear of the right-hand low-pressure cylinder with tail rod slide and links to the air pump lever.

Horizontal Four Cylinder Triple Expansion Engine

Briar Mill, Shaw

The engine supplied to Briar Mill in 1907 was one of the largest horizontals made by George Saxon Ltd. It developed originally 1,800 h.p. and later 2,000 h.p. It drove 96,768 mule and 25,088 ring spindles in 1915. Cylinder diameters were 25in high pressure, 38in intermediate and 42in for both low-pressures. Stroke was 5ft, speed 65 r.p.m. and boiler pressure 180 p.s.i. The 26ft diameter flywheel weighed 80 tons and carried forty ropes over its 7ft 10in width. This engine was maintained in first-class condition and kept scrupulously clean so that parts were stripped off it when it was stopped in 1964 to keep the other Saxon engines in the Courtaulds Group running. When the photographs were taken in 1967, the engine house was being used as a store for electric light fittings. The high-pressure cylinder showed the later influence of the main steam pipe entering from above, otherwise the engine had the typical shapes and massive construction of other Saxon engines with Corliss valves and Dobson release mechanism on all cylinders.

The high-pressure side of Briar Mill engine. The main steam pipe and parts of the planished steel lagging have been removed.

The intermediate cylinder of the Briar Mill engine with Dobson release mechanism for the Corliss inlet valves.

Part of the flywheel and governor of the Briar Mill Engine.

The outside of the high-pressure side of the Briar Mill engine showing the spacious width and height of the engine house. The pedestal for the main crank bearing and the crosshead slides were separate castings bolted together.

Horizontal Cross Compound Engines

Finsley Vale Mill, Harle Syke, Burnley

In contrast to the engine at Queen Street Mill which was mounted high up to drive the line shaft directly, the one made by Burnley Iron Works in 1904 for two weaving sheds at Finsley Vale was at ground level with steps up either side of the flywheel to reach the top of the rope-race. It was one of Burnley Iron Works's later designs with elegant curved cladding over the tops of the cylinders which were 17in and 35in diameter by 4ft 6in stroke. The paintwork was a bright red. The 18ft diameter flywheel in eight sections had eighteen ropes, nine for each shed. The engine was designed for 500 h.p. although 2,000 looms probably required more. Indicator diagrams taken in October 1964 show that the engine was still producing 294 h.p. at 68 r.p.m. with boiler pressure 135 p.s.i. and a vacuum of 26 1/2 in. The engine stopped on 21 August 1970 and was selected for preservation at the Science Museum in London.

The engine at Finsley Vale Mill with high-pressure cylinder to the left. To the right, the horizontal air pump for the condenser is driven off the tail rod on the low pressure cylinder.

Above: The high-pressure cylinder with its Corliss valve gear at Finsley Vale Mill.

Right: The linkage to work the inlet valves on the low-pressure cylinder at Finsley Vale Mill.

The horizontal condenser and air pump at Finsley Vale Mill.

T. and H. Spinners, Facit

T. and H. Spinners was another mill that took the opportunity presented by the boom years at the beginning of the twentieth century to expand and reorganise. This resulted in Yates and Thom supplying an unusual cross compound engine in 1909 which had to be fitted into a cramped, almost triangular engine house bounded by the road to the back of the mill. This was one of the few engines seen with the tail rod of the 19in high-pressure cylinder driving the air pump, in this case a horizontal one. There was little space between the two. The low-pressure cylinder was 37in diameter. Corliss valves, trunk guides and a stroke of 3ft were common to both. The 19ft diameter flywheel with 13 ropes had two central castings with four spokes each to which the rim segments were bolted. At 82 r.p.m. with 120 p.s.i., this engine developed 850 h.p., a third of which was used to drive an alternator. The engine was stopped on 23 August 1966.

The low-pressure side of the engine at Facit taken from the top of the rope-race from where a single shaft led into the mill.

In between the two cylinders of the engine at Facit. There was no space to fit a tail rod slide on the low-pressure cylinder. The speed recorder was also graced with a clock.

The unusually shaped condenser and air pump situated close behind the high-pressure cylinder of the engine at Facit.

The massive bolts securing the two halves of the fly-wheel spokes on the engine at Facit. On some engines, there were also two steel rings shrunk on.

Saxon Mill, Droylsden

Saxon Mill was newly built in 1907 when Daniel Adamson installed this 1,500 h.p. engine. It was fitted originally with Wheelock valve gear but cracks developed round the valve seatings so that the 27in diameter high-pressure cylinder was replaced by George Saxon in 1941 during the summer holiday and the 56in diameter low-pressure cylinder at the same time in the following year. Saxons fitted Corliss valves with their Dobson trip gear. Stroke was 5ft and speed 67 r.p.m. The air pump was the Edwards type. In 1947/8, superheaters were installed in the boiler house to give 170 p.s.i. at 500°F. The flywheel was 24ft diameter for 36 ropes.

The cross compound engine at Saxon Mill with its later cylinders by George Saxon.

Trunk guides gave the engine a massive appearance, increased by the height of the cylinders off the engine room floor. Many later large cross compound engines had the exhaust valves of the low-pressure cylinder below floor level so that the flywheel was proportionately lower but this Adamson engine towered high above the enginemen oiling her. The iron castings were painted green, showing off the polished steel rods, while the wooden lagging of the flywheel was painted grey. The sweeping arch of the main steam inlet pipe, clad in planished steel something like a knight in armour, added to the commanding presence of this engine. A Whitehead governor was fitted. The engine was still running beautifully when stopped in 1967. Beyond the rhythmical clicking of the Corliss valve gear, there was hardly another sound when running. Once the steam was shut off, the engine immediately broke into a chorus of protests at being made to stop with all the valves clattering and banging as if in anger.

Below: The high-pressure side at Saxon Mill showing spring-loaded pressure relief valves.

The high-pressure side of the engine at Saxon Mill with tail rod slide.

The low-pressure cylinder with tail rod slide and air pump lever at Saxon Mill. The ladder gives an indication of the height.

The low-pressure cylinder Corliss valve gear had vertical dashpots at Walk Mill

E. and P. Riley, Walk Mill, Nelson

This cross compound engine supplied by W. Roberts in 1908 shared its engine house with a small tandem compound. The cylinder dimensions of this larger engine were 18in and 30in diameter by 3ft 6in stroke. At 75 r.p.m. and 160 p.s.i., its 600 h.p. was sufficient in latter years for supplying all the power needed. It was still running in 1968.

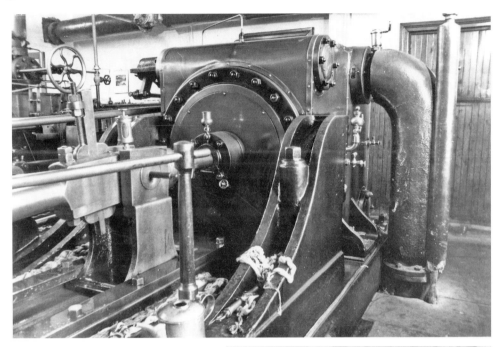

Above: The fronts of the cylinders at Walk Mill were firmly located by the swept-up portions of the engine beds. The single slipper crossheads were very tall.

Right: The governor at Walk Mill had cones for adjusting the setting of the Corlss trip mechanism.

Hawk Mill, Shaw

This fine engine lay awaiting scrapping in March 1967 after stopping in 1964. It had many standard features of Yates and Thom who installed it in 1908 in the newly built Hawk Mill. In 1915 its 2,150 h.p. was driving 108,120 spindles. Its vital statistics were cylinder diameters 27 7/8in and 56in by 5ft stroke with all Corliss valves. Speed was originally 70, later 71½ r.p.m. The flywheel for 37 ropes had twin pulleys 22ft in diameter and a total width of 7ft 11in. The rim speed 4,939ft per min. Oil was fed to the main bearings by drip feeds while Sumners pressure feed lubrication was fitted to supply the Corliss valves.

Parts of the cladding on the low-pressure cylinder on the left of the Hawk Mill engine have been removed.

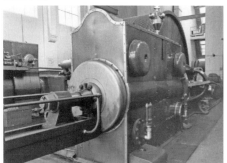

Above: The double curve to the top of the low-pressure cylinder on the Hawk Mill engine was a feature of earlier Yates and Thom engines.

Above right: An advantage of trunk guides was their accurate alignment with and their secure fixing to the cylinder with a ring of bolts.

Right: Trunk guides were another Yates and Thom feature as here on the Hawk Mill engine looking towards the flywheel.

Kent Mill, Chadderton

Kent Mill was built in 1908/9 for 90,000 mule spindles. The spindleage in 1923 has been given as 104,224. Power of 1,200 h.p. was developed in the Corliss-valve cylinders, 25in diameter high-pressure and 52in diameter low-pressure with 5ft stroke. The exhaust passed into a single condensing chamber which was cleared by two air pumps worked off the crosshead slides on either side. The 26ft diameter flywheel, 6ft wide with 30 ropes, turned at 62 r.p.m. Boiler pressure was 160 p.s.i. The flywheel and front half of this engine remained similar to those built by Saxon at Briar, Dawn and Magnet. However the steam pipe was arched over the high-pressure cylinder to give a freer flow and the pipes to the low pressure side were designed with equal care. Tail rods were fitted on both cylinders. Their slides were not the usual pattern of open troughs but were short bearings mounted on pillars through which the rods passed, with a round cylindrical cover stretching beyond. The engine worked until 1964 but had become sadly neglected when seen in May 1967 shortly before scrapping.

Much clutter lay around the Kent Mill engine and parts such as the pressure gauges had been removed from their board near the flywheel.

The high-pressure side of the Kent Mill engine showing the steam inlet pipes high above the cylinder and the tube covering the tail rod.

The exhaust steam passed under the engine to come up on the far side of the low-pressure cylinder in a pipe of ample dimensions. One link from the crosshead to the air pump lever can be seen on the Kent Mill engine.

The Kent Mill engine seems all ready to start. There is even some oil to feed into the banjo lubricator for the big end bearing.

Coldharbour Mill, Uffcombe

Fox Brothers had one mill at Wellington, Somerset, with Crossley Brothers producer gas engines later converted to diesel, as well as this mill at Uffcombe driven by a large suspension waterwheel. The 320 h.p. Pollit and Wigzell cross compound engine was added in 1910 to supplement the water power, probably when a new wool-combing shed was added at the rear of Coldharbour Mill in addition to existing spinning and weaving machinery. Cylinder sizes are 13in diameter high-pressure and 26in diameter low-pressure by 3ft stroke. Both cylinders are fitted with drop inlet valves and Corliss exhaust. Speed is 90 r.p.m. with flywheel about 10ft diameter to take 13 ropes. Both steam engine and waterwheel were used for commercial production until closure in early 1981. Both are now preserved as part of a textile museum.

The horizontal air pump and condenser were placed behind the low-pressure cylinder at Coldharbour Mill.

Above: The inlet drop valves were driven by eccentrics on a rotating shaft at the side of the cylinders while the Corliss exhaust valves were moved by a rocking shaft on the Coldharbour Mill engine.

Left: The side of the low-pressure cylinder at Coldharbour Mill with drop inlet valves on top and driving rods alongside.

Leigh Spinners Number 1 Mill

Leigh Spinners Number 1 Mill, finished in 1915, was designed to be extended although the second mill was not begun until 1925. Each mill had its own engine and engine house but the seven boilers and chimney were common to the two engines. The 1,200 h.p. engine for Number 1 mill was a cross compound with Corliss valves on both cylinders, 23¼in diameter high-pressure and 50in low-pressure. Stroke was 5ft and speed 67 r.p.m. The flywheel was a single pulley, 24ft diameter for 33 ropes. The condenser and air pump were behind the low-pressure cylinder under the floor. Perhaps the most outstanding feature was the decoration in gold leaf on the castings, much of which had disappeared with age.

One morning, the engineer was starting the engine when the steam pipe fractured above the main inlet valve. The rush of steam pinned him against the flywheel which had just begun to revolve. He was very lucky to escape with his life for it was a few minutes before steam could be shut off in the boiler house. The piping above the high-pressure cylinder was repaired and the engine carried on working until around 1960 when it was stopped, possibly due to a fractured cylinder.

The high-pressure cylinder of Leigh Spinners Number 1 engine built by Yates and Thom with the repaired steam inlet pipe above it.

The low-pressure side of Leigh Spinners Number 1 engine with Yates and Thom early form of double curved cladding. The Corliss exhaust valves are at floor level.

Above: The conical condenser and air pump below the tail rod of the low-pressure cylinder on Leigh Spinners Number 1 engine.

Left: The trunk guide for the high-pressure side of Leigh Spinners Number 1 engine with governor above it.

Nutters Ltd, Bancroft Mill, Barnoldswick

Although a date of 1914 has been given for this mill, the engine may not have been started until 1920. Bancroft Mill was perhaps the last new cotton weaving shed to be built in the area and this engine was probably the last large new engine supplied by William Roberts. It had a traditional layout with Corliss valves on both cylinders. The inclined dashpots were retained on the 16in diameter high-pressure cylinder and vertical ones on the 32in diameter low-pressure cylinder with 4ft stroke. The flywheel was 16ft 6in diameter with 13 ropes, all driving the main horizontal shaft into the shed. Power of 600 h.p. was generated at 68 r.p.m. with 160 p.s.i. The engineer, Stanley Graham, kept his engine superbly so that it was one of the last steam-driven cotton mills. While it closed soon after 1979 and the weaving shed was demolished, the engine has been preserved in its house.

Above: General view of the cross compound engine by Roberts at Nutters.

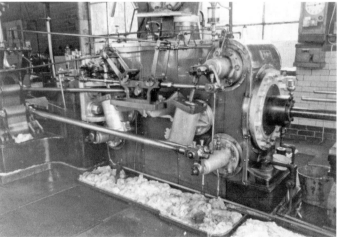

Left: The high-pressure cylinder with its inclined dashpots and Lumb governor on the Nutters engine.

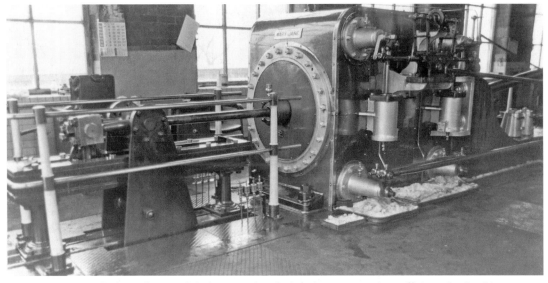

The low-pressure cylinder with vertical dashpots and to the left the air pump drive off the tail rod at Nutters.

Above: The rope drive from the flywheel to the main line shafting into the weaving shed at Nutters.

Left: The pressure gauge board in front of the flywheel at Nutters engine with Roberts' maker's plate.

Holmes, Mann and Co., Bradford

The cross compound engine *Dorothy* seen at Holmes, Mann sawmill driving a generator was a neat engine with clean outlines. It was supplied by Newton Bean and Mitchell, Bradford, in 1921 for H.D. Shaw and Co., woolcombers. Both cylinders had drop piston valves on top of the cylinders with horizontal piston exhaust valves underneath. The inlet valves on the 20in diameter high-pressure cylinder were controlled by a 'Bee' governor. Exhaust from the 40in low-pressure cylinder, stroke 2ft 6in, passed to the horizontal condenser and air pump behind the high-pressure cylinder. The condensate was pumped through a cooling tower. At 100 r.p.m. and 120 p.s.i., 660 h.p. was produced. To start the engine, the 15ft diameter flywheel with 12 ropes was turned by a second-hand single-cylinder Pollit and Wigzell barring engine. The engine was well loaded but running sweetly when seen in the spring of 1968. Its fuel supply from the sawmill was quite cheap!

The spacious engine house at Holmes, Mann looking towards the high-pressure cylinder and horizontal condenser.

The mechanism of a drop inlet valve on the high-pressure cylinder at Holmes, Mann with the 'Bee' governor.

The low-pressure side of the engine at Holmes, Mann.

The linkage from the eccentric to work a horizontal piston valve on the low-pressure cylinder at Holmes, Mann.

Leigh Spinners Number 2 Mill

The scale of Leigh Spinners Number 2 engine, *Mayor* and *Mayoress*, was not apparent when first entering the engine house because it was well proportioned and the floor level was high relative to the cylinders and crankshaft of this 1925 engine. The cylinder cladding lacked some of the ornate shape of earlier Yates and Thom engines yet the parentage could be seen distinctly in other parts. When one piece of the high pressure trip gear broke, the Number 1 engine was stripped and the appropriate part was discovered to be identical so the Number 2 engine was running again after the lunch break. This shows there was a certain amount of standardisation between engines by the same maker.

The engine developed 1,800 h.p. at 67 r.p.m. and 180 p.s.i. from Corliss-valve cylinders 30in and 61in diameter with 5ft stroke. The flywheel was 24ft diameter and 9ft 6in wide. It consisted of twin pulleys with 23 and 22 ropes. In November 1967, this was still an independent mill with spinning mules for cotton. It was intended to retain the engine and work it in the following manner. During the summer when there was no mill heating, electricity would be purchased from the grid. When the boilers had to be used for heating and charges were highest for electricity in the winter, the engine could be set to work again. Some of the boilers could be hand-stoked with coal, others were fired by a Bennis stoker and oil firing was also fitted so that the most economical fuel could be selected. When spinning ceased, the mill switched to carpet weaving and this engine was left in situ for some years.

Leigh Spinners Number 2 engine was well proportioned and low so its size was not at first impressive.

The high-pressure trunk guide of Leigh Spinners Number 2 engine with governor and flywheel in the background.

Above: Detail of the main steam valve operating gear and the Corliss valve inlet release mechanism on Leigh Spinners Number 2 engine.

Below: The large low-pressure cylinder of Leigh Spinners Number 2 engine had its exhaust valves below floor level so it appeared quite low.

Wilson's Woollen Mill, Dunblane

This woollen mill relied principally on water power, first from a waterwheel and then a Gilkes turbine. The final turbine produced 200 h.p. at 178 r.p.m. The Class E engine by Robey, Lincoln, was added in 1927 to supplement the turbine. With cylinders of 10in and 14in diameter by 2ft 6in stroke, it could develop 170 h.p. at 120 r.p.m. with 180 p.s.i. The steam circuit was arranged so that steam could be passed out between the high- and low-pressure cylinders for processing the wool. Inlet valves were the drop type and exhaust piston or slide. There were seven ropes round the 10ft diameter flywheel which drove at first spinning mules and later an alternator. Robey continued to build steam engines into the 1930s.

The high-pressure cylinder on Robey's cross compound engine at Wilson's mill. The crankshaft and flywheel are at the further end, driving back to the pulley wheel on the line shafting at the right.

The low-pressure side of Wilson's engine. Its size is apparent from the people looking at it.

Wilson's engine was fitted with Robey's normal trunk guides and disc crank.

CHRONOLOGY

BC

20000   Neanderthal sites in Dordogne have no fabricated textiles.

5000   Neolithic sites show evidence of spinning and weaving.

5000   In Chinese tradition, Foh-hi, the first Emperor, taught the people silk culture.

2500   First spinning and weaving in Britain.

1900   Spindle and whorl of this date for spinning flax found in Egypt.

1800   Representation of a fulling mill on tomb of Egyptian king Usertesen II.

1500   Wool combing in Sumerian civilization.

384–22   Aristotle mentions silk weaving.

370–287 Theophrastus writes about cotton cloth.

AD

530   Emperor Justinian takes the silk culture of Corinth under his patronage.

1068   Flemish weavers follow William the Conqueror into England.

1185   Earliest known water-powered fulling mill in England.

1248   Lucca, Italy, begins silk culture and manufacture.

1258   Export of wool from England forbidden, boosting weaving of broadcloth.

1272   A type of silk 'throwing' frame appears in Italy.

1298   Cotton noted being used for candlewicks in England.

1338   Luttrell Psalter has picture of great spinning wheel.

1348   Norwich worsted trade first noted.

1400   Soon after this date, spinning wheel with flyer and bobbin appears.

1530   Johann Jurgen fits crank to form Saxony spinning wheel.

1554   Fustians first made at Norwich.

1586	Loom for weaving multiple ribbons appears on the Continent, reaching London by 1616.
1589	Stocking frame invented by Revd William Lee.
1631	Calico cloth imported into England.
1685	Revocation of Edict of Nantes sends many skilled weavers to England.
1696	Calico printing by hand introduced into England.
1698	Thomas Savery's patent for a steam engine to raise water out of mines.
1700	Wearing of cotton goods prohibited in England.
1702	Thomas Cotchett sets up first English water-powered silk throwing mill at Derby.
1712	Thomas Newcomen's atmospheric steam engine erected at Dudley Castle for pumping water out of a coal mine.
1717	First mention of a 'flax' mill in Northern Ireland.
1718	Thomas and John Lombe's successful silk throwing mill at Derby.
1721	Act of Parliament fines £5 on the wearer and £20 on the vendor of cotton goods.
1733	John Kay patents flying shuttle.
1738	First patent of Lewis Paul and John Wyatt for cotton spinning machine.
1748	Daniel Bourn's patent for a carding machine with rotating cylinders.
1752	John Smeaton experiments with a model to find most efficient waterwheel.
1759	Jedediah Strutt patents Derby-rib attachment to stocking frame.
1764	James Hargreaves invents spinning jenny.
1765	Gartside's ribbon weaving factory in Manchester, powered by water, burnt down through arson.
1765	James Watt conceives idea of 'separate condenser' for the steam engine.
1769	Watt patents his separate condenser for the steam engine.
1769	Richard Arkwright patents roller drafting on a cotton spinning machine with flyers.
1770	Smeaton uses iron for some parts of waterwheels.
1770	Thomas Bell seeks advice from Watt about calico printing machine.
1771	Arkwright moves to a water-powered mill at Cromford.
1774	Parliament removes duties on all-cotton cloth produced in England.

1775   Act of Parliament extends Watt's 1769 patent to 1800.

1775   Arkwright patents series of machines for preparing cotton for spinning.

1779   Samuel Crompton reveals his spinning mule.

1780   Newcomen-type steam engine possibly working at Haarlem Mill, Wirksworth.

1781   Hunt's rotative atmospheric engine possibly installed at Shudehill Mill, Manchester.

1781   Attempts to adapt waterframe for worsted spinning.

1781   Jonathan Hornblower patents steam engine with two cylinders in which steam is used consecutively.

1782   One of Watt's patents covers sun and planet gear for rotative engines.

1782   Watt patents double-acting and expansive steam engines.

1783   Bell's first patent for calico printing machine.

1784   Watt invents his 'parallel' motion, the final part of his successful rotative steam engine.

1785   Edmund Cartwright's first patent for a power loom.

1785   Arkwright's patents annulled.

1786   First Boulton and Watt rotative engine in Robinsons' cotton spinning mill at Papplewick.

1787   John Kendrew and Thomas Porter patent flax spinning machine.

1787   Spanish merino sheep imported into England.

1789   Cartwright's first patent for wool combing machine.

1790   William Kelly at New Lanark tries to mechanise Crompton's mule.

1792   Kelly patents his mechanisms which fail to satisfactorily wind on the yarn.

1792   William Strutt's fireproof mill erected at Derby.

1793   In America, Eli Witney invents saw gin for removing seeds from cotton in the boll.

1794   First combing machine used in Bradford.

1795   Slubbing billy introduced.

1796   Robert Miller improves power loom.

1796   Charles Bage builds iron-framed flax mill at Shrewsbury.

1797   Neil Snodgrass, Johnstone, Scotland, invents scutching machine.

1798	Count Rumford experiments boring head of a cast cannon to determine nature of heat.
1799	William Murdock's slide valve for steam engine.
1800	Around this date, the throstle starts to replace the waterframe.
1800	Watt's patent for the separate condenser terminates.
1801	Batting machine used for opening cotton.
1803	William Radcliffe patents his first sizing machine in the name of Thomas Johnson.
1804	Arthur Woolf's patent for a compound steam engine with cylinders side by side.
1811	Richard Trevithick installs his first 'Cornish' boiler suitable for high-pressure steam.
1811	Whistle-mouth boiler developed by Butterley company.
1812	John Kennedy and Henry Houldsworth add differential motion to roving frame.
1812	Iron suspension waterwheel installed at Armley Mill, Leeds.
1813	Horrocks of Stockport drives slay on power loom by a crank.
1815	John Lewis, Brimscombe, patents rotary cloth-shearing machine.
1816	William Lewis, Brimscombe, patents woollen cloth milling machine.
1822	Richard Roberts patents his power loom with tappet mechanism.
1824	Condenser carding developed in America.
1824	Sadi Carnot publishes *Réflexions sur la Puissance du Feu*.
1825	Roberts takes out his first patent for a self-acting spinning mule.
1827	In France, Benoit Fourneyron awarded prize for his design of a water turbine.
1827	Platt and Collier's combing machine invented.
1828	Ring spinning patents taken out in America.
1828	Charles Danforth invents his cap spinning method in America.
1830	Roberts patents his quadrant winding mechanism for the self-acting spinning mule.
1834	John Ramsbottom and Richard Holt, Todmorden, patent a weft stop motion.
1834	Sharp Roberts in England purchase patent rights for ring spinning.

1836   Isaac Holden begins experimenting with combing machines.

1842   James Morris and J.J. Meyer patent their respective types of adjustable cut-off slide valves.

1842   Edmund Donisthorpe takes out his first patent for a combing machine.

1842   James Bullough, Blackburn, patents a loose reed for the loom.

1843   James P. Joule publishes his paper, 'On the Caloric Effects of Magneto Electricity, and on the Mechanical Value of Heat'.

1844   Method of firing the Lancashire boiler to consume smoke patented by William Fairbairn and John Hetherington.

1845   Edward Green patents his first type of Economiser.

1845   William McNaught patents receiver compound beam engine.

1846   Josué Heilman takes out a British Patent for a combing machine.

1849   In America, George H. Corliss patents his first form of valve gear named after him.

1850   James Thomson's patent for a water turbine.

1850s   Horizontal steam engines become more popular than beam engines.

1850s   Start of 'Limited' movement for building cotton spinning mills.

1851   Samuel Cunliffe Lister takes out his first patent for a combing machine.

1851   William and John Galloway patent improved Lancashire boiler.

1853   James Noble patents his type of combing machine.

1853   Saltaire Mill completed.

1853   In America, Wellman patents carding machine with self-cleaning flats.

1854   Founding of what later was called The Manchester Steam Users Association.

1855   Henry Bessemer patents his method of producing malleable iron or steel.

1858   In America, Charles Porter patents his 'loaded' governor for steam engines.

1858   Evan Leigh develops his successful 'flexible bend' for a carding engine on which the flats travel above the cylinder.

1861   First Corliss steam engine at work in Britain.

1861   William Creighton designs vertical conical beater to open cotton.

1862–64 Cotton famine.

1863	James Combe, Belfast, experiments with ropes to replace gearing for main drives in textile mills.
1870	E. Wigzell patents compound engine with cylinders back to back and three piston rods.
1874	Leonard J. Todd patents 'Uniflow' engine.
1877	Atlas No. 3 Mill, Bolton, lit by electricity.
1884	Shortly before this date, Gustaf de Laval develops his steam turbine.
1884	Charles A. Parsons patents his type of steam turbine.
1890	Superheat in steam engines becomes more common.
1894	Important patents for the Northrop loom taken out.
1894	H.F.C. Whitehead replaces the 'load' weight on the governor with springs.
1894	F. Edwards patents his air pump with no valves in the bucket.
1898	Edwin Reynolds in America designs the Manhattan type of steam engine.
1899	Formation of Calico Printers' Association.
1900	James Lumb improves the regulator on the governor.
1902	First Northrop looms imported into Britain.
1904	Acme Mill, Pendlebury, supplied with electricity from Radcliffe power station both to light and drive the mill.
1907	Times No. 2 Mill, Middleton, erected with 160,000 spindles, then the largest in the world.
1908	Prof. Johann Stumpf in Germany successfully develops the Uniflow engine.
1909	Musgrave, Bolton, construct first British Uniflow engine.
1912	Fernando Casablancas patents his high draft system for spinning cotton.
1913	India Mill, Stockport, driven by a Parsons Steam Turbine.
1918	Fine Cotton Spinners and Doublers Association formed.
1919	Henry Pilling, Galloways, patents hydraulically operated drop valves.
1926	11 December, engine at Wye No. 2 Mill, Shaw, started, the last reciprocating engine supplied to any British spinning mill.
1927	Last traditional multi-storey spinning mill, Sir John Holden's, Bolton, built as an all-electric mill supplied by Back-o-th-Bank power station.
1929	Lancashire Cotton Corporation formed.

GLOSSARY

Air Pump A pump on a steam engine for removing the condensate and air from the condenser.

Atmospheric Engine (or Newcomen Engine) A steam engine invented by Thomas Newcomen for pumping water out of mines. Atmospheric pressure forced the piston into the cylinder in which a vacuum had been created by condensing steam.

Backing Off Operation performed on completion of spinning a length of yarn on the great wheel, jenny or mule in which the spindle is turned backwards to unwind the coils of yarn from the tip to the cop.

Batting Early method of opening the raw cotton by beating it with sticks ready for carding.

Beam A roller on which a series of yarns are wound side by side and placed at the rear of the loom to form the warp. It is also the roller at the front of the loom on which the cloth is wound.

Beam The main horizontal link between the piston and cylinder at one end of a beam engine and the connecting rod at the other. It is pivoted at or near its centre.

Beetling Irish method of finishing the surface of linen cloth by beating it with wooden hammers.

Bobbin A round flanged spool for holding yarn.

Boll Seed-head of a cotton plant containing the cotton fibres.

Broadcloth Originally any cloth made on the broad loom, probably with two weavers; later applied to a fine, plain-weave woollen cloth heavily milled.

Calender Method of giving a smooth finish to linen cloth by passing it between heavy rollers.

Calico All-cotton cloth, usually plain weave.

Cap spinning A form of continuous spinning machine introduced in the later 1820s principally for worsted.

Card A fine but stiff wire brush by means of which fibrous materials may be disentangled prior to spinning. The term is also used as a verb.

Carding A preliminary treatment before spinning to open and mix the fibres. The word derives from the Latin name for teasels.

Carriage The carriage in a mule supports the spindles and allows them to be moved away from or towards the drafting rollers.

Clove A moveable clamp used to hold roving on a jenny while drawing and spinning.

Comb The preparatory process for long wools by removing the short fibres (the noil), leaving the long ones (the tops) straight and parallel.

Comb A toothed blade for removing fibres from the doffer cylinder of a carding engine.

Compound The use of steam first in a high-pressure cylinder then followed by a larger low-pressure cylinder.

Condenser In a steam engine, where the steam is condensed after passing through the cylinders.

Condenser System A system of spinning in which strips of fibres are rubbed together to form rovings as they leave the carding engine ready for spinning.

Cop A cylindrical yarn package spun on a plain spindle so constructed that the yarn may be pulled off substantially axially from one of the conical ends without rotation of the cop itself.

Count Number describes fineness of yarn. For cotton, the count is the number of hanks, each of 840 yards, in one pound of yarn.

Counter Faller Horizontal wire stretched behind the spindles on a mule designed to take up the slack and provide tension while winding on.

Creel A frame to hold bobbins.

Devil An opening and cleaning machine with spikes around a rotating cylinder used in the cotton and woollen industries.

Distaff The cleft stick that holds the carded fibre for hand spinning.

Doffer Cylinder The last cylinder on a carding engine from which the fibres are finally taken off.

Doubling Twisting two or more yarns together. On a spinning wheel, the wheel is turned in the opposite direction to spinning.

Drafting The drawing out of slivers, slubbings or rovings to straighten and parallelise the fibres. The sliver or roving will become thinner.

Drafting Zone The space between two pairs of drafting rollers.

Draw That part of the cycle of operations when spinning with the plain spindle by hand or with the jenny or mule during which the fibres are thinned out and some twist inserted.

Draw Loom The early form of loom for fancy weaving.

Dressing The application of an adhesive paste to yarns to facilitate the weaving process.

Duty The amount of water in pounds raised one foot by burning one bushel of coal weighing 84 pounds.

End An individual warp thread.

Enter Threading the warp ends through the healds and reed on a loom.

Faller Device to guide the yarn onto the cop during winding on. On jennies and mules it is usually a horizontal wire.

Filament The strand of silk unwound from a cocoon.

Flats Bars of wood with card clothing on their underside, positioned over the main cylinder in a cotton carding engine.

Flax Wheel A variant of the Brunswick, Saxony or flyer spinning wheel.

Flyer The rotating U-shaped arm on a spindle of the later type of spinning wheel, silk throwing machine, waterframe, throstle and preparatory machines for rovings, etc. in a continuous process.

Flying Shuttle A shuttle invented by John Kay in 1733 which could be sent through the warp by one hand of the weaver operating a picking stick.

Fork Two-pronged feeler that acts to stop the loom if the weft is missing.

Fulling The cleaning, shrinking and thickening of woollen cloth, now called milling.

Fulling Stocks Method of fulling using water-powered hammers to pound the cloth.

Fustian A cloth with linen warp and cotton weft.

Gig The teasel-covered raising machine.

Great Wheel The first type of spinning wheel with a plain spindle, using an intermittent process.

Hackling/Heckling Process of drawing handfuls of flax fibre through a series of combs known as hackles.

Hank Unit of length: of cotton, 840 yards; of worsted, 560 yards.

Headstock The major assembly of mechanical components which control the operations of a mule.

Heald/Heddle A cord formed with an eyelet through which a warp yarn is passed. In the loom, these healds are raised and lowered to allow the passage of the shuttle between the warp yarns forming the shed.

High Draft Recent drafting systems which make a high attenuation of the roving possible.

Horizontal Loom A loom in which the warp threads lie horizontally.

Jacquard Loom used for weaving fancy cloth which replaced the older draw loom. Its pattern selection system was invented by Joseph Marie Jacquard between 1801 and 1806.

Jenny A spinning machine invented by James Hargreaves in 1764 in which the plain spindles were mounted on the main framing.

Lap In textiles, a sheet of fibres which might be wound round a roller.

Lap In steam engines, an extension on the inlet side of a slide valve to give an early cut-off.

Milling A later name for fulling which came into general use with the development of the rotary milling machine.

Mule A spinning machine with an intermittent process invented by Samuel Crompton before 1779 in which the plain spindles were mounted on a moveable carriage and the cotton fed to them by rollers.

Mule Jenny An early form of mule partly driven by power.

Muslin Fine quality all-cotton cloth.

Nap The furry surface on a cloth.

Newcomen Engine See Atmospheric Engine.

Nip The point where a pair of rollers meet and grip the fibres.

Nip The clasp holding the fibres in some combing machines.

Noils Short wool or silk fibres removed by combing. This wool became an important material for the woollen trade.

Open End Spinning Recently invented continuous method of spinning which replaced both the mule and ring frames.

Opening Breaking up the lumps of cotton taken from the tightly packed bales in which it has been shipped.

Picker An attachment that drives the shuttle out of the shuttle box.

Picking Stick Part of John Kay's invention of the flying shuttle. It is a stick which the weaver uses to throw the shuttle from side to side, being connected by cords to the pickers.

Pirn Yarn package wound on a small spool which can be inserted into a shuttle.

Quill Similar to pirn.

Race Horizontal strip of wood in front of the reed on which the flying shuttle runs.

Raise The production of the nap on cloth.

Reed A frame fitted with thin strips of reed or metal carried on the slay of a loom to keep the warp threads spaced correctly and to beat up the weft into place.

Reel Revolving frame upon which hanks of yarn are wound.

Retting Process where water, fungi and bacteria break down or rot the gummy substance that binds the exterior of the flax stems, permitting the flax fibre to be exposed.

Ring Frame A continuous spinning machine on which the yarn passes through a traveller to be wound onto the package.

Rippling Process of removing the flax seed from the plant by pulling the stems through a coarse comb.

Rollag A short, carded roll, usually of wool.

Rollers In drawing, roving and spinning frames, several pairs of rollers, each pair rotating at a higher speed than its predecessor in the yarn path, draft the fibres as they pass from one pair to the next.

Roller Drafting The process of spinning in which the fibres are drawn out by pairs of rollers turning at progressively faster speeds.

Roving A thin length of lightly twisted, substantially parallel fibres from which yarn is spun.

Roving Frame In cotton manufacturing, a machine for imparting further draft and twist to the carded and drawn sliver.

Scribbling Carding process for wool.

Scutch Term used for separating flax fibres.

Scutching Machine A machine with a rotating beater which struck fibrous material in order to loosen it and release impurities.

Shear Either to cut the wool off sheep or to cut the fibres off the face of woven cloth to produce an even surface or nap.

Shed The opening in the warp that permits the passage of each weft thread.

Shuttle A long, pointed wooden block which contains the weft inside its hollow centre. It leaves a trail of weft as it is sent through the shed in the warp.

Shuttle Box A box with an open top added by John Kay at each end of the slay to receive the flying shuttle.

Size A solution of flour, starch or glue applied to the warp in cotton weaving to impart strength.

Slay The swinging frame on a loom between the healds and the woven cloth which carries the reed and supports the shuttle.

Sliver A thick, soft rope of fibre with no twist coming off the carding engine or drawing frames.

Slub A thick part in a yarn.

Slubbing A soft-twisted strand of fibres, prepared from a sliver for drawing out into roving.

Slubbing Billy An important machine during the early part of the nineteenth century for taking carded sliver or slubbings and drafting them, giving a modicum of twist before being spun on the jenny.

Snarl When yarn is relaxed, it is liable to twist itself into a snarl.

Snift The noise made when steam is blown through a condenser to remove the air, or the act of blowing through.

Spindle A rotating shaft around which the spun yarn can be wound either directly or onto a bobbin placed on it.

Staple Length The length of the fibres being used.

Stocking Frame A domestic knitting machine invented by the Revd William Lee in 1589.

Stop Motion A device that automatically halts a machine whenever the material being processed is broken or exhausted.

Strick A bundle of flax fibres ready for spinning on hand wheels.

Teasel The seed head of a sort of thistle which has hooks on it.

Temple Device in a loom to keep the woven cloth at the right width.

Traveller In ring spinning, the metal hook that, when pulled around its ring by the yarn, inserts twist in the yarn and guides the yarn onto the spun package.

Thread Two or more yarns plied together.

Throstle A continuous spinning machine using roller drafting and flyer spinning driven by a single set of gears at one end and developed from the waterframe.

Throwing The process of twisting the long silk filaments.

Tops Slivers of wool which have been combed to remove short fibres, becoming the main raw material for worsted spinning.

Tow The short broken flax fibres left in the hackle after hackling.

Twist Cotton yarn with high twist intended for warp.

Velvet A warp pile weave in which the pile is produced by a pile warp that is raised in loops above a ground weave through the introduction of rods during the weaving.

Vertical Loom A loom with the warp threads entered vertically.

Warp The threads in a loom which are entered first and through which the weft is woven.

Waterframe The name given to Richard Arkwright's continuous spinning machine with roller drafting and flyers through being powered in a mill by a waterwheel.

Weft The second set of threads woven across the warp, usually with a shuttle.

Whorl A small disc or pulley secured to the spindle.

Winding On That part of the cycle of operations in spinning when the spun yarn is wound onto the spindle in the form of a cop.

Woollen Yarn A woollen yarn is a soft spun full yarn made from carded fibres, nowadays prepared on the condenser system.

Worsted Yarn A smooth yarn spun from wool fibres that have been combed and laid parallel to each other.

Yarn A spun thread, usually only a single ply.

BIBLIOGRAPHY AND SOURCES

Aikin, John, *A Description of the Country from Thirty to Forty Miles Round Manchester*, J. Stockdale, Manchester, 1795, reprint David & Charles, Newton Abbot, 1968.

Alban, E., *The High Pressure Steam Engine*, London, 1848.

Alderson, M.A., *An Essay on the Nature and Application of Steam, with an Historical Note of the Rise and Progressive Improvement of the Steam Engine*, Sherwood, Gilbert & Piper, London, 1834.

Andrew, C.S., *Fifty Years Cotton Trade*, 1887.

Apling, Harry, *Norfolk Corn Windmills*, Norfolk Windmills Trust, Norwich, 1984.

Armstrong, R., *Practical Essay on Steam Engine Boilers as now used in the Manufacturing District around Manchester*, Manchester, 1838.

Ashmore, Owen, *The Industrial Archaeology of North-west England*, Manchester University Press, 1982.

Ashworth & Parker, *The Parker Engine*, no date.

Aspin, Chris, *The Water-Spinners, A New Look at the Early Cotton Trade*, Helmshore Local History Society, 2003.

Aspin, Chris & Chapman, Stanley D., *James Hargreaves and the Spinning Jenny*, Helmshore Local History Society, 1964.

Atkinson, Glen, *Worsley Textile Mills: A History of the Mills of Worsley, Walkden, Little Hulton and Boothstown*, Richardson, Radcliffe, 2004.

Bailey, Michael R., 'Robert Stephenson & Company, 1823–1829', *Transactions of the Newcomen Society*, Vol. 50, 1978–9.

Baines, Edward, *History of the Cotton Manufacture in Great Britain*, H. Fisher, R. Fisher & P. Jackson, London, c.1835.

Baines, Edward, *Account of the Woollen Manufacture of England*, 1875, reprint David & Charles, Newton Abbot, 1970.

Barlow, Alfred, *The History and Principles of Weaving by Hand and Power*, Sampson Low et al., London, 2nd edn 1879.

Barton, D.B., *The Cornish Beam Engine*, D. Bradford Barton, Truro, 1965, new edn 1969.

Bessemer, Henry, *Sir Henry Bessemer, F.R.S., An Autobiography*, Engineering, London, 1905.

Birmingham Central Library, Boulton and Watt Collection and James Watt Papers.

Bourne, John, *Recent Improvements in the Steam-Engine*, Longmans Green & Co., London, 1869, new edn 1880.

Boyson, Rhodes, *The Ashworth Cotton Enterprise, The Rise and Fall of a Family Firm, 1818–1880*, Clarendon Press, Oxford, 1970.

Burgh, N.P., *A Practical Treatise on Boilers and Boiler-making*, London, revised edn 1881.

Burn, R.S., *The Steam Engine, Its History and Mechanism*, London, 1854.

Butt, J., ed., *Robert Owen, Prince of Cotton Spinners*, David & Charles, Newton Abbot, 1971.

Butterworth, Edwin, *Historical Sketches of Oldham*, Oldham, 1856.

Bythell, Duncan, *The Handloom Weavers, A Study in the English Cotton Industry during the Industrial Revolution*, Cambridge University Press, 1969, reprint 1977.

Calladine Anthony & Fricker, Jean, *East Cheshire Textile Mills*, Royal Commission on the Historical Monuments of England, London, 1993.

Cameron, H.C., *Sir Joseph Banks, The Autocrat of the Philosophers, 1744–1820*, Batchworth Press, London, 1952.

Cardwell, Donald S.L., *From Watt to Clausius: The Rise of Thermodynamics in the Early Industrial Age*, Heinemann, London, 1971.

Carnot, Sadi, *Reflections on the Motive Power of Fire*, 1824, ed. E. Mendoza, Dover, New York, 1966.

Catling, Harold, *The Spinning Mule*, David & Charles, Newton Abbot, 1970.

Chaloner, William H., *National Boiler, 1864–1964: A Century of Progress in Industrial Safety*, National Boiler, Manchester, 1964.

Clapham, Sir John, *A Concise Economic History of Britain*, Cambridge University Press, 1949.

Clark, Daniel K., *The Exhibited Machinery of 1862*, Day & Son, London, 1864.

Clark, Daniel K., *The Steam Engine: A Treatise on Steam Engines and Boilers*, Blackie, London, 1890.

Colyer, F., *A Treatise on Modern Steam Engines and Boilers*, E. & F.N. Spon, London, 1886.

Cooke, Anthony, *Stanley: From Arkwright Village to Commuter Suburb, 1784–2003*, Perth & Kinross Libraries, 2003.

Cooper, Brian, *Transformation of a Valley: The Derbyshire Derwent*, Heinemann, London, 1983.

Crocker, Glenys, *The Godalming Water Turbine,* Godalming, 1982.

Crump, W.B., *The Leeds Woollen Industry, 1780–1820*, Thoresby Society, Leeds, 1931.

Dale, Peter, *Bolton A Century Ago*, Landy Publishing, Blackpool, 1991.

Day, Lance & McNeil, Ian, eds, *Biographical Dictionary of the History of Technology*, Routledge, 1996.

Derry, T.K. & Williams, Trevor I., *A Short History of Technology from the earliest times to AD 1900*, Clarendon Press, Oxford, 1960.

Dickinson, Henry W., *James Watt, Craftsman and Engineer*, Cambridge University Press, 1936.

Dickinson, Henry W., *A Short History of the Steam Engine*, Cambridge University Press, 1938.

Dickinson, Henry W. & Jenkins, Rhys, *James Watt and the Steam Engine*, Oxford, 1927, reprint Moorland, Ashbourne, 1981.

Dickinson, T.C., *Cotton Mills of Preston, The Power Behind the Thread*, Carnegie Publishing Ltd, Lancaster, 2002.

Dickinson, T.C., 'Preston Mill Engines', University of Manchester MSc, 1979.

Edwards, Michael M., *The Growth of the British Cotton Trade, 1780–1815*, Manchester University Press, 1967.

Emerson, William, *The Principles of Mechanics*, 3rd edn, London, 1773.

Engineer and Machinist, 1850.

Engineering.

English, W., *The Textile Industry*, Longmans, London, 1969.

Ewing, Sir J.A., *The Steam Engine and Other Heat Engines*, Cambridge University Press, 1926.

Fairbairn, William, *Mills & Millwork: Part I, On the Principles of Mechanism and on Prime Movers; Part II, On Machinery of Transmission and the Construction and Arrangement of Mills*, Longmans, Green & Co., London, 3rd edn 1871.

Fairbairn, William, 'On the Economy of raising Water from Coal Mines on the Cornish Principle', Manchester Geological Society, 29 October 1840.

Falck, N.D., *An Account and Description of an Improved Steam Engine*, B. Law, London, 1776.

Farey, John, *A Treatise on the Steam Engine, Historical, Practical, and Descriptive*, London, 1827, reprint David & Charles, Newton Abbot, 1971.

Farnie, Douglas A., *The English Cotton Industry and the World Market*, Clarendon Press, Oxford, 1979.

Fitton, R.S., *The Arkwrights, Spinners of Fortune*, Manchester University Press, 1989.

Fitton, R.S. & Wadsworth, A.P., *The Strutts and the Arkwrights*, Manchester University Press, 1958, 2nd edn 1964.

Fowler, W.H., *Fifty Years' History of the Development of Green's Economiser*, G. Falkner, Manchester, 1895.

Fowler, W.H., *Stationary Steam Engines*, Scientific Publishing Co., Manchester, 1908.

Fox, T.W., *The Mechanism of Weaving*, Macmillan & Co., London, 1911.

Gaskell, P., *The Manufacturing Population of England*, London, 1833.

Giles, Colum & Goodall, Ian H., *Yorkshire Textile Mills, The Buildings of the Yorkshire Textile Industry, 1770–1930*, HMSO, London, 1992.

Glithero, John P., 'The History of Engineering in Hyde to 1914', PhD, University of Manchester Institute of Science and Technology, 2002.

Goodeve, T.M., *Text-Book on the Steam Engine*, London, 1884.

Green Fuel Economizer Co., *The Book of the Economizer*, Matteawan, New York, 1910.

Gurr, Duncan & Hunt, Julian, *The Cotton Mills of Oldham*, Oldham Leisure Services, 1985.

Hann, James, Gener, Justo, & Gener, Placido, *The Steam Engine for Practical Men*, E. & F.N. Spon, London 1854.

Harris, T.R., *Arthur Woolf, The Cornish Engineer, 1766–1837*, D. Bradford Barton, Truro, 1966.

Harte, J.H., *Volledig Molenboek*, A. van der Mast, Gorinchem, 1849.

Haynes, Ian, *Dukinfield Cotton Mills*, N. Richardson, Radcliffe, 1993.

Haynes, Ian, *Mossley Textile Mills*, N. Richardson, Radcliffe, 1996.

Haynes, Ian, *Stalybridge Cotton Mills*, N. Richardson, Radcliffe, 1990.

Hick, Benjamin, 'First Order Book', October 1833 to March 1836.

Hills, Richard L., 'Glossop: The Rise and Fall of a Textile Town, 1790–1950', Manchester Statistical Society, 2003.

Hills, Richard L., *James Watt, Vol. 1: His Time in Scotland, 1736–1774*, Landmark, Ashbourne, 2002.

Hills, Richard L., *James Watt, Vol. 2: His Time in England, The Years of Toil, 1774–1785*, Landmark, Ashbourne, 2005.

Hills, Richard L., *James Watt, Vol. 3: Triumph through Adversity, 1785–1819*, Landmark, Ashbourne, 2006.

Hills, Richard L., *The Life and Inventions of Richard Roberts, 1789–1864*, Landmark, Ashbourne, 2002.

Hills, Richard L., 'Peter Ewart, 1767–1842', *Manchester Memoirs*, Vol. 127, 1987–88.

Hills, Richard L., *Power from Steam: A History of the Stationary Steam Engine*, Cambridge University Press, 1989.

Hills, Richard L., *Power from Wind: A History of Windmill Technology*, Cambridge University Press, 1994.

Hills, Richard L., *Power in the Industrial Revolution*, Manchester University Press,

1970.

Hills, Richard L., 'A Steam Chimera: A Review of the History of the Savery Engine', *T.N.S.*, Vol. 58, 1986–7.

Hills, Richard L. & Gwyn, David, 'Three Engines at Penrhyn Du, 1760–1780', *T.N.S.*, Vol. 75, No. 1, 2005.

Hoblyn, R.D., *A Manual of the Steam Engine*, Scott, Webster & Geary, London, 1842.

Hogg, James, ed., *Fortunes Made in Business*, Griffith, Farran, Okeden & Welsh, London, new edn c.1913.

Hunter, Louis C., *A History of Industrial Power in the United States, 1780–1930*, Vol. 1, *Waterpower*; Vol. II, *Steam Power*, University of Virginia, Charlottesville, 1979–85.

Ince, Laurence, *The Neath Abbey Iron Company*, De Archaeologische Pers Nederland, Eindhoven, 1984.

Ince, Laurence, *The Soho Engine Works, 1796–1895*, International Stationary Steam Engine Society, 2000.

Jamieson, A., *Elementary Manual on Steam and the Steam Engine*, C. Griffin, London, 1898.

Jeremy, David J., *Transatlantic Industrial Revolution: The Diffusion of Textile Technologies Between Britain and America, 1790–1830s*, Blackwell, Oxford, 1981.

Kanefsky, J., 'The Diffusion of Power Technology in British Industry, 1760–1870', PhD thesis, Exeter, 1979.

Law, Brian R., *Fieldens of Todmorden, A Nineteenth Century Business Dynasty*, G. Kelsall, Littleborough, 1995.

Law, Rodney J., *The Steam Engine*, HMSO, London, 1965.

Lawton, Bryan, *Technology and Change in History, The Early History of Mechanical Engineering*, Brill, Boston, USA, 2004.

Lee, C.H., *A Cotton Enterprise, 1795–1840: A History of M'Connel & Kennedy, Fine Cotton Spinners*, Manchester University Press, 1972.

Leigh, Evan, *The Science of Modern Cotton Spinning*, Palmer & Howe, Manchester, 3rd edn 1875.

Lindqvist, Savante, *Technology on Trial*, Almqvist & Wiksell International, Stockholm, 1984.

Lipson, E., *A Short History of Wool and Its Manufacture*, Heinemann, London, 1953.

M'Connel & Co., Ltd, *A Century of Fine Cotton Spinning*, Manchester, 1905.

Manchester Steam Users' Association for the Prevention of Steam Boiler Explosions and for the Attainment of Economy in the Application of Steam, *A Sketch of the Foundation and of the Past Fifty Years' Activity*, Taylor, Garnett, Evans, Manchester, 1905.

Mann, Julia de Lacy, *The Cloth Industry in the West of England from 1640 to 1880*, Clarendon Press, Oxford, 1971.

Marsden, Richard, *Cotton Spinning: Its Development, Principles, and Practice*, G. Bell & Sons, London, 1891.

Marsden, Richard, *Cotton Weaving: Its Development, Principles, and Practice*, G. Bell & Sons, London, 1895.

Mechanical World.

Montgomery, James, *The Theory and Practice of Cotton Spinning; or The Carding and Spinning Master's Assistant*, J. Niven, Glasgow, 1832, 3rd edn 1836.

Montgomery, James, *A Practical Detail of the Cotton Manufacture of the United States of America and the State of the Cotton Manufacture of that Country Contrasted and Compared with that of Great Britain*, J. Niven, Glasgow, 1840.

Morton, W.E., *An Introduction to the Study of Spinning*, Longmans, Green & Co., London, 1937.

Muirhead, James Patrick, *The Origins and Progress of the Mechanical Inventions of James Watt*, J. Murray, London, 1854.

Murphy, William S., *The Textile Industries: Practical Guide to Fibres, Yarns & Fabrics*, Gresham Publishing Co., London, 1910.

Musgrave, J. & Sons Ltd, *Illustrated Catalogue of Vertical Quadruple Expansion Engines, Horizontal & Vertical Triple Expansion Engines, Compound Engines, Simple Engines, Barring Engines, Lancashire Boilers, Globe Safety Boilers, Sectional Boilers, Mill Gearing, Indicators, etc.*, no date.

Musgrave, J. & Sons Ltd, *The 'Una-flow' Patent Steam Engine*, Bolton, 1910.

Musson, A.E., & Robinson, Eric, *Science and Technology in the Industrial Revolution*, Manchester University Press, 1969.

Nasmith, Joseph, *Recent Cotton Mill Construction and Engineering*, J. Heywood, Manchester, 2nd edn c.1900.

Newby, George A., 'Behind the Fire Doors: Fox's Corrugated Furnace 1877 and the "High Pressure" Steamship', *T.N.S.*, Vol. 64, 1992–3.

Perry, F.B., 'The Uniflow Steam-Engine', *Proceedings of the Institution of Mechanical Engineers*, 1922.

Pole, William, Ed., *The Life of Sir William Fairbairn, Bart., Partly Written by Himself*, Longmans, Green, London, 1877, new edn 1970.

Ponting, Kenneth G., *The Woollen Industry of South-West England*, Adams & Dart, Bath, 1971.

Postlethwayte, M., *Britain's Commercial Interests Explained and Improved*, London, 1757.

Rankine, William J.M., *A Manual of the Steam Engine and Other Prime Movers*, Griffin, Bohn & Co., London, 1861.

Rees, Abraham, Ed., *The Cyclopaedia; or Universal Dictionary of Arts, Sciences, and Literature*, London, 1819, extracts reprinted David & Charles, Newton Abbot, 1972.

Reynolds, Jack, *The Great Paternalist: Titus Salt and the Growth of Nineteenth-Century Bradford*, M. Temple Smith, London, 1983.

Reynolds, M., *Stationary Engine Driving: A Practical Manual for Engineers in Charge of Stationary Engines*, London, 1885.

Reynolds, Terry S., *Stronger than A Hundred Men: A History of the Vertical Water Wheel*, Johns Hopkins University Press, Baltimore, 1983.

Rigg, A., *A Practical Treatise on the Steam Engine*, E. & F.N. Spon, London, 1888.

Rogers, Kenneth, *Wiltshire & Somerset Woollen Mills*, Pasold Research Foundation, Edington, 1976.

Rose, Mary B., *The Gregs of Quarry Bank Mill: The Rise and Decline of a Family Firm, 1750–1914*, Cambridge University Press, 1986.

Royal Institution of Cornwall, 'Trevithick Papers'.

Scott Russell, John, *A Treatise on the Steam-Engine*, A. & C. Black, Edinburgh, 1846.

Shaw, John, *Water Power in Scotland, 1550–1870*, J. Donald, Edinburgh, 1984.

Smiles, Samuel, *Industrial Biography: Iron Workers and Tool Makers*, J. Murray, London, new edn 1879.

Stumpf, J., *The Una-flow Steam Engine*, R. Oldenbourg, Munich, 1912.

Tann, Jennifer, *The Development of the Factory*, Cornmarket, London, 1970.

Tann, Jennifer, *The Selected Papers of Boulton and Watt, Vol. 1: The Engine Partnership, 1775–1825*, M.I.T. Press, Cambridge, Massachusetts, 1981.

Textile Manufacturers' Year Book, Emmott, Manchester, 1939.

Throp, Arnold, *The Last Years of Mill Engine Building*, Stationary Power No. 7, International Stationary Steam Engine Society, 1988.

Tippett, L.H.C., *A Portrait of the Lancashire Textile Industry*, Oxford University Press, 1969.

Tomlinson, Charles, ed., *Cyclopaedia of Useful Arts and Manufactures*, G. Virtue, New York., c.1854.

Triewald, Marten, *Short Description of the Atmospheric Engine*, Stockholm, 1734, English Translation by Newcomen Society, Cambridge, 1928.

Turner, Trevor, 'History of Fenton Murray & Wood', University of Manchester Institute of Science and Technology MSc, 1966.

Uhland, W.H., *Corliss Engines and Allied Steam-motors . . . with Special Reference to the Steam-Engines of the Paris International Exhibition of 1878*, E. & F.N. Spon, London, 1878.

Ure, A., *The Cotton Manufacture of Great Britain*, London, 1836.

Van Natrus, L., *Groot Volkomen Moolenboek*, J. Covens & C. Mortier, Amsterdam, 1734.

Wadsworth, A.P. & Mann, Julia de Lacy, *The Cotton Trade and Industrial Lancashire, 1600–1780*, Manchester University Press, 1931, reprint 1965.

Watkins, George, *Stationary Steam Engines of Great Britain*, Vol. 1–10, Landmark, Ashbourne, 2000.

Watkins, George, *Stationary Steam Engine Makers, Vol. 1 & 2*, Landmark, Ashbourne, 2006.

Watkins, George, *The Textile Mill Engine, Vol. 1 & 2*, David & Charles, Newton Abbot, 1970.

Williams, Charles Wye, *On Heat in its relations to Water and Steam; embracing new views of vaporisation, condensation, & explosions*, Longman et al., London, 2nd edn 1861.

Williams, Mike & Farnie, Douglas A., *Cotton Mills in Greater Manchester*, Carnegie Publishing Ltd, Preston, 1992.

Wilson, Paul N., *Water Turbines*, HMSO, London, 1974.

Wood, James L., 'The Sulzer Steam Engine Comes to Britain', *T.N.S.*, Vol. 59, 1987–8.

Zonca, V., *Novo Teatro di Machine et Edificii*, Padua, 1607.

INDEX

People and Places

Subjects

A

Air Pump, 37, **37-8**, 58, **58**, 61, **98**, **136-7**, 137, **141**, 156-7, 161-2, 167, **197**, **209**, **211**, **218**

Air pump, Edwards, 154, **154**, 177

B

Beetling, 15

Bleaching, 8, 15, 52

Boiler, 31-3, 63, 87, **89**, 106, 110, 119, 132, 149, 162

Boiler, Cornish, 88, **88**

Boiler, Egg-ended, 88, **88**

Boiler, Haystack, 87, **87**, 88.

Boiler, Lancashire, 89, **89**, 90, **90**, **92**, 99, 106, 149, **149**

Boiler, Wagon, 87-9, 87

C

Calico, 19, 26, 83

Calico Printing, 19, 52, **52**, 147, 183

Carding, Hand, 9-10, **9**, 22

Carding, Arkwright, 26-7

Carding, Bourn, 25

Carding, Paul & Wyatt, 21

Carding, Machine, 25, **25**, 30, 50, 77, 77, 106-8, **107**

Coal, 29, 36, 38, 57, 99, 118, 222

Combing, 9, **9**, 77-9, **77**, **79**

Compensator, see Governor.

Condensing Steam, 31, 33-4, 37-8, **37**, 62, 91, **98**, 99, 111, 113, 135, 153-4, **154**, 161, 177, **179**, **209**, 211, 218

Cotton, 19, 24-5, 28, 40-1, 51, 70-1, 77, 79, 104, 108

Cotton Gin, 47

Cotton Manufacture, 7, 17, 19-20, 26-8, 41, 43-4, 50, 65, 71, 73, 85, 104, 146

Counts, 20, 47, 105, 109

Crank & Comb, **25**, 26, 50

Cut-off/Expansion of Steam, 61, 87, 95, 125-7, **126**, 133, 171-3.

D

Devil Machine, 48, **48**

Drafting, 11, **11**, 24

Drafting, Casablancas, 148, **148**

Drafting, Rollers, 23, **23**

Drawing Frame, 26, **26**

Drying Machine, 52, **52**

Duty, 32, 36, 38, 119

Dyeing, 8

E

Economiser, 90-1, **91**, 157.

Electricity, 137, 165-6, 179, 181-4, 193.

Electric Generation, 137, 140, 164, **165**, 169, **179**, 182, **183**, 184

Electric Lighting, 179, 181-2

Electric Motors, 184

Extraction Engine, see Pass Out

F

Flax, 7-8, 14, **14**, 24, 51, **51**, 79

Flyer, 11, **11**, 23, 49-50, **50**

Fulling, 13, **13**, 52, **52**

Fustian, 10, 19, 20-1, 27

G

Governor, 63, 127, 130-2, 150-2, 155

Governor, Hartnell, 150, **151**

Governor, Higginson, 131, **131**, 135, **136**, 199

Governor, Lumb, 99, 152, **152**

Governor, Porter, 69, 131, **131**

Governor, Watt, 63, **63**, 69, 101, **125**, 130

Governor, Whitehead, 150-1, **151**, **183**, 212

H

Healds/Heddles, 9, 12, 83

Heat, 32, 37, 111-4, 117, 171

Horsepower, Animal, 24, 29-30, **29**, 32, 35, 39, 70

Horsepower, Mechanical, 27, 32, 36, 50, 54, 57, 63-6, 73-4, 93, 105, 110, 117, 124, 143, 159, 161, 164, 169, 172, 174, 184-5